The Principles

of Hypnotherapy

THE PRINCIPLES
OF
HYPNOTHERAPY

Dr. Dylan Morgan

M.A.(Oxon.), D.Phil.(Oxon.), MNCP, Acc.Hyp.

Publisher:
    Eildon Press,
    Suite 5, Floor 6,
    Manor Buildings,
    2 Manor Row,
    Bradford,
    West Yorkshire,
    BD1 4NL.

Copy Editing and Proofreading:
    Trudi Morgan

Printed by:
    Antony Rowe Ltd.,
    Bumper's Farm,
    Chippenham,
    Wiltshire,
    SN14 6QA.

Correspondence with Author:
    9 Richmond Place,
    Ilkley,
    West Yorkshire,
    LS29 8TJ.

ISBN 0 9525620 1 4

Dedicated to my parents
Morien and Elaine,
for everything.

CONTENTS

THE BOOK is arranged in three parts: A, B and C.

Part A, like the root system of a plant, is a foundation. It brings into mind some of the materials that will be needed for the remainder of the book. These chapters are only loosely connected to each other.

Part B, like the stem of a plant, develops the central theme of the book, which is the key processes involved in Hypnotherapy. These chapters are strongly connected and should be read in order.

Part C, like the leaves or fruit of a plant, spreads out again. These chapters are all developments from the ideas of Part B, but are not otherwise connected strongly. They can be read in almost any order, and are intended to stimulate thought in a variety of new directions.

This describes the kind of book you are reading. It is a book which is devoted to presenting a unified theoretical view of the subject. In this way it is new and unique. It does not present any new facts, but rather arranges the facts in a new light. It presents a new paradigm for Hypnosis.

Here we make sure that we know what certain key words will mean in this book. The word Hypnosis will refer ONLY to the subject and not to some hypothetical state or condition.

Hypnosis and Hypnotherapy are particular fields of human knowledge. We may delimit such fields of knowledge by their subject matter: the phenomena they deal with. A brief overview of some of the standard phenomena of Hypnosis is given to remind the reader of what the subjects involve.

A very important idea which is central to future development is that of *systems*, and particularly organic systems. This chapter introduces some of the basic properties of systems which will recur throughout the book, primarily their level of activity, and the most basic ways in which they might affect each other. An important shorthand notation is also presented.

It is useful then to examine various other theoretical approaches which have been taken to the subject. This overview will deepen the understanding of the newcomer. The range of theories is classified with an eye on the way in which they can be related to particular organic systems. It will be seen that the systems approach gives a way of unifying discussion and analysis of the whole field. The primary conclusion is that previous theoretical models have been based on noticing that Hypnotic techniques change the functioning of one particular system of the mind or body and then extrapolating to the idea that this particular system or change is the key or definitive feature of Hypnosis. Each theory therefore has some truth to teach, but none provides a complete picture.

In this chapter the reader is reminded of many other organic systems with which he or she is familiar, such as organisations, ecosystems, economies and families. The purpose is to activate in the mind certain patterns of organised thought; certain dynamic images; a certain organic approach to a subject which is a useful one when we develop the "Morganic" approach to Hypnotherapy.

In this chapter we take a rather closer look at the central systems with which we deal in Hypnosis, in order to perform a rough classification. There are those subsystems which interface with the external environment, which can be classified into active, e.g. muscular, vocal; and responsive, e.g. vision, hearing. Then there are those subsystems which deal with the internal environment, e.g. emotions, internalised speech, visualisation and a variety of maintenance and defence systems. Important among this last class is the "flight or fight" process. This elementary classification is then used to illustrate the principles along which Hypnotherapy can proceed.

This brief chapter takes a closer look at the matter of distinguishing *processes* as opposed to distinguishing structures. It also considers yet another complex system as an example of an organic system: an orchestra. The particular virtue of this example is that it provides us with a concrete image of what we mean by a process of a system: it is akin to the score of an orchestral work. Another very important point made, which is neatly illustrated by this example, is the distinction between the *kinematics* of a process - *how* a thing proceeds - and the *dynamics* - *why* it proceeds as it does. No amount of analysis of subsystems will in principle enable us fully to understand an organic process by merely analysing its subprocesses: we must also always be aware of the influence of larger systems and processes of which it is in turn a subprocess.

Anyone familiar with Hypnosis will know many "tests" of Hypnotic responsiveness. These are used in an attempt to determine how readily a potential subject will respond. The purpose of this chapter is to re-evaluate such tests within a systems framework as follows. The tests remain tests, but tests not of Hypnotic responsiveness but of how readily one system of the brain or body activates another in a given individual.

"Hypnotic inductions" are traditionally thought of as processes that the Hypnotist goes through in order to "Hypnotise" the Subject. But they are mostly presented with little or no explanation of how they work, or of what is the purpose of their various parts. From a systems point of view it becomes much easier to see what the purpose of an induction is, and examples are given to illustrate this way of thinking. The result is a more precise, flexible and accurate approach to this area within the field of Hypnotherapy.

This central part of the book takes a very close look at the process of Hypnotherapy, in more or less the order that it arises in real life, starting with the initial diagnosis. In doing this the value of the systems approach and the notation we have outlined in Part A become more apparent and develop real strength, throwing further light on how a variety of Hypnotic phenomena are produced.

This chapter starts to look at the process of diagnosis by looking at the presented symptom. It then describes the first step in a process of diagnosis which involves looking at precursors and resultants of the presented symptom.

A precursor is a system, a change in the activity of which produces the symptom. A resultant is a system whose activity changes as a direct result of the symptom. In this way we build up a clear picture of the dynamics of the problem. The typical picture is a chain of systems each affecting the next, with the problem symptom somewhere in the middle. A situation of considerable importance arises if the chain forms a loop, colloquially termed a vicious circle.

The notion of a vicious circle is part of a more general set of ideas which deal with what are known as feedback loops. These are of enormous importance in organic systems, and this chapter outlines their principles. We distinguish positive feedback loops from negative feedback loops, and increasing from decreasing feedback loops. Any of these can at times create the problem we are supposed to be resolving, or prevent a change we want to make, or, on the other hand, be the means by which we are removing a problem or ensuring that the changes we make are permanent.

The next step in diagnosis involves looking at the question of what would happen if the problem symptom were to be removed. The importance of this comes from the observation that the problem may well only remain in existence because of a negative feedback loop which ensures that any reduction in the problem leads to consequences which start it up again. It is essential in successful therapy that such situations be recognised.

As a preliminary to deciding what to do to change things for the better this **very important chapter** builds on the analysis of cybernetic processes to emphasise a general and very central technique of Hypnotherapy. We start from the general principle that *amplification* is involved and the observation that organic systems are typically provided with a multitude of increasing positive feedback loops which act precisely like amplifiers. Many Hypnotic phenomena are shown to centre around the principle of deliberately creating and activating such loops. As a secondary but still important principle we note that in many other cases a pre-existent loop of this nature is present but is held in check by the activity of another system. In such cases it is enough to inactivate the controlling system in order to tap into the activating power of the loop. But even then the inactivation is likely to be achievable by means of establishing a positive feedback loop.

Chapter 14: The Process of Hypnotherapy. Stage 3: Planning a Change.   129

In this chapter attention is focused on the process of deciding a strategy in Hypnotherapy for reducing the problem symptom. There is no *one* way of tackling a given symptom, or helping a given person. But there is a strategy which has a good chance of producing a short list of the most effective and efficient ways.

Chapter 15: Reinforcing Changes.   139

In the context of Hypnotherapy it is important to ensure that changes to the Client are *reinforced* by factors in the environment. This amounts to ensuring that there will be an increasing positive feedback loop to make the change grow in strength. This is contrasted with a form of therapy in which any new behaviour is reinforced only by the therapist, which can result in undue dependence. The principle is that "Life must provide the reinforcer".

PART C   153

In this third part of the book each chapter is relatively independent. Each takes up one particular aspect of our subject and looks at it from the perspective of the principles that have been developed.

Chapter 16: Dynamic Rebound and Paired Systems.   155

In this chapter we focus on a particular and very important principle of organic systems. This is the fact that to maintain homeostasis - a reasonable equilibrium - there evolve *pairs* of systems which act in opposite directions to maintain any important parameter within range. If one increases, then the other decreases. This is coupled to the principle that if we attempt to override a system it will tend, over a few cycles, to strengthen. We may then often find that the most effective strategy in dealing with a problem is analogous to vaccination: we act in the short term to produce the very thing which we are trying to prevent in the long term, with the aim of *strengthening* a natural system which will produce the required change. The converse of this is that a *direct* attempt to change a system is more analogous to drug therapy: it can be very effective in the short term, but in the long term weakens a natural system which would do the same job, thus creating potential long-term problems.

This chapter draws attention to the general point that in *any* complex system there are subsystems which may or may not affect each other. If two have no direct effect on each other they may be called totally dissociated. If the effect is only one way we may call it a partial dissociation. The dissociation may also be weak or strong - in the latter case there will be some third or higher system which acts so as to prevent the strongly dissociated systems from affecting each other. Examples are given of these phenomena and an interesting point is made regarding the difference in emphasis between Hypnotists, who tend to create dissociation, and Hypnotherapists, who tend to eliminate it.

The asking of appropriate questions is a theme which runs through the whole book. One particular aspect of this is asking questions of the Client. Problems can arise when we want to know things about subsystems of which there is no conscious awareness. This chapter deals with some of the techniques specific to Hypnotherapy which deal with such a situation. In brief they involve bypassing the verbal system and connecting the system of interest to some other system (using the characteristic Hypnotic techniques of eliminating distractions, amplifying responses by means of feedback loops, etc.). The alternative systems are usually the visual imagination or the motor or emotional systems. Examples are given to illustrate this.

This chapter underlines the value of the very clear theoretical structure presented in this book when it comes to making meaningful experiments. Since it has proved impossible to find an agreed objective answer to the question, "When is a person Hypnotised?" the experimentalist who wishes to be scientific is working on shaky foundations. Within our framework, however, the basic question as to whether a particular system is active or not is much more tractable and answerable. It should then be possible to build a strong experimental structure on the basis of clearly defined experiments on the component parts of Hypnotic procedures.

Family therapy is an area of human psychology which has already incorporated to some extent a systems way of thinking. The background to this is presented for the sake of its similarities to our systematic approach to Hypnotherapy. Some examples are used to illustrate the fact that the approach and notation developed in earlier chapters continue to be precisely as valuable when the primary system is a family and not an individual. The general point is made that the practice of a therapist is characterised by the *choice of systems he recognises as important*. The different fields of family therapy are associated with different assumptions as to the subsystems of importance. The same holds for Hypnotherapists: the subsystems they regard as important characterise and at times limit them.

Different schools of psychotherapy tend to focus their attention on different subsystems of the human mind, and apply different techniques to them. This chapter very briefly outlines some of the major approaches in order to provide an idea of the context of Hypnotherapy. It is concluded that Hypnotherapy, in the sense of this book, is broader than most forms of psychotherapy as it may deal with systems of many kinds and all levels from the comparatively simple reflexes of the nervous system up to social systems. It involves a prescriptive diagnostic process, a crisp theoretical framework, a sense of the dynamics of feedback systems and a wide variety of procedures to change them.

This chapter presents a precise scientific definition of the key notion of *activity* which has run through this book. The activity of a system is defined as the rate at which it increases the entropy of the universe - a quantity which is in principle always measurable or calculable. It also has the property of always being positive. It is approximately proportional to the power output of the system in watts. If we wish to extrapolate the notion of activity to socio-economic systems (which are also organic) then a more useful measure will be the rate at which money is spent: £/sec.

The use of analogies or metaphors in Hypnotherapy is common and important. In this chapter their use is related to the general principles running through the book. The key idea is that the principles allow us to uncover the abstract dynamic pattern of the problem and solution. The same abstract pattern may be embodied in many particular forms, each of which thereby provides an analogy for all the others. In helping a Client we generate an analogy which draws on his or her experience, and present the change that is required to resolve the problem in terms of the related change in the analogy. These ideas also throw some further light onto the nature of the theory of this book: although many analogies have been presented for

Hypnotic phenomena, their purpose is to enable the reader to grasp the *general* or *abstract* principles which are involved in both Hypnosis and the other fields from which the examples or analogies are drawn.

This brief chapter gives an outline of an approach to the very difficult question of consciousness. The essence of the approach is the theme, which runs through this book, of the twin perspective on any system both as being part of a larger system or systems and also as containing subsystems. The point is made that when we ask of a system a question based on "How?", then we are looking for an answer in terms of its subsystems. On the other hand when we ask a question based on "What?" we are looking for answers in terms of its supersystem or supersystems. Anything like a full understanding of a system can only be obtained by answering *both* the "How?" and the "What?" questions. Applying these principles to human consciousness, which is taken to involve the highest order of systems within the individual brain, leads inevitably to the conclusion that although research has gone a long (though not the whole) way towards answering the "How?" questions, the answers to the "What?" questions *must* lie in a higher system, which must at least include very many other human beings. The fact that traditionally the "What?" questions regarding human life have been answered in terms of higher systems than the individual human being is therefore accepted to be the right approach in principle.

This brief chapter points towards the way in which the analysis of Hypnotic phenomena promoted in the body of the book could be developed in such a way that it would connect up with the large existing body of mathematical theory of cybernetic and biological systems. A single very small example of mathematical modelling is given in the hope that even the non-mathematician may get an idea of the potential of such an approach.

PART A

INTRODUCTION

WHAT KIND of book is this?

This question is an important one. In order to get the best out of a book we need to approach it with the right mind-set.

This book is a paradigm-changing book: it aims to present a fresh way of looking at the field of Hypnotherapy.

It was in 1962 that Kuhn introduced the notion of a paradigm shift to describe a process that has happened in many fields of science at many times. The second edition of his book will be found in the list of References under Kuhn (1970). It concerns a fundamental change in the way in which the phenomena of the field are viewed, and consequently in the way things are done. In Kuhn's view such a change has the nature of a revolution. His book itself introduced a paradigm shift in the field of the theory of scientific ideas. A good survey of his ideas and of those of others who do not agree with him is given by Casti (1989).

Since this book presents a paradigm shift it is a book of *ideas*. It will therefore stand or fall on the success of these ideas. They will be a success if they help others to *make sense* of Hypnotherapy.

We may contrast this with some books which it is NOT.

It is NOT a book which claims to present any new FACTS about Hypnosis. If it were it would contain a number of detailed accounts of specific new experiments and their results: it does not.

It is NOT a compendium or encyclopaedia of known facts about Hypnotherapy. If it were, it would contain thousands of references to the work of thousands of other workers and what they have discovered: it does not. It would also be a great deal thicker.

It is NOT a history. If it were it would deal exclusively with ideas and practices from the past. It does not.

It is NOT a handbook of techniques. Although various techniques will be mentioned, they are there only to illustrate and illuminate the theory. A handbook would aim to give extensive lists of techniques. This does not.

It is NOT a "Teach yourself Hypnotherapy" book. Although you will learn a lot about Hypnotherapy, this book will not, in itself, qualify you to be a Hypnotherapist. That requires in addition a lot of practical experience and a lot of detailed information that you would need to acquire from the kinds of books mentioned above.

It is NOT one of those Elixir of Life books which claims to have found some totally new and remarkably simple method of solving all human ills.

It is none of those things. It IS a book which aims to change in a fundamental and useful way the manner in which we think about the subjects of Hypnosis and Hypnotherapy. Books of this nature are rare - and they are exciting.

Not only does it give a new perspective, it generates new insights into the processes used. Furthermore it leads to a clear and original description of the process of diagnosis in Hypnotherapy - something which is notably absent in other books on the subject.

The association of Hypnosis with therapy is not new. By that name it was first used by the Scottish doctor, James Braid, then practising in Manchester, in the 1840s. Related practices, under other names, were used in healing by Mesmer and his followers in the 17th century and by priest and shaman as far back as the dawn of recorded history.

Over the centuries many books have been written about Hypnosis in the context of therapy. The common characteristic of all these books is that they deal extensively with HOW to create the many phenomena we associate with Hypnotism but give very little idea of WHY the methods work. There is very little theory. They are therefore of little help when a method does NOT work, which is a matter of some importance to the practitioner of Hypnotherapy.

The early days of most sciences are marked by this same feature. Early chemistry consisted of a collection of recipes, "If you add *this* to *that* then the following happens..." There was no real understanding of WHY or HOW it happened. Early medicine was the same. It had a large collection of procedures and treatments, but only vague ideas as to HOW they worked (when they did). In the light of our present understanding, moreover, we can see that the theoretical ideas they did have - such as the Hippocratic idea of Humours - were inadequate and faulty in the extreme, leading for example to quite unnecessary and potentially dangerous bloodletting on a massive scale.

When a science has reached a certain degree of maturity, as a result of the accumulated experiences of many workers, there comes a stage in which partial, and hard-won, experiences may coalesce to form one uniform picture which makes sense of a whole field. An example of this was the introduction into chemistry of the atomic theory by Dalton (1808), which was a big paradigm shift and the foundation of all subsequent understanding in the field.

It is the contention of this book that Hypnotherapy has come of age, and that it is now possible to describe in some detail a theoretical framework within which Hypnotic phenomena can be produced and understood in a systematic way.

This book is written with three classes of readers in mind. The central class consists of students: people who are learning the skills of Hypnotherapy. There are increasing numbers of these as this form of therapy becomes more popular. They can expect to find this book a unique aid to understanding what it is that they are learning to do.

On one side of these are individuals who already have an extensive understanding of Hypnotherapy, whether as practitioners or as experimentalists. For these individuals this book may be seen as a codification of ideas that are floating in the pool of common consciousness of Hypnotherapists in this day and age: it crystallises these ideas; it makes them more definite and clear; it unites them in a common pattern. Some of the ideas presented here have already been published in journals read by professionals and found a ready response. The paradigm shift involved does not involve the shattering of existing ideas for most professionals. It is more a matter of drawing together all that we know and do in a systematic way and then building on that foundation a strong new understanding.

On the other side of the centre is the group of intelligent readers who want to know what Hypnosis and Hypnotherapy are all about, though with no intention of using them in person. This will include students of psychology and medicine, but also many of the millions of people who like to know "how things work", and in particular "how people work". Hypnotherapy is intimately involved with the ways in which people's minds and bodies work: arguably *the* most fascinating subject for everyone outside their own speciality.

With this readership in mind the language has been kept comparatively simple. A minimum level of specialised vocabulary is used, and a minimum amount of prior knowledge assumed.

Having said that, it has been my experience that the concepts are grasped most readily by men and women who are working at the higher levels of many fields such as management, education or consultancy. They seem naturally to think in terms of systems and processes: an ability that I suppose is correlated with degree of intelligence. It may well be then that a certain level of intelligence is a prerequisite to grasping the ideas in their abstract form. However, I have supplied many concrete examples to minimise this problem.

The theoretical framework described here, although proposed as a basis for understanding Hypnotherapy, is in fact rich and powerful enough also to provide a fresh perspective on a very much wider arena of human behaviour, whether individual or in groups such as families or organisations. It is hoped that it will open up new ways of thinking to others as it has to the author.

It will seem to outsiders that the Hypnotherapist does not hold a central position in the world of ideas: I certainly thought so myself at one time. But I have gradually come to realise that in terms of understanding how people work it is a position second to none.

This is because it combines the maximum opportunity for observation with the maximum opportunity for making changes and seeing the results.

The Hypnotherapist sees people from all ranks of life. People open up and disclose their innermost feelings and thoughts to the Hypnotherapist, so that a full picture emerges of the entire course of people's lives.

The Hypnotherapist is not restricted to working with people in whom there is a severe mental malfunction as are Psychiatrists for the most part. He or she is instead often working with healthy and typical people who want help with a single problem in an otherwise satisfactory life or to improve their performance in some way. Consequently the Hypnotherapist can form a clear idea of the range of ways that people normally deal with life: there is not the Psychiatrist's exclusive emphasis on severe malfunction.

Compared with many other related fields such as counselling or psychoanalysis, the Hypnotherapist is expected to a far greater degree *actively to change things*: a variety of things in a variety of people. This seems to me to be of far-reaching importance. The scientific revolution which began around the seventeenth century was a result of men who were not, in the Greek tradition, restricted to contemplation and reflection in the pursuit of truth, but who had *hands-on experience*.

There is nothing like trying to make a change and failing, to drive home the fact that you do not understand what you are doing. When your livelihood depends on making successful changes it concentrates the mind still better. If, on the other hand, it is possible to take an ivory-tower approach and to build a theory on the basis of what has been merely read, then there is little chance of any immediate feedback to prove the theory wrong.

Later on in this book we will find much on the importance of feedback loops. In the present context I will observe that improvement in any skill or ability depends on a feedback loop in which execution is followed by an assessment of how successful that execution has been, which is followed by an appropriate modification and further executions. That is how the Wright brothers learned to fly. That is how anyone learns to play golf. That is how babies learn to co-ordinate their limbs. That is how science has grown.

The Hypnotherapist is in the position of having immediate feedback, perhaps within minutes, quite usually within an hour and always within days to test how successful he or she has been in effecting a change.

As a matter of contrast, many Psychoanalysts work over periods of years with a Client. The feedback is so slow, I wonder it can ever have any effect on practice. Research Psychologists are disciplined to work with a very small area of human psychology; each experiment can take months or years, and can lead only to knowing a lot about very little. Psychologists who build theories on the results of the work of such painstaking research inevitably spend most of their lives in libraries and laboratories: they have little chance to get *any* feedback by putting their ideas into any kind of practice. Many counsellors are constrained by present conventions to be non-directive: that is to say they are supposed NOT to make direct changes, but rather to somehow create an environment in which the Clients will make changes for themselves. Since there is so little action, there is limited scope for feedback also.

In addition, many such professionals are working in salaried positions: which has two drawbacks. One is that they involve extensive costs in terms of the time that has to be spent on the organisation - the committees, the paperwork, the administration, etc. - which reduces either or both of the time available for original thought and the time spent dealing with clients or patients. The second is that since the salary cheque is only very, very loosely connected with success at helping people as contrasted with making a good impression on the System, there is not the same direct and immediate incentive to improve at the cutting edge of the work.

The Professional Hypnotherapist - by which I mean an intelligent man or woman who devotes his or her whole life to the field, not someone who is a professional in some other field like medicine and does a little Hypnosis on the side - is, by contrast, in a perfect position to devote ALL his or her time to studying and changing the functioning of other people with ample and immediate feedback available. This is the optimum position to be in in any field. I, personally, have adopted *and then discarded because they failed me in practice*, hundreds of different partial theoretical structures before finally evolving that which is presented in this book, which has passed the hard test of day-to-day work and also exposure to my professional peers.

My initial training and doctorate were in Mathematics with a strong leaning to Theoretical Physics. These force you to think clearly and deeply and honestly about the structures and dynamics of things. Ideas must be as crisp as possible: woolliness of thought is a sin. When I plunged into the world of Hypnotherapy, I found none of the precision of thought I was used to, no systematic approach, no theory worthy of the name. I also found my ego very badly hit every time I failed to help someone. Furthermore I had no salary: Clients are not reimbursed by Health Insurance Policies for Hypnotherapy as yet; neither can they get it free on the National Health Service. When Clients are paying with their own money, they require evidence that the service is worth it. And this is even more true in Yorkshire. The fact that if you make no progress you make no money concentrates the mind wonderfully, I find. If an idea does not work you reject it at once. Those that survive and evolve in this tough environment are fit and strong and lean and healthy. I hope you will find these qualities throughout this book.

Finally I come to a small matter of how to refer to the approach to Hypnotherapy which has evolved in this way. In my first articles for the European Journal of Clinical Hypnosis, I referred to it as a "Systems-oriented Paradigm for Hypnotic Phenomena". This is a bit of a mouthful, and the Journal used, as a more useful label, the phrase, "the Morgan Proposition". Neither of these lends itself to the formation of a useful adjective: "systematic" is a possible one, but this is too general a word.

As you read the book, you will find that central to the approach is the notion of the functioning of *complex organic systems*. An alternative adjective could therefore be "organic", but this again is too general. Finally I stumbled on an adjective which is concise, reminds us of this aspect of the theory, is specific and easily memorable: "Morganic". So when, from time to time, it is necessary to distinguish between the approach of this book and other approaches I will use this coined word as a convenient shorthand.

OUR

CHAPTER 1

Clearing the Ground

OUR TOOLS for understanding are ideas and words. To do a good job tools must be clean and clear. This short chapter does some of this necessary preparation.

Let us begin with the word "hypnosis". It has been used in a number of senses. It is sometimes said that a person is "in hypnosis". Or it might be used in a phrase such as "experimental hypnosis" to mean a field of expertise.

In this book the words "hypnosis" and "hypnotherapy" will refer ONLY to fields of knowledge and skill. They are in the same class as the words "chemistry", "medicine" (as a discipline), "physics", etc.

The reasons why this is important will become clearer later. Briefly it is because the other use conjures up a picture of a subject in a unique "state of hypnosis". Detailed experiments have failed to establish any way of defining such a state or distinguishing it from other, "non-hypnotic states". For the same reason the phrase "an hypnotic trance" will not be used.

On the other hand a field of knowledge is comparatively easy to define. It is characterised by an interest in a certain class of phenomena. The field defined by interest in the weather can be labelled "meteorology", of interest in the past, "history", in books, "literature", in the nerves, "neurology" and so on. Notice that it is the *phenomena* that define the subject and not the *theories* or the *practices*. For example, the techniques used in chemistry have varied enormously over time. Modern equipment is vastly different from nineteenth century equipment: Bunsen didn't start using his burner until 1855! Chemical theories have also changed enormously over time: Dalton's atomic theory only goes back to the beginning of the nineteenth century. In a similar way both the ideas that people have had about the field of Hypnosis and the methods they have used have changed considerably, but the phenomena of interest have remained relatively fixed.

What the Hypnotist is interested in is a certain class of *changes in the functioning of the mind and body brought about in a non-physical and naturalistic way.* Later on we will list in more detail most of the common such changes, but here we will note a few such things: analgesia - a loss of a sense of pain; amnesia -an induced forgetfulness; involuntary movements induced by suggestion alone; and distortion of the messages of the senses, in which a lemon may be made to taste like an apple, a clearly visible object may not be perceived, or an object may be "seen" though not present.

The Hypnotherapist is more interested in a rather different class of changes, such as recovery of lost memories, removal of old habits or patterns of thought, elimination of tensions, changes in perceptions to bring them more in line with reality, changes in mood and so on: in brief to change things which are perceived as "problems".

When we say that these changes are to be produced in a *non-physical* way, it implies that the changes are NOT produced by the application of drugs, electricity, magnetism or other physical agency. To say that the changes are produced in a naturalistic way implies that neither are they produced by some strange or unnatural force, power or phenomenon. Hypnotic phenomena are a result of using the natural modes of functioning of the mind and body, but in focused or particular or unusual ways, to produce the desired changes.

It is because we are using only modes of functioning which can exist naturally that no hard line can be drawn between a "state of hypnosis" and any other "state" or mode of functioning of a person. For many people this point cannot be emphasised too much. In the uninformed mind there is a simple picture that being "under hypnosis" is rather like going "under" an anaesthetic: a sudden and dramatic departure of consciousness. While the stage Hypnotist will at times work (with his better Subjects) to approximate to this state of affairs, it has been found by careful experiment that the same phenomena which can be produced under those conditions can also be produced under conditions where there is no such dramatic change.

A related error can be typified by a recent enquiry to me: "Can Hypnosis be used to improve my memory, so that I could pick up and learn a telephone directory?" This is effectively equivalent to being able effortlessly to be a chess Master, a scratch golfer, etc. The normal rules of functioning of the mind and body demand that practice, and a lot of it, is necessary to develop such skills. Hypnotic techniques may be used to increase motivation, to reduce distracting thoughts and to optimise the results of practice, but they are always working on natural systems which have their own rules and therefore limitations. You cannot make a silk purse out of a sow's ear.

There is a lot of power and potential in Hypnotic techniques, but they are not magic: not contrary to the laws of physics, chemistry or neurology. It is easily possible to get a person to feel themselves too heavy to get off a chair. But it will not result in any extra pressure on the chair.

Two other words that will be used in this book are **Subject** and **Client**. The former will normally refer to a person whose functioning is being changed by a Hypnotist, and the latter by a Hypnotherapist. Some Hypnotherapists use the term Patient in place of Client.

SUMMARY

HYPNOSIS is the area of knowledge concerned with certain naturalistic changes in the functioning of the mind and nervous system.

HYPNOTHERAPY is the application of such knowledge to help individuals with a related class of problems.

We will not use the concept of a "state of hypnosis" in this book.

CHAPTER 2

Hypnotic Phenomena

IN ORDER TO GET a clearer view of the subject matter of Hypnosis we will next look at some of the more common phenomena which have been reliably produced in certain people in an experimental setting as well as by Hypnotherapists or stage Hypnotists.

There is no real disagreement about the existence of these phenomena. Others may be added to the list below and there can be disagreement over the precise nature of what is happening in them and also about theories designed to explain how they are happening. But there is general agreement that the phenomena *do* characterise the field of Hypnosis.

In each of these examples it must be remembered that no claim is made that the particular phenomenon can be produced with equal ease in everyone, nor that it will be possible in everyone. Remember that we are dealing with *naturalistic phenomena*.

The fact that some individuals are colour blind does not invalidate the phenomenon of full colour vision in others. The fact that some individuals have poor memories and take a lot of time to learn things does not negate the achievements of certain individuals who can memorise enormous amounts quickly. The fact that not everybody can run a mile in under 6 minutes does not affect the fact that a great number could, with practice, or that there are many who can run it in under 4 minutes. Neither does the fact that the world record time has been reducing allow us to deduce that a 2 minute mile will some day be possible.

The general principles of ALL human behaviour or achievement are that there is a range in the capacity of different individuals to produce certain behaviour; that anyone's capacity can be improved by proper practice; and that there are natural limits to what can be done.

If Hypnosis dealt with phenomena which did NOT obey these principles it would be a very strange subject indeed.

Consequently in reading the following, remember always that each example is something that can be produced to a high degree quite easily in some people, to a lesser degree and/or in more time in others, and finally to no significant extent in any reasonable time with yet others. It is also a fact that there is only a loose correlation between an individual's capacity to produce one phenomenon and another, rather in the way that if you are very good at geography there is a better than average chance that you will also be good at history, but it is far from certain.

The stage Hypnotist works within these constraints of nature by selecting from the audience, by means of various tests, those individuals in which the phenomena of interest can be produced most easily. The Hypnotherapist, who has to work with a wider range of individuals, will tend to use more time and a variety of methods in order to offset the limitations that may arise in a particular individual.

Some Hypnotic Phenomena

In the following list the phenomena are grouped into those areas of the brain or nervous system or body which they involve.

VOLUNTARY MUSCULAR SYSTEM

At one time it was a popular part of a demonstration of stage Hypnotism for the Hypnotist to get a Subject to go completely rigid. So great was this rigidity that the Subject could be supported on two chairs by his head and heels alone. And as if this were not enough the Hypnotist would be able to sit or stand on the supported body with no complaint from the Subject or yielding of his body! This has now been banned in the UK by the Hypnotism Act of 1952, as it could lead to physical damage.

At the opposite extreme from this, it is comparatively easy to induce in those same large muscles of the body an extreme limpness or relaxation which is so great that the Subject feels unable to move them.

In between these extremes there are a variety of phenomena in which a large group of muscles - those of an arm, perhaps - will move in response *not* to the perceived will of the Subject, but rather in response to verbal suggestions from the Hypnotist.

INVOLUNTARY MUSCULAR SYSTEM

There are many muscles in the body which we do not normally expect to be able to control at will. These include the heart, which is one big muscle, the small muscles which expand and contract to control the flow of blood through veins and arteries, and the muscles of the stomach and alimentary system which push the food along its way.

Hypnotic techniques have been shown to be able to affect these. Heart rate may be increased quite a lot, and reduced to a lesser extent. The flow of blood can be altered so that, for example, it can be increased to warm the feet or decreased to cool them. The flow of blood to the face can be altered in order to induce or reduce blushing. And so on.

SENSORY SYSTEMS

Another popular phenomenon for the stage Hypnotist is to get a Subject to eat an onion under the impression that it is an apple. In order for this to be possible - and with every indication of enjoyment - there must have been changes in that person's perception of taste, smell and also vision.

In general it is possible to change the messages from any sense. The sense of touch can be altered either so that a certain kind of numbness results in which a touch cannot be felt at all, or, conversely, so that it reports the presence of a stimulus which has no basis in reality - for example, that an insect is crawling over the skin. Glove anaesthesia is a term often used in Hypnotherapy to describe a situation in which nothing is felt in one or both hands up to the wrist - as if a thick glove is being worn which makes it impossible to feel things.

The related sense of pressure can likewise be affected, all the way from feeling no sensation of the pressure of the body on the chair to a great sensation of pressure on the chest which has no outward cause, for example.

The sense of smell may be affected either to produce anosmia - the absence of all sensation of smell - or to change the perceptions so that one smell becomes interpreted as another. A pleasant scent can be made to smell like hydrogen sulphide - rotten eggs - or ammonia like a rose.

The related sense of taste can likewise be affected to change either the quality of the taste or its intensity. Sweet can turn to sour and vice versa, or can simply vanish.

The sense of hearing can be affected so that the Subject fails to respond at all to a certain class of sounds, while remaining aware of others - for example, he may remain aware of the Hypnotist's voice, but unaware of anyone else or any background noise.

The sense of sight can be affected in a similar way so that things which are there may not be noticed and things which are not present are visualised as vividly as if they were there. A popular stage trick is to give the Subject "X-ray glasses" which seem to be able to see through the clothes of anyone looked at.

The sense of orientation may be altered so that, for example, a feeling of lying at a steep angle can be induced in a person lying horizontally, or a feeling of falling in someone who is standing vertically.

The sense of temperature may be affected so that a part or whole of the body is perceived as being either hotter or colder than it is in reality, though there is no change measurable by a thermometer.

The sense of pain, though it is so much more acute than the other senses, follows the same pattern. Because of its importance it has received a great deal of experimental attention and the basic facts have been established conclusively. It is indeed true that a person can be induced by Hypnotic procedures to be consciously aware of less pain in a given circumstance, or, on the other hand, of more.

HABITUAL SYSTEMS

A typical habit is a complex pattern of behaviour which is carried out automatically with little or no conscious thought. Although it may involve the same groups of muscles that are involved in the phenomena mentioned above, it is really a higher order phenomenon of the nervous system. Such habits are regulated primarily by a part of the brain called the cerebellum - and altering habits is therefore altering the functioning of a part of the brain.

For the stage Hypnotist the task is often to establish a *new* habit, such as standing and declaiming something when a certain piece of music plays. For a Hypnotherapist the task is the more difficult one of preventing a long-established habit, such as smoking or nail-biting, from continuing.

EMOTIONAL SYSTEMS

The emotions tend to shade into each other more gradually than do the senses: it is hard to put a clear line between a pleasure and happiness in the way that we can distinguish touch and pain, for example. But the principles we have seen above in the senses continue to hold in the sphere of the emotions. Whether we consider love, liking, excitement, pleasure, happiness, or fear, anger, grief, guilt, depression or any other shade of feeling, it is true that they can be induced or suppressed or altered in quality.

Although feelings do not seem to us to be localised, in terms of our physiology they are primarily a function of a certain structure in the brain called the limbic system. So in altering emotions we are again dealing with a part of the brain. This part is in direct contact with a small gland in the brain called the thalamus, which produces hormones which in turn affect other endocrine glands in the body. The best known of these are the adrenal gland and the ovaries or testes.

If a person is induced by some Hypnotic technique to feel fear or excitement then the adrenal glands respond as a part of the process. This underlines the fact that Hypnotic techniques can also affect the functioning of the endocrine system. Another example might be the arousal or suppression of sexual feelings, which would be accompanied by changes in the level of sexual hormones.

RELATIONSHIPS

Of very great importance to most people are their relationships with others. A relationship is a complex pattern of feelings and habitual actions and responses in two or more people, so it involves systems which have been mentioned above. Very often the problem presented to the Hypnotherapist lies in this area, and the task is to sort out what parts of the complex pattern it is best to change in order to improve matters. Insofar as it is possible to alter feelings and actions by Hypnotic techniques, it is by the same token possible to alter the course of a relationship.

IMMUNE SYSTEM

Scattered through the literature on the subject there are accounts of the use of Hypnotic techniques to influence the body's ability to react to a wide range of illnesses, including cancer. Perhaps the best evidence underpinning the validity of these reports is the very well-attested fact of the Placebo Response. This simply says that for virtually any illness there will be a certain proportion of sufferers who will recover significantly better if they are given something that they *believe* will work, even if it is totally neutral medicinally. Insofar as Hypnotic techniques can evidently change an individual's belief about all manner of things, as we have seen, there is every reason to suppose that it can act as well as, if not better than the beliefs involved in the Placebo Response to help people's bodies to heal themselves.

MENTAL SYSTEMS

We have seen that emotions and habits are both properly seen to be functions of the brain, though they may not be thought to be so by the man in the street. We will now consider a few more functions of the brain which are more obviously so.

Memory is a particular function of the brain which has also been demonstrably affected by Hypnotic procedures. It, also, can be enhanced, inhibited, made selective or falsified. On the stage a popular alteration is to make the Subject forget some quite simple thing, like the name of a colour or the number 7. The Subject may struggle very hard to recall the missing fact but fail totally. An alternative is to get him to believe that something is true or has happened which has not. If a Subject is induced to "remember" that another person has cheated him in some way, he will start to act in a way which is amusing to the audience. But the serious side to this is that certain individuals can be influenced to believe that they have remembered episodes or early sexual abuse which never in fact happened. The problems that can arise from this are termed the False Memory Syndrome.

Concentration is another high-order mental faculty which can be intimately affected by Hypnotic techniques. It is not uncommon to come across cases in which the Subject responds exclusively to the voice of the Hypnotist, and seems totally oblivious to all else. This is a particular case of total concentration. Equally it can be possible to make concentration on any subject very difficult.

More generally the entire mental framework can be altered, as when a Subject can be induced to imagine himself to be Elvis Presley, or some other person, and act, respond and answer questions from the viewpoint of that person.

Since this book is not encyclopaedic there is no need to list ALL possibilities. Enough has now been said to indicate something of the range of changes that have been recorded.

SUMMARY

Hypnotic procedures have been demonstrated in laboratories and elsewhere to produce a wide range of changes in the functioning of human beings. Something of the range has been listed above.

CHAPTER 3

Introducing Systems

IN THE LAST CHAPTER the word "system" frequently arose. In our growing understanding of the functioning of body and brain, scientists have come to recognise the nature and modes of functioning of many systems in the body. There are the nervous system, the digestive system, the cardiovascular system, the limbic system, the endocrine system, the immune system, the muscular system and so on.

Each of these systems has an identifiable **structure**. The nerves are the physical structure of the nervous system; the heart plus veins and arteries and their associated small muscles form the structure of the cardiovascular system, and so on. But equally, if not more, important are the **processes** which the system undergoes. The existence of the heart has been known since prehistoric time. But the fact that it circulates the blood only became understood with William Harvey (1578-1637) in the early seventeenth century. The existence of the major planets of our solar system was also known from prehistoric times, but the principles of their movements were only properly described by Newton (1642-1727) in the latter half of the seventeenth century. To get any proper idea of a system we must know how it works; what kinds of processes it undergoes; what are the principles governing those processes.

The difference is related to the difference between seeing a thing in *static* terms and *dynamic* terms. This great change has taken place in a multitude of sciences, and each time has heralded a great increase in understanding. Darwin's Theory of Evolution is an example of a change from a view which held that species were *fixed* to one in which they *changed* in certain ways for specific reasons. The theory of continental drift has similarly transformed geology.

As a simple analogy illustrating this matter from another angle, consider the position of a car mechanic. He might well be able to put quite a few things right by following a few tried and tested procedures that he has found to be effective in some instances. But unless he understands the principles governing the function of the various parts of the machine, his ability is going to be strictly limited: he will have no real idea of why the changes he makes are effective, and so his work will remain rather hit and miss. He has to know how and why the parts move or operate in order to understand things properly.

It will be clear from the last chapter that the field of interest of Hypnotherapy is intimately involved with the functioning of effectively **all** the major systems of the mind and body. In order to understand what we are doing we are therefore **forced** to give thought to understanding the nature of these organic systems, and in particular to understanding their modes of functioning and interacting. There is no option. The phenomena are clear. That they involve changes to systems of the body is clear. That the changes are not to their structure (we are not surgeons) is clear. That we change the behaviour is clear. Consequently we are dealing with the **dynamics of complex organic systems**. If we are to form an idea of the principles of Hypnosis we are therefore forced to start with a picture, however simple, of the dynamics of the organic or biological subsystems of human beings.

The study of the dynamics of organic systems in general is a growth area: it is highly relevant to economics, ecology, sociology and biology, and has been approached from all those areas. I have not been able to find an existing approach, however, which is well-adapted to the kinds of systems and dynamics involved in Hypnosis. The following language and methodology is therefore designed specifically to be useful in our field, though it can be generalised to others.

How does one start to design a dynamical theory? It is a tried and trusted principle that one should as far as possible work with **observables**. To base a theory on unobservables is to be working in the dark: there is no way of verifying if the theory is right or wrong and no way of refining it. What observables therefore can we say are applicable to all the systems of mind and body in which we are interested?

The answer which I will adopt is: **the level of activity**.

It is possible, by means of very fine electrodes, to measure quite precisely the level of activity of a single neuron (nerve cell). It is easily possible to measure the mean activity of the heart - the heart rate. It is possible to get a good measure of the level of activity of a muscle by means of seeing what force it can resist, or by its oxygen consumption. The overall level of activity of a region of the brain can be estimated by measuring the rise in temperature of that region (a method used over a century ago) or more modern methods involving measuring electrical activity (EEG) or local blood flow and metabolism - positron emission tomography (PET) and magnetic resonance imaging (MRI). The activity of various glands can be estimated by measuring the concentration of the hormones they produce in the blood. And so on. Although the functions of the various systems are of course distinct, we can in each case form at last a qualitative and very often a precise quantitative measure of its activity at a given time, and hence how its activity is changing with time.

Later, in Part C, we will discuss a more exact definition of activity, applicable to all systems, but at this introductory level it is enough to note that the intuitively clear notion of activity is something that is in principle observable for systems of the body. We will therefore base our theory on the notion of **the activity of a system**.

Let us now take a very brief look at a simple Hypnotic process with this idea in mind. A fairly typical Hypnotic induction as used by a Hypnotherapist today may proceed as follows. First of all the Subject's eyes may be induced to close, by one of a number of methods which usually involve fixing the gaze on some point, and

Eildon Press

Dr. Dylan Morgan
9 Richmond Place
Ilkley
West Yorks
LS29 8TJ

Dr David Gower
Course Director, MSc in Clinical Hypnosis
Psychology Dept (Torrington Place Building)
Dept of Psychology
University College
LONDON WC1E 6BT

25 July 1996

Dear Dr. Gower,

Thank you for taking up the offer of a copy of *The Principles of Hypnotherapy*.

If you can find time to let me know any thoughts of any kind you have regarding it, I would of course be grateful.

Yours sincerely,

Dylan Morgan

some form of verbal suggestion that eyes will get tired until they close. However it is done, it is clear that the **result** must be a great *reduction in the activity* of the whole of the part of the visual system involved in viewing the external world. With the eyes closed all the nerves from the retinas to the visual cortex will become quiescent.

A typical second step is to encourage physical relaxation. This again may be accomplished in a variety of ways: each group of muscles may first be tensed so that there will be a natural rebound into a more relaxed state; there may simply be a focus of attention on groups of muscles and a suggestion of relaxation; there may be the creation of an imaginary scenario such as a warm beach, which is designed to induce relaxed feelings. But however it is done the **result** is a *great reduction of the activity* of the main voluntary muscles, and very often the involuntary ones as well.

It will be noticed that a typical induction process is a one-way affair. Unless a question is asked, the Client does not talk. This is usually accomplished by the Hypnotist maintaining a steady flow of speech in which there are no cues for the Subject to respond verbally. But however it is done, the **result** is that the active speech-producing system often becomes *very inactive*.

The pattern is clear. The Hypnotherapist is reducing the activity of nearly all systems one by one. Higher-order faculties which are harder to observe, such as an internal verbal analysis of what is going on and a critical analysis of its content, are typically also reduced. There is, however, at least one exception to the general rule that systems are inactivated: and that is the aural system. The Subject must continue to be able to hear the Hypnotherapist. Ideally this system should become *more active* than usual: the intention is for the listener to respond more than usual to what is said by the Hypnotherapist. This may be accompanied by a reduction of attention to other sounds. Another possible exception will be a particular other system that the Hypnotist is aiming to change: it may well be that the goal is to enhance its activity. The Hypnotherapist may, for example, be aiming to *enhance* a memory or to *activate* the imagination.

So the total pattern of what the Hypnotherapist is doing can be charted in reasonable detail by noting the levels of activity of various systems and whether their activity is tending to increase or decrease.

It may be useful to some readers to picture things as follows. Let every major system of the brain and body be represented by a large dial, and an adjacent knob. Beneath each large dial can be placed a collection of smaller ones indicating the level of activity of the subsystems. Through the course of a normal day the needles on the dials are flickering, and most of the time indicating quite large levels of activity for most of the systems. The above Hypnotic induction can then be pictured in terms of the Hypnotherapist slowly turning knob after knob, turning down all those systems which are not relevant to the task in hand, and turning up those which are.

This brief example should illustrate the relevance of the level of activity of systems in the context of Hypnotherapy. It should show why it is worthwhile considering the dynamics of organic systems at a more abstract level.

In a general form the basic question which underlies understanding any complex thing is, "If I change *this*, how will it affect *that*?" We **must** be able to give at least a qualitative answer to questions of this form if we are to claim to understand what we are dealing with.

As an example of this, Newtonian physics is based on the twin observables of force and acceleration. The basic rule of the dynamics is that, "If I change the force on a particle, then I change the acceleration instantaneously in exact proportion: i.e. if the one doubles, then so does the other."

In our present theoretical structure the only dynamical variable we have so far is the level of activity. The central question we need to answer is therefore, "If I change the level of activity of *this* system, how will it alter the level of activity of *that* system?"

In general, such is the complexity of the systems with which we are dealing, we will be unable to give a quantitative answer to this question. But what we may at least be able to do is to discover whether an increase or decrease in the activity of one system acts so as to increase or decrease the activity of another. In other words we may simplify our central question to being one of *sign*.

Given any two systems A and B, in a given individual, we would like to know whether an increase in the activity of A leads to an increase or decrease in B or has no effect. Likewise we would like to know the effect on B of a decrease in the activity of A.

It might be supposed that if an increase in the activity of A leads to an increase in the activity of B, then a decrease will lead to a decrease in its activity. However this is not necessarily the case when we consider biological systems. We may take as an amusing and illustrative example the analysis in *Parkinson's Law* (Parkinson (1957)) of the figures for such organic systems as the Colonial Office or the Navy. It is understandable that as the empire increased or the number of ships increased then there should be a corresponding increase in the administrative staff. But the corresponding assumption that the *reduction* of the size of the empire, or a *reduction* in the number of fighting ships would also lead to a *reduction* of the administrators turns out to be quite wrong. If anything the facts suggest that their numbers continued to *increase even faster!*

Within the human body, an increase in the activity of the nerves running to a muscle typically produce a quick increase in the activity of the muscle, which will contract. A reduction of the activity of the nerves does NOT cause the muscle to expand again. To reverse the effect of that muscle, another muscle has to be called into play. That is why we see the general principle of *pairs* of opposing muscles throughout the body. There is, for example, a muscle to turn our eyes right, and another to turn them left; one to turn them up and another to turn them down. Other pairs handle diagonal movements.

As another example, the thought of going for a walk may activate the process of walking. The mere fact that this thought is then displaced by another does not stop the walk. It has to be stopped by activation of the thought, "Time to stop".

In the most general terms we may say that the most fundamental organic activity is that of *growth*. Growth may be activated, and that strongly and exponentially (i.e. doubling repeatedly in a characteristic interval of time), if a favourable environment is provided. On the other hand a removal of that provision does not necessarily lead to an equally rapid decline in the system, for it is the nature of organic systems to be self-preserving. A Government may induce activity in an area of the economy by putting some money into it. But when they stop doing so, that area will not immediately cease activity. Indeed it may respond to the challenge and become even more active.

Within the human body a sight of danger leads to an immediate fear response. The removal of that sight does not immediately induce relaxation. There is a strong asymmetry. It may even be the case that the removal of the sight actually increases the fear, on the grounds that it is better to be able to see a danger than to have it reappear unexpectedly.

Although this point has been emphasised in the case of organic systems, the principle is familiar even in certain mechanical contexts. Motor vehicles have a brake and an accelerator, one to slow you down and the other to speed you up. Simply taking your foot off the accelerator does very little indeed to stop you. Simply taking your foot off the brake does not cause you to accelerate at all. And notice that in order to drive a car you need only know which pedal is which. You only need to know the *sign* of their effects. The exact mathematical expression for how the velocity of the car varies with the pressure on the pedals is immaterial to the basic operation.

And this illustrates in the context of controlling organic systems why it is often enough to know the *sign* of the effect of one system on another.

The next step we will be taking is to streamline the discussion. It is a very good principle of thought, used extensively in mathematics, that if a phrase or sentence arises frequently, a shorthand expression should be found for it. Our brains are **severely limited** in their capacities. The *compression* of concepts makes the most of such capacities as we have.

This is a principle I personally find sadly lacking in application in books written by psychologists who should know better. There are too many people who seem to reason as follows: "Much valuable work is hard to understand. Therefore work which is hard to understand must be valuable. For my work to be valuable it must be hard for others to understand. I will therefore make the syntax and vocabulary as abstruse and complex as possible." It is as if they reasoned, "Most stately homes are hard to find your way around in. Therefore houses which are hard to find your way around in must be stately. For my home to be stately it must be hard for others to find their way around in it. I will therefore fill it with large furniture, screens, wardrobes, etc. which are all as large and difficult to negotiate as possible."

I am acutely aware of the smallness of my mind, and so have to work hard to keep it free from clutter by keeping things as simple as possible in finding my way around complicated things.

So in place of the phrase "an increase in the activity of system A" I will introduce the symbol "↑A". In place of the phrase "a decrease in the activity of system A" I will use "↓A". In place of the sentence, "an increase in the activity of system A leads directly to an increase in the activity of system B" I will use the expression "↑A → ↑B".

Expressions such as ↑A → ↓B, ↓A → ↑B and ↓A → ↓B can then be read easily.

Since it is useful to discuss situations in which a change in the activity of one system leads to no change in the activity of another, I will also use the symbol "○B" in place of "no change in the activity of system B".

If we let S = {sympathetic nervous system} and let P = {parasympathetic nervous system} and H = {heart} then we may say that the basic regulation of H follows the pattern that:

$$↑S → ↑H, \quad ↓S → ○H,$$

while

$$↑P → ↓H \text{ and } ↓P → ○H.$$

I.e. the action of the sympathetic nervous system activates the heart, while a reduction of the heart rate is produced by a direct action of the parasympathetic system (Rathus (1987)). They are rather like accelerator and brake in a motor vehicle.

It is worth noting that the basic concepts introduced so far have a range of applicability from the level of individual nerve cells - neurons - right up to the level of economies or ecosystems. It is known that the direct effect of one neuron on another with which it is in contact is either to excite it (increase its activity) or to decrease it (reduce its activity). The rule does not change from moment to moment or day to day. The pattern of working of the brain is dependent ultimately on the complexity that can arise from such basically simple interactions, when repeated by the billion.

Likewise in an ecosystem in which we may measure the mean activity of a species by its numerical strength, then the effect of a change in the activity of one species on another is also fixed in time. Foxes always prey on rabbits. Rabbits never prey on foxes. If F = {foxes}, R = {rabbits} then:

$$↑R → ↑F → ↓R → ↓F → ↑R → \ldots$$

which is shorthand for "an increase in the number of rabbits leads to an increase in the number of foxes (since they have more to eat), but an increase in the number of foxes acts to decrease the number of rabbits (since they are eaten); such a decrease in the number of rabbits will, in a while, lead to a decrease in the number of foxes (some starve to death), and that in turn will allow the numbers of rabbits to increase again. An increase in the number of rabbits ...." Such a pattern of interaction results in a cycling of the activity of each group. It is actually a negative feedback loop of a kind we will discuss in far more detail in Part B.

It is known from a careful analysis of definite models of organic systems that the result can readily become *chaotic*, in the strict mathematical sense of the word (Murray (1993)). Roughly speaking this means that even if we know the precise form of the dynamical equations it soon becomes impossible to predict with any accuracy the size of a population at a time in the future. And since in practice we are unlikely to know either the exact form of the equations, or the starting population accurately, the difficulty of exact prediction becomes that much harder. Consequently the analysis of precise models may well tell us very little more than our simple model, which by merely noting the sign of the effects of change actually contains a lot of the useful qualitative dynamics.

These considerations lead to the conclusion that we have found a strong and robust foundation for our subject in the above simple considerations. They are very general, but very clear. They get to the heart of the matter. We will be building on this foundation in Part B, to some effect.

Important note on abbreviations.

There may be some readers who are put off by the notation I have introduced. Anything new can be hard to adapt to. Please note that it is only a form of *shorthand*. If you think of it as being like the use of abbreviations, such as NCP&HR for the National Council of Psychotherapists and Hypnotherapy Register, you may find it easier to understand what it is about.

But shorthand *does* take a little time to master. I suggest that when at first you see some you avoid the temptation to let your eye skip over it and simply expand it into the full phrase or sentence it represents until you become familiar with its meaning. In time you will then be able to work simply with the shorthand. Compared with the task of a secretary learning Pitman's shorthand the time and effort involved is very small indeed.

The great strength of a shorthand lies in its simplicity and compactness. We will find this useful when we come to analysing different kinds of processes which arise. I re-emphasise that even arithmetic could not have developed without the use of a good shorthand for the numbers. But of course the use of a shorthand in itself is not mathematics.

The weakness of a shorthand is that it has to be *accurate*. A one letter mistake in the degree MA can make a Master of Arts into a Doctor of Medicine - MD - something that cannot be achieved by a one letter change to the full phrase.

Finally, for the sake of exactitude, I will make explicit a convention that if a word or phrase is in { } it refers to the *activity of a system*, while if it is in ( ) it refers to some quantity that is not. Thus it can be useful to write ↑(temperature) →

↑{sweating}, which would be shorthand for "An increase in the temperature of a person leads to an increase in the activity of the perspiration system". The subtly different expression ↑{temperature} → ↑(sweating) would mean "An increase in the activity of the sensory system which registers temperature leads to an increase in the measurable sweat produced". This distinction is not of great importance at the level of this book, but could be important as the methods become increasingly precise. For it is NOT always the case that the perceived temperature is the same as the actual temperature and it may not be the case that a given level of activation of the perspiration system always leads to the same level of perspiration.

SUMMARY

The notion of a system has been elaborated mainly through examples.

The notion of the **activity** of an organic system has been introduced, together with a notation which expresses in a compact form the essential facts regarding the way changes in the activity of one system may affect the activity of another.

It is important to note the general principle of organic systems that reversing the cause does not necessarily reverse the effect.

It has been emphasised that Hypnotic techniques have the effect of altering the level of activity of a very wide variety of systems in the brain and body, which is why this systems-oriented approach to the subject is invaluable if we are to analyse what is happening.

CHAPTER 4

Other Theoretical Approaches

THE PREVIOUS CHAPTER outlined the concise and general framework for theoretical Hypnosis which will be used in this book. We may now take a look at earlier theories to see how they can be related within this framework.

Although the Hypnotic phenomena described in Chapter 2 have been observed for a very long time - hundreds if not thousands of years in some cases - the nature of what was happening has been understood in very different ways. This chapter will describe the various *ideas* of what is involved. For convenience these ideas will frequently be associated with the names of their originators or chief proponents. The order in which they are described will be loosely chronological but the intention is not to give a history but rather an overview of the kinds of ways in which our subject has been thought about over the years. In any case the historical development of ideas is seldom straightforward. Similar ideas have a way of arising in several places at the same time, and returning in modified forms at different times. Many different ideas can coexist at the same time. For anyone who is interested in the detailed history of Hypnosis there are some excellent books now available (Gauld (1992), Crabtree (1993)).

The main theoretical approaches can be summarised as follows:

1. Spirit possession.
2. Vital energy effects.
3. Neurological.
4. Suggestion.
5. Sociological.
6. Information.

1. Spirit possession.

When we look back in time through the eyes of history we find that most people most of the time had a total and unquestioning belief in all manner of disembodied spirits. These could be the spirits of the dead - humans or animals, ghosts, evil spirits, good spirits, gods and demons. (Even in this secular age the majority of people I meet seem to retain some form of belief in such things.)

In societies with complete faith in such spirits there would be individuals who claimed to have special powers with regard to them. They might be called shamans or priests or witch-doctors or oracles. Some of their early practices foreshadowed professions which have since become quite distinct. Their practice would often be tied in with the movements of the moon and planets, and so in that way they are the forerunners of astronomers. They would often work with the healing spirits they associated with various substances - animal, vegetable and mineral - and in that way are forerunners of medicine and even chemistry. In creating theories of the origin and meaning of the universe they were the forerunners of philosophers and cosmologists. In their use of music and dramatic enactment to enhance their effect they are also the forerunners of actors and musicians.

It is not therefore surprising that their work also contained the seeds of Hypnotherapy. To our eyes it seems clear that they often used a variety of means to induce in their listeners certain powerful expectations which would then very often have been realised. In terms of healing, a modern interpretation of what they did would be that they used a greatly enhanced placebo response to great effect.

If we stand back and look at the pattern that seems to run through the practice of such people we see the following.

The Practitioner goes through some procedure which he (or she) claims to lead to his or her possession by some powerful spirit. Today this might be termed entering a trance. The usual personality disappears and another takes its place - that of the spirit or god. This powerful spirit then acts on the Client's behalf. Rather more problems would be tackled in this way than we might contemplate today: they could include not only health problems but also divination or procuring good fortune or revenge on an enemy. Notice that the whole focus of attention is on the *Practitioner*. Although we can expect that the Client will also become strongly expectant of change, and might at times be acted upon to remove a supposed evil spirit which might possess him or her, the focus of the activity is the possession of the Practitioner by a powerful spirit.

It should be noticed that this approach to problems has not died out in the world. There are many today who continue to work within this paradigm. For example there are those working within the healing ministry of various churches who are portraying themselves as channels through which the healing spirit of God can come down for others. Even more similar are the mediums who go into a trance in which they might be "taken over" by the spirit of a Red Indian Guide or the like, and it is that spirit which then supposedly advises or helps.

The only trace of this theme in modern Hypnotherapy is that the Practitioner will typically adopt a professional persona while at work. This has a faint flavour of the practice of the shaman. It is saying non-verbally, "I am no longer the ordinary person you meet in the street. I am now embodying wisdom, knowledge and power to help you. These transcend my personal self."

It is worth looking at a few phenomena from our field to see how they might look from a spirit-world perspective.

There is an established Hypnotic phenomenon of automatic writing. In some Subjects it is not only possible to make a hand rise up into the air with no conscious volition, but also to get it to write words which seem to the Subject to be totally unwilled and unpremeditated. Indeed if the hand is hidden from view there may be no knowledge even that the hand has done any writing (e.g. Gauld (1992)).

A natural spiritual possession interpretation of this is that clearly a foreign spirit has taken over the functioning of the hand, and that the Hypnotherapist has simply acted in such a way as to facilitate it.

Another phenomenon which arises in the field of Hypnosis is that of Clients who seem vividly to recall events which are clearly set in times before they were born. The spiritual possession view of these would naturally be again that the body (like that of the medium) has temporarily been taken possession of by the spirit of someone else who had lived that earlier life, and again that the Hypnotist has acted in a way to facilitate this.

Alternatively it may be said that this phenomenon concerns only one spirit who first lived the past life and is now living the present one. This interpretation is fairly popular with many people today, and is termed Past Life Regression. Examples of instances of the use of Hypnotic techniques to elicit details of past lives are provided by Iverson (1976). The belief harmonises well with those Eastern philosophies and religions which believe in repeated incarnations of each individual soul. I know of no attempt to distinguish by experiment or theory between the above two interpretations.

Most of the phenomena which today are interpreted as being the results of the functioning of "the subconscious" would be interpreted as being the results of the functioning of "the spirits". We see echoes of this in phrases such as "he is showing his animal spirits", "spirit of inquiry", "she is inspired", etc.

The relief of some bad feeling like a depression or jealousy would be seen as the removal or exorcism of a bad spirit that was possessing the person. The cure of a disease would be by removing the possessing spirit or by placating or neutralising the evil power that was causing it. A cure of insomnia would be seen as the removal of the "wakeful spirit" that was inducing it, and so on.

We have seen how some of the phenomena of our field look from the point of view of someone who believes in spirit possession. Now let us see how that paradigm looks from the perspective of our present systems approach.

The starting point is the idea that the mind is composed of many subsystems. At times, as in the case of split personalities, these different subsystems can be distinct and very complex, each having its own memory and pattern of behaviour. We will later meet other aspects of this phenomenon, which go by such names as dissociation, "the child within", "the hidden observer", etc.: all attest to the fact that for most of us the mind is best seen as a complex network of interacting systems, many of considerable complexity and often having a high degree of autonomy. In such cases they can function like sub-personalities.

There is really very little difference *in practical terms* between such a picture and that of spirit possession. Any differences centre around such essentially pragmatic questions as, "How do such subsystems arise in the mind or brain?" One school of thought will say that it can only be as a result of an elaboration of physical information which has come through the normal senses or is implicit in the genes. The school of thought at the other extreme will say that they can arise by some paranormal process: that a distinct spirit, unbounded by space and time, may enter the mind or brain and take root.

The systems paradigm cannot, of course, resolve this conflict: that can only come as a result of very careful examination of the phenomena. What it does do is to provide a comparatively neutral language and framework which could be shared by proponents of both views and which might lead to some agreed experiments to determine the actual facts. If, for example, we are examining a case of automatic writing, then it could be agreed by both sides that there is a subsystem of the person which is acting outside the scope of the normal personality. The content of the writing might then be examined to see if it is explicable on the basis of previous experience in this life, or not.

If, as another example, we are dealing with a case of "past-life regression", it could be agreed it involves a complex subsystem of the person which is functioning in some ways like that of a person who lived in the past. (There is nothing too strange about this in itself: actors can do it regularly.) It can be presumed that this subsystem would have some effects on the present behaviour of the person, and that any changes a therapist might make to the "past-life" system, including making it more conscious, would have some effect. Such changes are valid whatever the assumption made about the origin of the phenomenon. In principle, however, it might be possible for some criteria to be agreed which might clarify the question of the origin of such systems. A clear case in which a "past-life" report revealed a complete knowledge of the meaning of a written language which up until then had been totally obscure would, for example, be strong evidence for the transference of a mental system of thought by other than the ways we accept on a daily basis: i.e. primarily through what we have seen or heard - at first hand or perhaps on the TV, video, radio or in a book.

In brief then, IF it were to be established as a pragmatic fact that spirit possession in the traditional sense takes place, THEN we would simply include such systems and their workings within the current theoretical structure of systems. This is parallel to the observation that IF it were to be established that mental communication - telepathy - is possible between minds then this would not affect the framework of the theory, based as it is on the effect of one system on another: it would simply add an additional method by which one mental system can affect another - like the addition of radio or television.

2. Life-force effects.

Mesmer (1734-1815) is one of the best known names in the history of Hypnotism (Burranelli (1975)). He can be taken to herald in a new paradigm. In this, the old idea of powerful spirits with wills, intelligences and feelings is displaced by a belief in powerful life-forces akin to gravity, magnetism and electricity. Mesmer was first influenced by Newton's theory of gravitation. To begin with he called the force *animal magnetism*, though he later came to regret the term since too many people then confused it with ordinary magnetism. This force could be stored in certain objects. He, other things and other people could be a channel for it. If its flow was blocked in a person, it could lead to illness. Healing resulted from restoring the proper flow.

Such ideas are congenial to certain kinds of human minds in certain ages, it would seem, since others independently arrived at similar theories, in which the force was given different names. A Baron von Reichenbach (1779) claimed the discovery of what he called the Od force with similar properties. In America the so-called Electro-biology of Grimes (1839) had the same flavour. In this century we find Reich with his orgone energy which could likewise be stored and used. And to the present day the concept of a life-force floats freely through New Age literature.

We also find notions of "psychic energy", "repressed (perhaps sexual) energy" and the like entering into some psychoanalytical writings and thought without a great deal of attempt to pin down the notions precisely, so that they are scarcely distinguishable from the other forces mentioned above.

I am not aware of a proponent of this way of thinking who has worked the ideas out in detail. There seems a certain nebulous vagueness about the supposed force which is mirrored in a similar vagueness of the thought about it. Thus Mesmer himself simultaneously saw the "magnetism" as being capable of passing through *anything*, but as being reflected from mirrors and also of being stored in certain things! In his list of 27 propositions concerning animal magnetism we find the following propositions (Mesmer (1779)):

13. Experience shows a diffusion of matter so subtle that it penetrates all other bodies, apparently without any loss of potency.
15. It is like light in that it can be reinforced and reflected by mirrors.
17. ... (it) can be accumulated, concentrated, and transported from one place to another.

This is such a strange combination of properties that you would expect it to suggest all forms of questions in the mind, but it did not to Mesmer.

As an example of how this theoretical approach might treat a typical phenomenon, we may consider a fairly typical response of many of Mesmer's patients which was that at some stage in the proceedings they would go into some form of convulsion - a crisis. This is not something that happens in modern Hypnotherapy, but then it is not expected. If we were to suggest it, then undoubtedly there would be Subjects who would respond in that way. (Stage Hypnotists have been known to get people to respond as if they have just received a strong electrical shock.) But to the Mesmerist this was a clear manifestation of a release of the blocked energy.

As another example, I can say to someone: "Hold your hands six inches apart. I will now place mine one on either side of yours and a few inches away from them. You will then start to feel a powerful force coming from my hands forcing yours together." And when I do this it will normally work. If there is a belief in the existence of some vital force then this will seem to be very strong confirmation that I *am* producing that force.

However, all it really proves is the power of the *idea* and not the existence of the force, for *it works equally well* if I simply say (and, usually, repeat until it happens), "Hold your hand six inches apart. Try to keep them that distance apart. They will in fact, whatever you do, be drawn together." In neither case will any flow of energy be measurable from me to the Client. All I have done is to establish a *system of thought* in the person's mind.

Notice that a Practitioner like Mesmer would still be credited with some power, though it is not now the power of a possessing spirit, but some sort of power of his own to direct this life-force. It might be manifest in his eyes or in his hands. He might well have his effect by moving his hands over the patient's body, with or without touching it. The norm in the practice of Mesmerists seems to have been a great deal of contact, which was often very vigorous. There are certain "healers" in the present day who claim some form of this same power.

In the longer term the most valuable consequence of the shift of perspective that we may associate with Mesmer is that the phenomena came to be thought of as things that might be analysed in a controlled way. A big problem with the old spirit-world picture is that spirits are, of their nature, not easy to measure or control. Once the phenomena are assumed to be the result of something more like forces they are open to examination. And it must be said that when the notions of Mesmer *were* put to the test by the Royal Commission appointed in France to look into his claims, it was found that his claims for the existence of a force of "animal magnetism" were unsubstantiated. For example a patient who would react appropriately to a tree when he had seen it being "magnetised", reacted at random to trees if he had not seen which one had been treated. The Commission concluded that Mesmer's results were a result of the belief and expectation of people together with the fact that some spontaneous remissions are to be expected in any case (*Rapport...* (1784)).

This report did not have very much effect on the continuing use of Mesmeric techniques which gradually changed in the hands of various people over the next half century from the end of the eighteenth century into the nineteenth. Over this period most of the common Hypnotic phenomena were being evoked regularly, and it would appear that the repertoire of travelling Mesmeric showmen of the day would be rather similar in content and tone to that of many a modern stage Hypnotist, though their "explanation" of what was happening would be different.

What are we to make of vital energy explanations?

To the best of my knowledge all properly conducted examinations of detailed predictions of this theory have led to essentially the same conclusion as that of the

Royal Commission: there is no evidence for a transfer of energy or of there being any vital force or similar.

But from the perspective of our current systems approach we may perhaps build a bridge to such theories as follows. What we *can* certainly do is to activate in another person a new pattern of thought. This, in itself, is not a process which is essentially energetic. It has more to do with *ordering*, with changing the *patterns* of thought. But the new pattern of thought can lead to an increase, or of course a decrease, in the activity of a variety of subprocesses in the person. For example, if a person is shouted at, it can arouse strong feelings of anger or even actual violence. In such a case it can look as if the person has received energy from the shouter. But an even stronger response can be evoked by a piece of paper, such as an Income Tax demand, where there is negligible energy involved, only information.

So, we transfer patterns, order, information, and this may lead to an activation of energy out of all proportion to any minute amounts of energy that are actually involved in the sound waves or other media which convey the change. The *amplification* that this involves will be made the subject of Chapter 13.

3. Neurological theories

It is convenient to associate the start of this approach with the name of James Braid (1795-1860). In his book of 1842 he gave the world the results of what his rational Scottish mind had discovered about the Mesmeric phenomena of the day. He also gave us the word Hypnosis (Braid (1842)).

The essence of his theoretical conception is that he discovered that he could greatly depress or prodigiously exalt (his terms) the arousal of selected parts of the nervous system. The name he chose to describe the phenomena was, in full, Neuro-Hypnosis, or a sleep of the nerves. This is a reference to the condition of greatly depressed activity of most groups of nerves in his Subjects. But he was quite clear that this was distinct from normal sleep, and that it could be combined with a greatly exalted condition of other groups of nerves.

In terms of the concepts that have been introduced in this book, Braid's idea was that the level of activity of particular subsystems of the nervous system could be increased or decreased freely and dramatically. In this respect his ideas are clear precursors of those in this book.

He also demonstrated that the standard phenomena of Mesmerism, which were supposedly a result of the power of animal magnetism, could be produced as readily with no passes, contact from the Practitioner, etc.

Braid, however, also thought in terms of a Hypnotic *state*. This is a natural conclusion from his experiences. He used one and only one induction procedure. He expected the one form of response. With our present understanding it is not surprising that he should therefore have discovered a seeming uniformity of response.

In the one hundred and fifty years since then, the notion of *a unique* Hypnotic state has continued to run through our subject. There have been many attempts in more recent years to find one single clear defining criterion for this supposed state which will effectively distinguish it from other states - but to no avail. And indeed, surely the *a priori* assumption is that a single state is far too simple a concept to explain the fact that the phenomena of Hypnosis can arise in conditions as different as the very relaxed calm office of a modern Hypnotherapist and the emotionally charged group sessions of Mesmer which were characterised by patients falling about in convulsions and having to be taken into adjacent rooms to recover from their crises?

Associated with the notion of a single state has been a more modern tendency to try to determine ONE neurological structure which is involved in Hypnosis. Some workers have been inclined to think that it depends on the inhibition of the activity of the left (verbal) hemisphere of the brain and a simultaneous activation of the right hemisphere (Shone (1983)). Clearly such a process comes within the definition of Hypnosis used here in that the above lateralisation of brain activity is *one particular example* of the general principles of Hypnosis which involves a relative change in the activities of various systems. But there is no clear evidence that this particular change is either necessary or sufficient for the production of any other particular Hypnotic phenomenon.

A modern refinement of this theory maintains that the balance between the hemispheres can be altered by forced uninostril breathing: breathing through the right nostril tends to increase the activity of the left hemisphere and vice versa (Rossi (1993)).

Another theory, which has also only been presented in a superficial way, is that the key system is the Ascending Reticular Activating System (RAS) in the brain stem (Waxman (1981)). This is certainly involved in general levels of arousal or activity in the brain, and presumably any global changes in mental activity will involve the activity of the RAS. So while it is quite consistent with the general principles of Hypnosis that it should be possible to affect the activity of the RAS, there is again no evidence that changes to it are either necessary or sufficient for the production of a given phenomenon. We have already remarked on the fact that Hypnotic phenomena may be observed in Subjects with both very high and very low levels of arousal.

Closely related to this is the idea that Hypnosis involves simply a form of sleep, for there are certain key nuclei in the brain stem - the nuclei of Raphe - whose activation will either switch on sleep or switch on arousal. This idea, in one form or another, goes back a long way in the history of Hypnosis. The suggestion of sleep was used as least as far back as De Puységur (Tinterow (1970)).

Now sleep may seem to be a simple thing or state, but more recent research has shown a number of things about it. The first thing is that it is not a *state*. Measurements of brain activity show a continuously changing pattern. Within this pattern there are episodes of dreaming in which there is clearly a lot of mental activity of a particular kind. In addition we may note that it is during sleep that the level of growth hormones in the brain is at its maximum, which strongly suggests that *some* processes are very active.

Having said this it is also clear that sleep is characterised by the almost total elimination of the activity of certain high-order brain functions: those we associate with consciousness. Thus it is within the bounds of the general principles of Hypnosis that it is possible to change the pattern of activity in similar ways to those in sleep - and indeed when suggestions of sleep have been given it has been found possible to measure electrical waves in the brain which are characteristic of sleep. But again we must emphasise that this has not been shown to be either necessary or sufficient in order to produce any other Hypnotic phenomenon.

Attempts have also been made to detect other specific changes in brain wave patterns which can be associated with a unique "state" of Hypnosis. Again the weakness of this approach is that an experimenter may well find it possible to record certain changed patterns of activity in the brain in certain Subjects, such as those mentioned above, since, as I have continually noted, the changing of the patterns of activity is the central theme of Hypnosis. But there is again a lack of evidence that any *particular* change is either necessary or sufficient for the production of any other Hypnotic phenomenon.

Another theory in this area, promoted by Rossi (1993), involves linking Hypnotic phenomena to the natural cycles of wakefulness and sleepiness during the day - the diurnal cycles. There are such cycles, which are a continuation of cycles which have been observed in sleep also, which have a period of roughly 90-120 minutes. Roughly speaking this means that the degree to which a person is more active and outward looking as opposed to being more passive and inward looking will fluctuate with time. Since quite a lot of Hypnotic phenomena involve a certain amount of inwardness it is reasonable to suppose that they could be evoked *more easily* at certain points on the cycle than others. However this is a far cry from establishing that this particular phenomenon is at the basis of all Hypnotic phenomena.

Another line of thought seems to go to the opposite extreme from the sleep theories, and to emphasise the strong focus of attention which can characterise mental activity in many Hypnotic procedures. It can be noted that at times the attention of the Subject can be narrowed so that there is no awareness of anything but the Hypnotist's voice and the current thought which it is generating. It is certainly true that this can happen, and that many Hypnotic procedures have this as a goal. Braid himself thought on these lines and at one time attempted to change his nomenclature and to drop the word Hypnosis in favour of mono-ideism, which is a reference to the single-mindedness characteristic of many Subjects. The narrowing of attention is often a very useful tool in the practice of Hypnosis, and we will come across it often, particularly when it is sharpened by the constant use of the question, "Exactly which systems is it being limited to?" At the same time it is a fact that other Hypnotic techniques and phenomena are aimed at broadening of attention and even to a seeming elimination of any focused attention at all, so that we could not define the subject entirely in terms of focused attention without losing valuable material. If we regard attention as an aspect of the functioning of the brain, then it is natural within the systems paradigm to see Hypnosis as involving the increase *or decrease* of attention to a particular area according to the needs of the task in hand.

Finally under this classification comes one of the simplest pictures of what Hypnosis involves. This picture sees the brain in terms of conscious plus subconscious. All functions of systems of the brain involved in conscious behaviour are lumped into one supposed entity, "the conscious mind", and all those others of which there is not normally conscious control or awareness are lumped into another, "the subconscious mind" (cf. Bowers et al. (1984)). The process of Hypnosis is then seen as being the displacement of the conscious mind - it is "sent to sleep" - and the Hypnotist then speaks to the subconscious mind directly. This idea is not one that can be clearly associated with one person. It is implicit in the work of Puységur and subsequent workers in our field, and it is probably the case that it was the cumulative experience of those working with Hypnotic phenomena in the nineteenth century that led to the notion of the subconscious that nowadays is associated with Freud.

There are other versions of this model which go by the name of dissociational theories. Anyone who has read the literature on clear cases of split or multiple personalities will be familiar with the picture of one body which seems to contain a number of personalities which are at variance with each other. Despite the fact that such extreme cases seem to be very rare, they provide a simple picture which can be carried over into thinking of people who do not suffer from any problem.

The most recent proponent of a form of dissociational theory is Hilgard, an American psychologist who has done some excellent work on the use of Hypnosis in pain (Hilgard & Hilgard (1975)). Some of his experiments demonstrated that it would be possible for there to be no *conscious* awareness of pain in certain individuals, but there was clear evidence that it was being perceived at some level of the mind.

Such theories are quite in harmony with a systems approach, the only difference being the amount of detail. A systems approach will expect there to be a multitude of systems at many levels. Under some conditions the situation may simplify into effectively two systems, just as a society may at some times be seen for simplicity as a governing class and a governed. But this view of things will far more often be too naïve and simplistic to be of universal value. Things are seldom this clear cut. For example such a model of a nation has little to tell us about improving the educational system or the health system or the transportation system of a country. Similarly the fact that there is no conscious awareness of a system says very little about it: it may involve a "split personality" or a repressed memory, or simply an automatic action, or an automatic regulation of weight.

Finally in this section we may mention a common "definition" of the supposed "state of Hypnosis", i.e. as "an alternative state of consciousness". The main thrust of this definition is that Hypnosis does not involve the Subject becoming unconscious. It does not say what the difference is between a supposed "normal" state of consciousness - is this the "state" of being in a rage, or in a race, or watching a video or making love? - and the "alternative" state - is this relaxed, or doing the cancan on stage, or expressing deeply repressed emotions?

However, this idea can be expressed rather more precisely in terms of the systems approach as follows. Hypnosis will generally involve activating systems in a rather different pattern from those which are customary for the individual in order to achieve the required change. There will be no ONE different pattern for each person, but nevertheless the difference will be perceived by the individual, and during the process of experiencing this different pattern we might loosely say that he or she "has an altered consciousness".

It should be apparent by now that the theories mentioned in this section can be seen to have the following common pattern. 1. A phenomenon is observed in the course of some Hypnotic procedure. 2. It involves some particular system or function of the brain or nervous system - which we will call X. 3. An unwarranted generalisation is made that ALL Hypnotic phenomena are a result of X.

The argument of this book is that all such overgeneralisations are invalid. Each of the systems mentioned can, at certain times, be relevant to the practice of Hypnosis, but none can be seen as central. Of the theories mentioned above in this section Braid's is perhaps the least limited in that it comes quite close to the perception of the multiplicity of effects which can be achieved, though of course he did not know nearly as much as we do today about the workings of the very many complex systems in the human body and nervous system.

4. Suggestion.

The fourth major approach to Hypnosis is based on the simple idea that all the phenomena are a simple result of suggestion. We may associate this idea with Bernheim (1840-1919) (Bernheim (1884)).

We may present the argument for this approach in the following way. It is a commonplace fact that we generally act in accordance with our beliefs. If, then, these beliefs can somehow be changed, our behaviour will change. In this view Hypnotic phenomena are simply a result of changing beliefs.

Inasmuch as any thought is a mental process, the initiation of a new belief involves the activation of a particular new and specific process in the brain. Likewise, since the acceptance of a new belief will often mean the rejection of an old one, it will also be necessary to inhibit or reduce the activity of a second system of thought. Therefore the process of suggestion comes within the framework of Hypnosis we are developing in this book.

By approaching things in this way we can avoid futile discussion about a supposed *difference* between simple suggestion and Hypnosis. Even Bernheim found that he could produce dramatic changes in people's behaviour by simple suggestion with no "Hypnotic" induction at all. He found, for example, some individuals who, if charged confidently with a theft of which they were totally innocent, acted in every detail as if they were guilty - even to seemingly recalling the details of the incident.

Is it any wonder then that a stage Hypnotist can find individuals who can believe with total conviction the innocuous, if unlikely, things he suggests to them?

Proper experiments have, in fact, failed to produce evidence of any incontrovertible difference between "simple" suggestion and "Hypnotic" suggestion. The search for such a difference is largely motivated, consciously or unconsciously, by the concept of a unique Hypnotic state.

The limitations of a theory based entirely on the idea of suggestion are that 1) it omits any details of how the suggestions lead to the desired results, and consequently 2) it cannot explain why some suggestions are effective and some not. Finally 3) it does not answer the question of what suggestions should be made other than the simple, "The problem will go".

By contrast the systems approach, as will become clearer in later chapters, is in a position to determine a causal chain by which a suggested idea will lead to changes in other systems, which will in turn lead to further changes, until we reach the system of interest. It can indicate better what changes should be suggested, and in which systems; it can also discriminate between cases in which direct suggestion can be expected to be effective and those in which it cannot.

5. Sociological.

At the opposite extreme from Braid, who saw the phenomena as being essentially intrinsic to the Subject, we find theories which are based on looking at the combined system of Subject plus Hypnotist.

There are those such as Ferenczi (1916) who see what happens as being essentially that the relationship of the two individuals becomes that of parent and child. The Hypnotist adopts the parental role and the Subject acts like an obedient and unquestioning child.

It is certainly possible for this sort of thing to happen. Given suitable cues it is relatively easy to evoke a pattern of behaviour which was current at an earlier time. The standard Hypnotic phenomenon of regression to an earlier age is a particular form of this. In the language of systems we may say that it is certainly possible for a childlike behavioural system to be evoked in a Subject, and that for the Hypnotist to adopt a suitable parental role is one way of achieving this.

So it is helpful to see certain aspects of Hypnosis in this light. What would be misleading, however, would be to see the whole of the subject from this angle, since there is no evidence that it is either necessary or sufficient for a Subject to enter into such a childlike relationship with the Hypnotist in order to evoke any other Hypnotic phenomenon.

Another common relationship which has been used as a model for the Hypnotist-Client system is that of sexual love. Freud seems to have thought on these lines for a while. It is true that if a person falls in love with another, then she or he is at that time very open to the influence of the beloved. Consequently if feelings of romantic love for the Hypnotherapist were to arise in a Client, then an increase in responsiveness would be likely: possibly this does arise in certain cases. But this phenomenon is again really too limited to be a suitable foundation on which to erect a theory of our subject. It would make self-hypnosis very hard to explain and would lead to the expectation that Hypnotic phenomena would arise only, or at the least far more easily, between members of opposite sexes than of the same sex - an expectation which is not substantiated by any evidence I have come across.

There is a third significant social phenomenon which has not, I believe, been used explicitly as a foundation for a major theory, though it might have been, and which is included here for comparison and completeness. This is that of the implicit obedience of an inferior to a superior in either the armed forces or any other strongly hierarchical part of society. It is certainly the case that in the earlier days of this century books on Hypnosis would say that members of the armed forces made good subjects. The presumption is that they were so accustomed to obeying orders without question that it was easy for the Hypnotist to build on this basis an unquestioning acceptance of his suggestions. We may surmise that some of the easy success of early practitioners such as Mesmer and Braid may have been based on the fact that many of their patients would have been used to accepting what their social superiors said without any question in a way which is far from common today. Insofar as the Hypnotist was of a higher class, it would have been comparatively easy for him to obtain many Hypnotic phenomena which depend on a simple and unquestioning acceptance of the Hypnotist's statements.

A fourth social phenomenon (related to the above but without the hierarchical overtones), which has been used as the basis for an explanation of Hypnotic phenomena, is that of social compliance. This idea is usually associated with the name of Spanos (1986). In essence this theory views Hypnotic phenomena as being the acting out of a role by the Subject which will meet the expectations of the situation. The situation includes the Hypnotist, but also any other people involved and the physical situation. Thus the situation in a consulting room is different from that on a stage. In the latter situation the Subject will have an expectation that dancing the rumba is only to be expected. In the former it would not be. Consequently it would be much harder to elicit such dancing in the consulting room. More generally there are certain expectations of what Hypnosis involves which are diffused through society and which change over time. An example is the expectation of a "crisis" - a going into convulsions - which Mesmer's patients did frequently because it was expected and which does not happen today because it is not.

It is certainly true that people will do quite extraordinary things as a result of social compliance, as numbers of psychological experiments have proved (Milgram (1974)). People *will* change their behaviour or ideas in response to the social situation that they are in, though of course this is not the same as saying that all people will do so equally. It must therefore be regarded as *one* of the mechanisms involved in certain Hypnotic phenomena. However this again seems far too limited a basis to explain all the phenomena of Hypnosis.

Perhaps we may put all the social theories into perspective by considering a hypothetical intelligent race which has no pair bonding, no nurturing, no hierarchies and no social groupings. Some form of intelligent reptile comes to mind. Would any form of Hypnosis be possible in such a species? A proponent of each of the above theories should say, "No. Since the particular form of interaction I am assuming as the whole basis of Hypnosis is not present, nothing can be done." Yet there is every reason to suppose that if you carefully manipulated the creature's *imagination*, you could produce many of the responses we regard as Hypnotic. Many such phenomena are produced in humans purely in response to pictures in the imagination. If, let us suppose, we were to give such a creature a journey into a virtual reality world which we control, then by manipulating the world appropriately we could manipulate its thoughts and feelings and actions. By creating pictures of the world as it was when it emerged from its shell, it would seem that we would have a good chance of activating childlike behaviour patterns, i.e. regression. If we wanted to stop it smoking, we should be able to do some simple conditioning involving introducing some painful/fearful images with every introduction of the image of a cigarette, and so on. Practising Hypnotherapists will see that this hypothetical scheme reproduces much of what they do without the need for any common language, or any social compliance factor at all. So in principle there would still be a subject of Hypnosis as I have defined it even in the absence of social factors.

On the other hand the existence of such factors does make the subject richer and in many ways easier. Since the objective of Hypnotherapy is to make some change in the functioning of some internal system of the Client, it is going to be much facilitated if, as a preliminary, the Client can be encouraged to activate a receptive and responsive mode towards the Hypnotherapist. To some extent such a pattern must be based on relationships which the Client has known in the past. They may be parent-child, teacher-pupil, man-woman, friend-friend, shopkeeper-customer, doctor-patient, etc. The *art* of Hypnotherapy lies in utilising whatever capacities are present in order to achieve a given end, and a good Hypnotherapist has to have a reasonable degree of flexibility in order to activate such social systems as are present and appropriate in the Client.

We should note also in this context the Freudian notion of *transference*. This is the phenomenon whereby a patient in therapy may transfer into his or her relationship with the therapist some of the feelings and characteristics of an earlier relationship with a parent or other significant figure. This can happen spontaneously and is discouraged by certain schools, while others encourage it. Clearly the mechanism of transference involves the stimulus of the therapist's presence activating a particular pattern of feeling and behaviour in the patient, and is therefore a particular aspect of the above.

This section of theories may be summarised as follows. They all regard the primary system of discussion *not* as the individual Subject, but as the larger system of Hypnotist plus Subject, or the even larger one of the society within which the two individuals are a subsystem. Each theory tends to focus on one particular aspect of such larger systems and to view *it* as the central aspect of Hypnosis.

The position taken in this book is that while all such aspects can be of importance in the field of Hypnosis, none of them is either necessary or sufficient to the production of Hypnotic phenomena.

It should be clear, moreover, that the concept of an organic system which we have used as a foundation for our subject can deal as naturally with systems consisting of two or more individuals as it can with two or more subsystems of the human nervous system. This aspect of the subject will be developed in more detail later, but here we may note that the basic element of Hypnosis, considered as an aspect of the two-person system, is that of the activation of some particular process - - which we will label A - within the repertoire of the *Hypnotist*, which leads to some required change (an increase or decrease) in the activity of some corresponding process B in the *Subject*:

$$\uparrow A \rightarrow \updownarrow B.$$

A is typically a linguistic process, but may well have behavioural and affective components: i.e. the Hypnotist is primarily talking, but the body language and the emotional tone in what is said will also contribute.

The successive application of this form of interaction leads in time to the change in the pattern of the mental and physical activities in the Subject which is aimed at by the Hypnotist.

6. Information.

A very recent theory of Rossi (1993) discusses Hypnosis in terms of information. This theory may be presented as follows. We have observed that there are many systems in the body. Where in this book we are starting with the more elementary idea that each may alter the activity of another, an information-theoretical approach says that each can communicate information to another. The effect of the communication of information will, of course, be to alter the activity in some way.

In his own words Rossi proposes that, "The cybernetic (circular) flow of information between our psycho-social world, mind and body down to the cellular-genetic level is the general domain of Hypnotherapy."

However at its present stage of development the theory is biassed towards showing how changes at a mental level may be communicated via a hypothesised process of "information transduction" to the chemical processes involved in healing, and there is little development at the level of analysing Hypnotic inductions, etc. The theory is also somewhat confused by its association with the rather limiting conception that Hypnotherapeutic suggestion is "the entrainment and utilisation of psychological rhythms generated by the cybernetic loops of mind-body communication" - the theory involving diurnal cycles described above.

By contrast the approach of this book is to be in broad agreement about the domain of Hypnotherapy: that it *does* involve the many cybernetic systems at the social, mental, physical and chemical levels. But within this scheme it unifies existing understanding rather than positing any new specific principles. We will also find that it makes far clearer the dynamics of the cybernetic processes, in many different contexts.

Conclusion

It will be apparent from the above brief accounts how many different aspects there are to our subject. Each has a certain virtue. But each is largely incompatible, as a theory, with the others because of its claim to exclusivity.

It is as if a continent has been surveyed by a number of individuals. Each has drawn a map of his own locality and regards the local terrain as archetypal of the whole continent. They therefore regard the others as being substantially in error.

But there comes a time when it is possible to unite the maps in such a way that they *add* to each other and help to form a composite map of the entire continent.

The uniting principle is the fact that all of the theories deal with one or more organic systems and their interactions. By using this principle we are able to make a consistent picture of the whole field. It provides a way for the proponents of different theories to talk to each other in a common language, and therefore makes it possible to explore common ground and differences constructively.

CHAPTER 5

Interlude: Analogous Processes

ABSTRACT PRINCIPLES are often grasped better if they are embodied in examples, analogies or metaphors.

This brief chapter contains a description of different types of organic systems from those normally found in Hypnotherapy. Though different in structure, they are in many ways similar in their processes. They are therefore analogues which can illuminate the general principles of our subject.

Consider first a large firm with many hundreds or even thousands of employees. They do not relate at random. There will be a considerable degree of organisation. Typically there will be many departments and subdepartments. For example there are likely to be groups whose primary concern is production or sales or accounts or maintenance or management or after-sales service or advertising or secretarial or stock control or transport or recruitment. In a large company these may be further subdivided, perhaps because there are different sites, or because a task is so complex that it is best subdivided into smaller ones and smaller subgroups are used to deal with each.

Although all large companies follow this general principle, they will each be different not only in the exact pattern or mix of departments but also in the way that they function.

Each department is an organic or biological system. Its *structure* consists of the people in it together with the buildings and things they use. Its *processes* are the things that they do.

In order to understand the functioning of a business it is necessary to have a grasp of the departments and *how* they interact with each other and also with any external factors - typically other businesses or other aspects of society. At the most elementary level this means being able to answer questions like, "If department P (production) increases its activity, what effect will this have on department S (sales)?"; "If department E (exports) reduces its activity, what effect will this have on P?"; "Does the action of M (management) on P increase or decrease its activity?"; "How does the action of the government (G) in raising VAT change the activity of S?" and so on. If we can't answer such basic questions then we cannot claim to understand the functioning of the company at all. There are countless theories of management (cf. Kennedy (1991)) but if they do not include the ability to answer the simple questions above, which in effect are, "Will a certain change make things better or worse?" then I would argue that they cannot be very useful.

Of course in a business context the word "activity" is not used, but instead money is generally used as a measure. Every activity of every department can be costed with reasonable accuracy. The costs involve such things as salaries, raw materials and a variety of overheads. The natural tendency of every department is to increase its costs - to grow - just as the natural tendency of organic systems generally is to grow. This growth is limited in a company because there are limited financial resources, and so the departments have to co-operate and/or compete. Any change in activity of one department will therefore change that of the others. But some changes can lead in the longer term to an overall increase of resources - normally by increasing profits - which will benefit each department, and each individual in it. Other changes may lead to a reduction in resources for each department - if they lead to a drop in profits. An intelligent analysis of the effect of each department on each other and of the effect of factors in the outside world - normally the market-place - on each department can lead to improvements all round.

Notice that the fact that two businesses have the same formal *structure* is no guarantee that they will *function* identically. There may be excellent relationships between management and workforce in one firm and terrible ones in another. In one, the accounts department may be very conservative and resist any request for money to be put into research and development, while in another it may be very co-operative. In one, the sales department is only concerned to feather its own nest, while in another the sales department is very much part of the team.

Notice that the above descriptions are *qualitative*, not *quantitative*. Although some aspects of the functioning of a company can be given a useful financial measure, the above thumbnail sketches show that the simple notions of whether one department will resist or co-operate with changes in another department could be of far more importance in assessing a company than the financial accounts, however exact, of each department.

In an abstract form, if we let A and B be two departments then the question of whether:

$$\uparrow A \rightarrow \updownarrow B \rightarrow \uparrow A \text{ or } \uparrow A \rightarrow \updownarrow B \rightarrow \downarrow A$$

is of great importance. Spelled out in detail these two expressions describe situations in which an increase in the activity of department A leads to a change in the activity of department B (which can be either an increase or decrease) which in turn leads *either* to a further increase in the activity of A *or* to a decrease. In the former case B acts to help A, in the latter to resist it.

The analogy with individuals should be clear. Two people might have identical mental and physical structures, but they could still be functioning in very different ways: have very different personalities. In one person, advantageous systems could be co-operating and the overall person would have inner harmony and do things with great efficiency. In another person, inner systems could be at variance in such a way that the main result is internal stress.

As a next step in our analogy let us suppose that there is a problem in the company. It may have been simmering in the awareness of some departments for some time, but it is unlikely that anything will be done about it until it reaches the attention of the managerial system. Attempts may be made at that level to solve it, but if that fails, recourse may be had to a Management Consultant.

This is an analogy of the situation in which an individual has some problem which may be simmering for some time without its being consciously recognised as one; then an attempt is made to resolve it; then a Hypnotherapist is called in to help.

The Management Consultant will first spend some time with the Management, hearing their interpretation of the problem. But even at this stage he is finding out as much as possible about the ways in which the company is organised, both in terms of the structure and also the functioning; i.e. he will be asking questions like those mentioned above.

Because he has experience of many other companies, some good and some bad, he will be able at least to guess at the likely cause of the trouble, which is probably localised in just a few of the departments.

He may then well want to check out his guesses by going and talking to the departments involved. Broadly speaking the attitude of management to this may on the one hand be co-operative and they may be prepared to let him get on with it, or on the other hand they may well want to be with him all the time. A skilled consultant should be able to handle either extreme.

If he operates like the classical or stage Hypnotist, he will attempt to eliminate any influence of the management and will want to take over the running of the company all by himself for a while.

If he operates like a modern Hypnotherapist, he is more likely to be happy to have the Management watching and learning as he goes along. It is so very often the case that real problems in life are only labelled "problems" because there is a failure to understand consciously how to cope with a situation. Consequently an approach in which there is conscious co-operation and conscious learning is normally far better in a therapeutic situation. In other words, although the Management may perceive the problem as coming from elsewhere in the organisation, the roots are often a managerial deficiency.

When it comes to implementing a change in practices, it should be evident that this is likely to be very difficult at a time when every department is stretched to capacity. Retraining is normally best done when there are few outside pressures. So ideally the Management Consultant would like to declare a general holiday and send home all the workforce except those in the "problem" departments. They will then be able to concentrate totally on the task of changing their practices. In a different language, we may say that ideally the Consultant will act to reduce the activity of all but the key systems to a minimum, so that there will be minimal interference with them. At the same time he will introduce quite high levels of activity, but of a specific kind - learning new processes - in the key systems.

This parallels the tendency in a typical Hypnotherapeutic session to reduce to a minimum the activity of all major systems of action and perception and thought in the Client, *other than* those of importance to the problem.

However, please note that the above is not the *only* possible approach. It is quite conceivable that a certain kind of Consultant could step in with such dynamic confidence that he will *command* the attention of all relevant departments, whatever else is going on. He might then create a major upheaval - an organisational convulsion - and in that way disrupt dramatically any established practices which are leading to problems. Such an approach would be more akin to some of the practices of the Mesmerists or exorcists, or might be likened to the modern practice of Electro-Convulsive Therapy in which certain serious mental problems may be relieved by the rather drastic procedure of delivering a series of electric shocks to the brain. There is little in the way of theoretical justification or understanding of this process, but when it works, it may work on the above principle of: "Let us disrupt the organisation and then hope that when it reorganises itself, it will do so in a better way."

So we have seen that some applications of Management Consultancy include the existing Management systems among those to be inactivated (*not* involved) during the change, and some include them among those to be activated (involved). Some involve a gentle retraining, some may involve drastic shake-ups. Some may involve a gentle holiday for most departments, some simply hold the attention of key departments so strongly that it does not matter what other departments are doing. But the job definition is the same: it is to produce change by altering the patterns of activity of the many subdepartments of the organisation.

Some applications of Hypnosis include conscious systems among those to be inactivated, and some include them among those to be activated. Some involve a gentle learning process, others involve dramatic shake-ups of existing ways of thinking. Some proceed via an initial condition of general relaxation, others simply arouse or activate key systems so strongly that it does not matter what other systems are doing. But the job definition is the same: it is to produce change by altering the patterns of activity of some of the many subsystems within the person.

In this analogy it should also be obvious that to say that "the company is in a state of consultancy" is not very informative. There is no unique defining characteristic of such a hypothetical "state", because companies are so different and consultancy styles are so different and the goals can be so different. But the absence of any such unique "state" does not invalidate consultancy as a skill or even a science.

Now let us consider a totally different class of organic system: that which is considered by ecology. In the classic book by Krebs (1994) ecology is defined as "the scientific study of the interactions that determine the distribution and abundance of organisms". Although ecology is a comparatively new science - it can perhaps be dated from the work of Charles Elton (1927) - its concepts have permeated our world to such an extent that it can be supposed that we all have some idea of its basic ideas. Quantitative ecology is now well-established in the A-level Biology curriculum, for example (Green et al. (1984)).

As an example of a problem faced within ecology let us suppose that there is a pest in a certain area of the world, and that an ecologist is asked to advise on how it can be eliminated or at least much reduced. How does she go about her job?

Notice that this goal can be approached in different ways. There is the chemical method: find a poison which kills the pest; apply it profusely; if the pest returns, apply more poison. Such a method is quick and will often produce remarkable improvements in the short term. The problems with it are 1) the cost of repeated doses, 2) the fact that the poison may start to affect other organisms, including people and 3) the fact that the pest can, if not totally eliminated, start to develop immunity so that ever-increasing doses of chemical are needed to control it.

The more ecologically sound method is to proceed on the following general lines. The pest species is regarded as one subsystem of the complex ecosystem of the region. The interactions between the pest species and other species of animals and plants is then carefully analysed. Interest is focused in particular on those species which act as food for the pest and those which prey on the pest. In terms of our simple notation we want to know all those species or systems X such that a change in the activity of X can lead to a change in the activity of our pest P:

$$\updownarrow X \rightarrow \updownarrow P.$$

Typically it is the case that:

$$\uparrow \text{Predator} \rightarrow \downarrow \text{Pest and } \downarrow \text{Predator} \rightarrow \uparrow \text{Pest,}$$

and

$$\uparrow \text{Food} \rightarrow \uparrow \text{Pest and } \downarrow \text{Food} \rightarrow \downarrow \text{Pest,}$$

though we must remember that behind these simple, first-order ideas there may be much complex detail.

Of course once the ecologist has found the other species which have a direct effect on the prey, she must go on and find out how those species themselves are affected by others, until she has achieved at least a fair working knowledge of the network of interactions. Notice again that she is going to start with a *qualitative* picture. It is going to be very hard indeed to gain a *quantitative* one, though it is not out of the question.

Her skill is then going to be employed in using this knowledge to discover some way of changing things which will lead to a new and stable mix of species which will have a lower level of the pest present.

This is not a simple job. A naïve approach is to introduce a new prey species. This may work. But there are instances where this has been disastrous because the consequences have not been thought through. The new prey species may turn out to prefer to eat not the pest but another species which competes with the pest for the same food supply. We then have the following simple pattern:

↑New Prey → ↓Competing Species → ↑Food Supply → ↑Pest,

and the result is the opposite from that desired.

However, if this job is done well - and note that the exact solution will be different in each case - it has the promise of being stable and long-term, with no further input of money or time being necessary.

Another way of altering the ecosystem is to work with the inorganic part: the physical environment. If the pest has a larval stage which flourishes in swamps, then the draining of the swamps will largely eliminate the pest. (↓Swamps → ↓Pest.) Of course this should not be done without thought, as there will be other consequences which should be thought through. For example, the swamps will be a necessary resource for many other life-forms which may suffer if the swamps are drained, and this may not be an overall improvement.

The equivalent perspective to the above in our field is as follows. The equivalents of the different species are the different systems within the brain, nervous system and body. The equivalent of the chemical solution is drug therapy. The introduction of a new thought or habit into a human mind has distinct parallels to the introduction of a new species into an ecosystem. It will inevitably affect the pre-existing thoughts or habits. It may be that the new thought will not flourish - the new species will not be able to survive. It may be that it will thrive very well but not have the intended effect, even to having a contrary long-term effect to the one intended. The equivalent of changing the physical environment of an ecosystem is changing the physical environment of a person. (This may not seem to have much to do with Hypnotherapy, but if it is the easiest way of solving a person's problem, it should not be overlooked on that account.) The equivalent of the careful and intelligent ecologist is the careful and intelligent Hypnotherapist who very carefully studies the personality of the Client until she has a good grasp of the complex interactions of the various systems involved before gently introducing an ecologically sound change, i.e. one that will take root and thrive, change things in the desired way and enrich the inner environment.

Note again that there is no real meaning to the phrase, "the ecosystem is in a 'state of ecology'" to describe the process of being studied or changed by an ecologist, but this does not mean that such studies and processes do not exist.

The field of ecology also teaches us that it is easy to make what on the surface seems an advantageous change, only to find that it results in something worse. As an example we may take the introduction of the Nile perch into Lake Victoria in 1960. The United Nations Food and Agriculture Organisation decided that these large fish would provide a good source of food, and introduced them without taking account of warnings by scientists at the time.

Here are some of the consequences (Murray (1993), p.88):

↑{Perch} → ↓{Cichlid fish} → ↑{aquatic snails}
    → ↑{human liver-fluke disease},

$\uparrow$ {Perch} $\rightarrow$ $\downarrow$ {fishing catch},

$\uparrow$ {Perch} $\rightarrow$ $\downarrow$ {Trees}.

The mechanisms are quite simple. The smaller cichlids which used to provide the fishermen with their catch not only added up to a bigger catch overall: they also controlled the aquatic snails, which were carriers of the liver-fluke disease bilharzia, which is invariably fatal in humans if not caught in time. In addition the perch are too oily to be sun-dried like the cichlids, and so precious trees have to be cut and burned in order to preserve them by smoking. So what was supposed to be a beneficial change turned out to be a disaster in more ways than one.

The moral for us in Hypnotherapy is clear. The internal interactions of the various systems in the human mind are also organised in complex webs, and a careless introduction of a change without thought of consequences could also be a disaster.

Another field with which we can draw analogies is economics. Here the systems of interest are such things as the building industry, the stock exchange, the transportation industry, the government, the media, the power industry and so on.

The task here is to be able to work out how changes in each of these affect the others. If the government changes the bank rate, how will this affect the activity of various sectors of industry? If manufacturing increases, how will that affect the demand for power or capital? There are many such questions that should be answerable if it is claimed that the workings of the economy are understood.

Economists actually try to produce very detailed and quantitative models of an economy. These can be complex indeed, and consequently the models can only be run on very large computers. As a result they give little *insight*. The answers, if available, to the above simple *qualitative* questions can be far more illuminating.

What is of interest here is analogies between certain patterns within an economy and within an individual. In an economy there can arise conflict between two sectors or subsectors competing for the same resources. This can happen at many different levels: between companies, between capital and labour, between industry and government, and so on. Similarly, within an individual there can also arise conflicts between two systems or subsystems: between a desire to smoke and a desire to stop, between a need to eat and a desire to be slim, between a desire for relaxation and a need for income, between an increasing sleepiness and an interest in the late night movie, between the previous intention to walk forward and the present perception that to do so will mean colliding with another pedestrian, and so on.

Large conflicts between systems can prove to be a problem both in an economy and in an individual. In recent years society has begun to generate numbers of subsystems which are designed to resolve such conflicts, such as the Conciliation and Arbitration Service in the UK. In many problems which come to a Hypnotherapist, the role of the arbitrator is taken by the Hypnotherapist, who may speak to each subsystem separately and then find a way to bring them together in a co-operative way.

It is worth noticing in this context the difference between short-term and long-term solutions. It may be possible to make a short-term change by throwing the weight of the arbitrator totally behind one of the sides, and overriding the other. But it is in the nature of organic systems of all kinds to react to attack by increased defence, and although this process may often be delayed, the long-term effect is that the side which was overridden will come back later even more determined than before to compete and resist. Thus for example if there is an internal conflict in a person about food which is "resolved" by a draconian diet, then when the inner system F which is concerned with eating food gets half a chance it will seize the opportunity and binge to excess. But this in turn will lead to an increase in the dismay of the other system W, concerned with reducing weight, and so when *it* gets its turn, it will become even more draconian in desperation.

In our shorthand:

$$\uparrow W \rightarrow \uparrow F \rightarrow \uparrow W \rightarrow \uparrow F$$

and we have what is colloquially called a vicious circle: the stricter the diet, the greater the binge, and the greater the binge, the stricter the diet. (We will be finding out a lot more about such vicious circles later.)

Within an economy or society the same pattern can arise in many ways. If two firms X and Y are competing for the same market then X may increase its advertising, which will result in Y increasing *its* advertising, which in turn leads to X increasing its advertising, and the budgets can spiral ever upwards. The net effect is a larger advertising industry and a more expensive product. Or we may find a conflict between different communities, possibly of different ethnic origins, which can similarly escalate into increasing levels of conflict as each reacts to aggression with yet higher levels of aggression in return.

As a final subject which parallels our own we may consider an example which is a little closer to home: family therapy. Here the basic system is the family, consisting of parents and children together with the more or less strong influences of grandparents or other related individuals. Here again we are looking at a dynamic system with recognisable subsystems: the individuals involved. There will be some specified "problem" which is often presented as a problem with a child. But in family therapy it is normally supposed today that the problem is far more likely to be a consequence of the dynamics of the family as a whole.

Suppose that the symptom is tantrums (T) in a child. In a simple case it may be discovered that the immediate cause of the tantrums is a tendency for the parents to quarrel (Q) with each other. Suppose also that a result of the tantrums is that they call a truce for a while to deal with the tantrums. The presented symptom then is clearly implicated in the loop:

$$\uparrow Q \rightarrow \uparrow T \rightarrow \downarrow Q.$$

Here we see that the tantrums are actually useful in holding the family together because they limit the amount of quarrelling. You cannot then remove the tantrums without considering the consequent change in the pattern of quarrelling. It might be, for example, that in removing the tantrums you will destroy the marriage! In a particular case it might, however, be relatively easy to resolve the cause of the quarrels, and then the tantrums, lacking a driving force, will quietly fade away.

The Family Therapist, in the process of handling each situation, will often be using principles which are formally identical to some used by Hypnotherapists. She may, for example, send everyone else out of the room while talking to one individual, which is equivalent to the Hypnotherapist rendering inactive or quiescent all subsystems but one in the individual. For the other members of the family to be present but listening is equivalent in Hypnosis to a lower than normal level of activity of other relevant systems. Getting the members of a family to rehearse new forms of behaviour is equivalent in Hypnosis to getting a new form of behaviour imagined. Getting them to relive, in the Therapist's presence, some earlier family trauma is equivalent to the Hypnotherapist getting an individual to relive a traumatic experience, with catharsis being the goal in each case. There are many such parallels.

In practice the Hypnotherapist can often be dealing with an internalised family in the sense that an individual will have character aspects which directly correspond to the dynamics of the family in which she or he grew up. So Hypnotherapy can often be likened to family therapy in which all the family is in the one head! As an example there is the commonly used notion of "the child within". It is not saying that an adult is always childlike, but that there are within most adults behavioural and emotional subsystems which are essentially those they developed in childhood, and which may influence life quite considerably from time to time. The "child within" which appears in the literature is usually unloved and hurt. But this is inevitable: anyone with a "child within" which is a consequence of a loved and loving childhood is unlikely to go to a therapist for help in that area! Therapy is often aimed at dealing with the dynamical interaction of an unloved "child within" and an internalised "parent within" - another mental subsystem which perpetuates the unloving attitudes to the person of a parent in childhood.

In shorthand the typical pattern of such an interaction, whether in a real family or an internalised one, is:

$$\uparrow \text{Upset of Child} \rightarrow \uparrow \text{Anger of Parent} \rightarrow \uparrow \text{Upset of Child,}$$

whereas in a loving relationship we have:

$$\uparrow \text{Upset of Child} \rightarrow \uparrow \text{Love from Parent} \rightarrow \downarrow \text{Upset of Child.}$$

The task of the Family Therapist or the Hypnotherapist is to change the former process for the latter. Chapter 20 deals with Family Therapy in more detail.

SUMMARY

This chapter has been an exercise in mind broadening, with an emphasis on the central idea of the dynamics of organic systems.

Four examples of complex systems have been referred to: the family, a company, an economy and an ecosystem. Each has natural subsystems. The basis of understanding the dynamics of each is to understand the complex interactions between these subsystems.

A human being is likewise a complex organic system with naturally arising subsystems - each of which can in turn be analysed into subsystems down to the level of a single cell and below. Each human being can also be regarded as a subsystem of larger systems: families, firms, countries or ecosystems.

Each organic system has its own detailed language and expertise. But it is argued here that if we put the language on one side and stick to the most essential features, we are left with a theoretical framework which is recognisably the same in each. In everyday language we may say that understanding in each area is based on asking the key question, **"If the behaviour of *this* system changes, how does it affect the behaviour of *that*?"** -though of course there are many other questions that can be asked, many of which vary from subject to subject.

This similarity has been emphasised by the use of a simple common notation which can be applied in **each** of the contexts.

It is expected also that the newcomer to the field will know more about at least one of the more familiar systems mentioned in this chapter than about Hypnotherapy. Since learning is often a matter of relating the new to the known, this chapter should have helped many readers to start to think about Hypnotherapy in a valuable way.

CHAPTER 6

A First-Order Classification of Subsystems useful in Hypnotherapy

IN THIS CHAPTER we will look at some of the systems which are important in Hypnosis. This is not intended to be a complete list, but rather to give some familiarity with some of the more central ones and with the systems approach to the subject. It will also lead to an elaboration of the simple picture of a Hypnotic process mentioned in Chapter 3.

A system consists of a structure and a collection of processes. We will begin by focusing attention on the structure. We are then normally able clearly to distinguish the system from its **environment**. We may therefore give meaning to the words **interior** and **exterior** as applied to a system.

There are times when there is a very clear boundary between system and environment: an individual person and an individual cell are both clearly distinguishable from their environment. On the other hand there is a certain arbitrariness about where we draw the line between a heart and the veins and arteries which are attached to it, or between the brain and the associated nervous system. But such fuzziness is inevitable in most systems of classification - where does red end and orange begin? - and does not give rise to large problems.

With this in mind let us next consider the question of useful ways of analysing the human being into major subsystems for the purposes of Hypnosis.

There is no one agreed way, but the following is a possible first-order approximation. We have noted that a system S can be distinguished from its external environment E. However it is not independent of that environment. It is continually being acted on by that environment ($\updownarrow E \rightarrow \updownarrow S$) and in turn it is acting on it ($\updownarrow S \rightarrow \updownarrow E$). In practice in complex organisms there are different subsystems which deal with these different aspects: the active and the responsive. A market research department (which responds to the market) is distinct from sales (which acts on it). Military intelligence (which is purely responsive to the state of the enemy) is distinct from the fighting force (which is primarily active). In the human being we may distinguish the sensory systems which respond to the environment from the motor systems which act on it.

These examples will motivate a first large analysis of the subsystems of any organic system. There are those which interface directly with the external environment and those which do not. We can divide the former into those that act on the environment and those that respond to the environment.

The main systems in the human being which respond to the outside world are responsive to the following: sight, sound, touch, smell, taste and acceleration and orientation in a gravitational field, and can be identified with the eyes, ears, nerves in the skin, nose, tongue and a mechanism in the inner ear respectively.

The main systems which act on the outside world do so by means of: force, sound, visual signs and smell, and are normally identified with the major muscles, the voice, the facial muscles together with bodily gestures and the pheromonal system respectively. (The pheromonal system is comparatively unimportant in humans compared with most land animals. It is a means of sending chemical signals through the air in the form of scents to affect other members of the species. The lucrative market in perfumes indicates that it is not totally irrelevant to us, however.)

There are other systems in both categories which might be mentioned but they are too slight to be included in our first-order list. There are, for example, reports of animals and some people being sensitive to magnetic or electrical fields. Some animals can generate electric fields strong enough to kill, and human beings generate detectable electrical fields at the skin (they are what enable an EEG machine to work) which might in principle affect the environment, but are generally too small and insignificant to be included in our list.

In the context of modern Hypnotherapy, though not of other subjects like gastronomy, the above lists can be simplified to four primary systems - two active and two sensory.

The two main sensory systems are vision and hearing which together give us the greater part of our information about the world, with touch coming a very poor third. (The modern Hypnotherapist does not usually touch the Client at all.)

The two main active systems of interest are the vocal and the muscular, with the emphasis being on the body language aspect of movement rather than on the moving of objects.

At the beginning of a Hypnotherapy session all four of these systems are active in the Client. Broadly speaking, current practice is for the Hypnotherapist to reduce the activity of the Client's muscles until relaxation is nearly complete, to eliminate all external vision by inducing the eyes to close directly or indirectly and to eliminate vocalisation either directly or much more often indirectly. The only major system that remains active is therefore hearing, and this the Hypnotherapist wishes to remain active the whole time as it has become the only channel of communication, though it may well be narrowed down to respond only to his or her voice and nothing else. Notice that this cannot be said of true sleep.

Notice also that although the above is the current practice, it has not been universal. At one time it was thought that the gaze of the Hypnotist's eye was very important. It was therefore important to keep the Subject's eyes open in order for this Hypnotic gaze to be effective.

We may note also that it was once a common procedure in stage Hypnosis to work first on the sense of orientation. The potential Subject was instructed to stand upright and rigid, and to gaze upwards. After a while suggestions of swaying would be made. These would tend to disorientate the Subject, who became unable to tell if he or she was vertical or not. The result was a falling against the Hypnotist, who would generally then gently lower the rigid body to the floor. (I have heard of a similar procedure being used in certain churches, in which the resulting condition is called "the sleep of the spirit".)

In current Hypnotherapeutic practice very little use is made of the sense of touch in the Client. At most it enters negatively, in that suggestions are made to the effect that it will become impossible to feel the chair, etc. In past times, particularly in Mesmerism, touch was used extensively. Stage Hypnotists today tend to use quite a lot of physical contact, though of a different kind. In principle the holding of a hand or a gentle stroking could, in the right circumstances, be used to advantage in Hypnotherapy to induce feelings of trust or relaxation, but in the present social environment in the UK such gestures could be taken amiss and tend therefore to be avoided in Hypnotherapy. The same social conventions allow them in Aromatherapy, however!

Equally little use is made of the sense of smell, though some therapists might use a pleasant background scent in their consulting rooms.

Having made this simple classification of subsystems which deal directly with the external environment, we now turn to a classification of subsystems which do not. Such systems must by definition respond to or act on only the *internal* environment of the body. We may say as a broad generalisation that the more complex the organism or organisation becomes, the greater, in proportion, become these purely internal systems. A large business, with more departments, needs far more people devoted entirely to maintaining the departments and regulating their interactions. A complex society develops a far larger service sector as opposed to a primary producing sector. This process has been noticeable in human societies generally over recent centuries. An organism as complex as a human being develops many internal systems to keep everything in order.

It is of overwhelming importance to any organism that it should maintain its viability. An organism as complex as a human being needs an enormous variety of subsystems whose function is simply to keep things going. Let us call these things Maintenance and Defence (M&D) subsystems. They include the immune system in all its complexity, which enables the body to react to and destroy an enormous number of invading pathogens. They include the healing systems that detect and repair breaks in bones and lesions in most tissues. The pain system is best seen as a part of this Maintenance and Defence system, serving to activate awareness of serious internal damage. The maintenance of body temperature, of blood sugar levels, fat reserves, oxygen levels and the levels of many other important substances such as salt, various hormones, etc. are vital functions which all involve some form of monitoring and control by the nervous system. We may include the digestive and excretory systems under this heading insofar as they are involved in the necessary maintenance job of maintaining energy levels and removing toxins and rubbish. This list can go on almost endlessly: skin has to be kept in good condition by means of continuous renewal from inside together with some oiling, the eyes have to be washed and swept clean, the joints have to be kept lubricated, bone strength and thickness is continually being adapted to conditions - thus in zero gravity conditions the body will lighten the bones since that additional strength is no longer necessary, red blood cell levels have to be continually topped up as the old cells die, and so on.

We tend to take all these things for granted - until they go wrong. The amazing thing is how well they work so much of the time. For remember that not only must the basic systems mentioned above be maintained, but there must be other subsystems which act to maintain the viability of the first-order maintenance systems. Auto-immune diseases are just one example of what can happen if a system which has a maintenance function itself goes wrong. In the analogy of a society, the function of a police force is primarily to maintain a reasonable fairness between individuals. But in order to prevent the police force itself becoming corrupt, it is necessary that it should itself be controlled. But that controlling body could itself go wrong unless it also is controlled. In a similar, though vastly more complex way, we should be aware in general, if not in detail, of amazing nested systems within the body which are balanced against each other, checking and correcting each other in a ceaseless interplay of action and reaction, or activation and inhibition, following paths that have been laid down sometimes over billions of years.

In recent years a great deal of progress has been made in the painstaking analysis of the simpler of these maintenance systems, and hence faults in them can often be corrected. For example, the process of blood clotting has been discovered to be a fourteen-stage process. Haemophilia is typically a result of just one of those stages not working properly (factor VIII). This can now be compensated for. No doubt we will see much more progress on these lines in the twenty-first century, which will dovetail with the systems approach to Hypnotherapy, as we see ever more clearly how the comparatively high-order systems which are easily accessible to Hypnotic techniques control and interact with the lower-order maintenance systems such as those mentioned above.

Although the maintenance systems are those which are of overwhelmingly the greatest importance as regards the internal environment of a person, they are not those which are most immediately affected by Hypnotic techniques - though there is one major exception which we will come to later. It is therefore more useful for us to start our classification as follows.

We will begin with the internal verbal system, the internal visual system and the emotional system as being the three most directly important internal subsystems in Hypnotherapy. The first two arise out of the complexity of the systems which have evolved to deal with the spoken word and with vision. This complexity has resulted in systems which can become active even in the absence of an immediate external stimulus. In everyday language this amounts to our being able to hold internal conversations with ourselves, or imaginary conversations with others, and to be able with more or less vividness to call to mind imagined scenarios - some of which are memories of past experiences, some of which are imagined future events and some of which are fantasy pure and simple.

The third system is that of emotion which, as mentioned in Chapter 2, is centred in the limbic system of the brain and is tightly connected to the hormonal system via the thalamus gland in the brain. I have not included it among the list of systems that deal directly with the outside world, but it is normally activated indirectly in response to stimuli from the outside world which enter via one of the sensory systems mentioned above. We recognise such feelings as fear, excitement, anxiety, hate, jealousy, guilt, happiness, rage, sexual excitement, love, affection, nostalgia and so on. Primarily they are responses to external stimuli, but again the complexity of mental systems is such that they can be activated spontaneously.

The emotions have a very central and powerful position in the economy of the body. Most of our decisions are ultimately based on some feeling or other.

If we label internal verbal processes V, verbal processes which are purely receptive of external voices L (listening), the external visual system S (sight), the imagination system I and the emotional system E, then a very common process in Hypnotherapy is to proceed as follows:

$$\uparrow L \rightarrow \downarrow V$$

$$\uparrow L \rightarrow \downarrow S \rightarrow \uparrow I \rightarrow \updownarrow E.$$

In words these shorthand sentences stand for two processes. The first is rather simple. By means of holding the Subject's attention on the Hypnotherapist's voice, any internal verbal speech is reduced or eliminated. This can be very important in some Hypnotic processes. As a very simple example, if as part of an induction a Hypnotist is repeating, "You are feeling sleepier and sleepier", but the Subject is repeating to himself, "I am getting more and more irritated by this", then the second suggestion will predominate. More generally, internal verbal activity can be simply distracting: "I wonder if I should be trying to feel more relaxed?", "I can still hear the sound of traffic", "What shall we have for lunch?", "Perhaps I will have time to do some shopping on the way home", "When is he going to come to the point?", "Is this going to work, I wonder?" All such thoughts are a hindrance to the changes that are generally aimed at in Hypnotherapy. Of course if the thoughts are favourable, then there is often no need to reduce them: it depends then on the particular goal.

The second shorthand sentence expands into the process of first inducing the Client to listen primarily to the Hypnotherapist; then of achieving eye closure so that external sight is eliminated; this in turn will make it easier to activate the internal visual system; by then using this to create images of emotionally significant scenes, the appropriate emotions can be evoked.

As simple examples of this, it is commonplace to use images of relaxing situations (a sunny beach, perhaps) in order to produce peaceful feelings. In treating phobias it is possible to induce the feeling of fear in a controlled way by suggesting images of the feared thing or situation, in order then to eliminate the phobia by a standard method of progressive desensitisation. This involves exposing the Subject to increasingly intense experiences of the (imagined) thing feared in a controlled way in order to reduce the fear felt. If the agreed aim of therapy is to uncover repressed traumatic material (which results when an experience was so emotionally painful that it cannot be consciously recalled), then using the imagination to set the scene of the experience will commonly be enough to allow in the associated emotions.

For many people the catch-all word "subconscious" refers almost exclusively to processes which are primarily to do with emotion, and when they think of "Hypnosis getting through to the subconscious", they are simply thinking of its power to influence feelings about things.

We may emphasise again at this stage the very important fact that in different individuals the different systems can function VERY differently. There are, for example, individuals who are very poor at imagining things, even though they can be strongly influenced by what they see around them - e.g. the TV. It may be that in a particular person words are a far better way of activating emotions than any amount of pictures. (A quick idea of the balance between the two can be obtained by asking the Client if she prefers a fictional book or a film for relaxation or entertainment.)

Although we have listed only the primary internal systems of imagination, internal verbal thought and emotion, there is no suggestion that this list is more than a first approximation, appropriate as an introduction to thinking in a systems-oriented way. We can also think in a kinaesthetic way, for example: I can imagine the sense and feeling that go with lifting a spoon without ever verbalising or visualising it. Music has not been mentioned, but it can be a strong activator of emotions, and some people can call it to mind at will as easily as a visual memory. And we can think in more abstract conceptual ways which are of a higher order and harder to locate as a cerebral function. And we should be aware that each of the above systems can be analysed into subsystems, and that they can combine in various ways. This is not an encyclopaedic book: it is intended to present a way of looking at things. The key idea is that practitioners in the field of Hypnosis should be aware of just what systems they are activating or inactivating at a given time, and some sort of classification is useful to detail their answers.

Now that we have looked at the main systems which are involved in the early stages of a Hypnotherapy session, it will be useful to return to the large class of Maintenance and Defence systems, and look at one in particular which looms very large in the work of the Hypnotherapist. The function of this system is to enable the body to respond to a perceived danger. It is defensive. The responses are often summarised by the phrase "fight or flight". The presumed origin of this system was in a more primitive world than our own, when most dangers could be met either by running away from them or by fighting the wild animal or enemy which posed the threat. It was seldom the case that threats could be met by drawing little marks on a white surface, or by quiet reason. It was far more useful to have the lungs drawing in reserves of oxygen, the heart beating fast, adrenaline flowing, the muscles ready for action, the stomach and/or bowels empty, perspiration starting to keep the body cooled and so on.

Problems involving this system which may be presented to the Hypnotherapist include anxiety, panic attacks, examination nerves, fear of flying, agoraphobia, "stress", bereavement, fear of dentists, and so on endlessly. Many cases of sexual malfunction, for example, involve this same defensive response, because another aspect of it is that it tends to switch off sexual drive. Consequently the man who gets anxious about his performance and therefore activates this defensive pattern will *further reduce* his sexual prowess. This will make things worse and a vicious circle begins.

In most of these cases the problem is that this particular defensive system is activated *inappropriately*. There are very few threats in modern life that call for these kinds of emotional and physical changes. Typically there is some sort of trigger - a place, a feeling, etc. - which is interpreted by a key mental system as DANGEROUS. This will immediately activate the defensive "fight or flight" system. One common strategy for the Hypnotherapist is to aim to change the first system so that it no longer regards the particular trigger as being DANGEROUS.

In principle an alternative approach might be forcibly to prevent it from activating the defensive system, but although this might work in the short term, it is potentially flawed in that the warning might later break through again. As an analogy, suppose that the accounts department of a company is (rightly or wrongly) saying, "We are in a financially dangerous situation. We must economise!" The effect of this will run through the whole business. Now we may prevent the accounts department making everyone feel demoralised by locking them up, or cutting their lines of communication. But not for long. Sooner or later they will get out and shout all the louder as a result of not being heard before. As management technique or Hypnotic technique that is bad practice. Correct practice is to pay attention to the system which is reporting danger and then demonstrate to it that the situation does not call for the drastic level of response that is being suggested.

There is evidence that Hypnotic techniques can in fact affect the functioning of Maintenance and Defence systems which operate at a lower level, such as the immune system. Rossi (1993) presents some details on the effect of Hypnotic techniques on healing. Another review of this area is provided by Walker et al. (1993). There is plenty of evidence - *vide* the placebo effect - that people's beliefs about their diseases can affect their course. But the exact pathway by which the mental process affects the physical one is not totally clear.

This is an area in which more research would be useful. It is to be expected that the theoretical approach being developed here would help to formulate precisely the questions that research will answer. For example, the useful question is not, "Does being Hypnotised cure a patient of cancer?", but "What systems can the Hypnotherapist usefully activate or inactivate in such a way that the internal environment of the body is altered in such a way that the body's defences against cancer can be activated more effectively?"

We cannot yet answer this in the way that we can see how Hypnotic techniques can reduce high blood pressure: high blood pressure is one consequence of an active "fight or flight response"; this system is activated by a sense of being under some form of attack. Hypnotic techniques can act on the perception of being threatened, to reduce the activity of the "flight or fight" system, which will in turn reduce the frequency of high blood pressure.

CONCLUSION

The first step or two on the path of methodically listing systems appropriate in Hypnotherapy have been taken *(less important ones in italics)*.

Externally oriented:
    active: muscular, vocal, *pheromonal.*
    responsive: sight, hearing, *smell, taste, orientation.*
Internally oriented: internalised speech, visual imagination, emotions, *kinaesthetic.*
Maintenance and defence: "Flight or fight", immune system.

These really only scratch the surface but are enough for our present purpose, which is to understand the PRINCIPLES of our subject. The principle is that we work methodically with a variety of interlocking systems to alter their functioning, hopefully to correct problems.

CHAPTER 7

Processes

IN CHAPTER 3 we saw a variety of examples of organic systems which were used to get our minds working on appropriate lines. This small chapter looks at yet another example, but with a specific goal in mind: that is to enable us to get a clearer idea of HOW we are to decide when two processes are different.

This is a part of the more general question, "When are two systems different?"

Because we have defined a system as consisting of an underlying structure and a set of possible processes, we may conclude that two systems are different if they have EITHER different underlying structures OR a different set of processes, or, of course, both.

The case of different structures presents no problems: it is normally quite easy to distinguish structures. There is no danger of confusing heart and lungs, or nerves and muscles, or the visual cortex with the motor cortex, or a school with a garage, and so on.

But processes are more subtle. One structure can be involved in many different functions. The physical structure which is a person can, for example, perform a seemingly endless variety of different actions. The different processes which can occur in the physical structure of your brain are known to you to be often very different, but how are we going to go about defining this difference within the theoretical structure we are developing?

A very natural definition would seem to be the following:

A particular **process** of a system is identified with a particular pattern of activation of its substructures.

Two processes associated with a given structure will therefore differ if the pattern of activation of its substructures is different in the two cases.

Thus we would assume that ultimately the difference between two thoughts (which are mental processes) is that each is associated with a different pattern of activation of neurons in the brain. The difference between two physical activities is associated with a different pattern of activation of the muscles, and so on.

In order to make these ideas somewhat clearer it will be useful to look at the promised analogue: an orchestra.

We could at any time measure the activity of each section of the orchestra - strings, woodwind, percussion, etc. - simply in terms of their loudness in the course of a musical work. This is a very rough and ready way of measuring an orchestral process (the playing of a work), but it would be more than adequate to distinguish between most works.

In order to identify a work more completely we would need to refine our analysis of the subsystems so that, for example, we measured the activity of each string on a violin, distinguished between the activity of a clarinet at different fingerings and so on: in other words we start to discriminate between different notes.

A musical score is a shorthand way we have of describing a musical process. The musical score is divided into time intervals by means of bar lines. Each major subsystem of the orchestra has its own set of horizontal lines - a stave - marked out by the vertical bar lines. If the score is looked at from a distance, it is possible by quickly casting an eye down the page between bar lines to say which sections are playing (active) and which are not, at a given time. If we look more closely, so that we can analyse the process of each section in more detail, we see the individual notes, which amounts to a more detailed analysis of each instrument into its subsystems (e.g. strings on a piano) and of its processes into patterns of activation of those subsystems.

We might use this idea in order to portray the pattern of activity of any biological system. We would first decide on an analysis into large subsystems. Each subsystem gets its horizontal line on the page. These lines are marked with time intervals - seconds perhaps. Along each line we might draw a graph of the level of activity of that subsystem. At a distance all that will be visible is a rough idea of whether there is a lot or a little or no activity of a particular subsystem in a given interval of time. This would be enough to distinguish many processes in the same way that we can distinguish many orchestral processes by a distant glance at the score.

If we wanted to analyse a process in more detail we would have to replace each horizontal line by several, corresponding to a further analysis into subsystems, just as the stave is resolved into many lines. We would then be able to represent the level of activity of each of the subsystems of the major subsystems, and characterise a process in more detail. This process of continual refinement could, if required, be continued many times.

Of course, it is not being suggested that this **has** to be done, nor has any prescription been made about the best way of representing the pattern on the above lines: whether a graph (which is a scientist's normal representation of a variable) is better than the discrete notes of music, for example. However some such representation is in principle possible for most biological systems insofar as a level of activity is measurable.

Furthermore, and perhaps more importantly, **it provides a useful mental image of what exactly is meant by a process of a system: one can think in a general way of the "score"**. Two different processes of the same system have different "scores".

We may now refine the statement on when processes can be distinguished as follows:-

Two processes will be regarded as different **relative to a given analysis into**

subsystems if the differences between the "scores" are significantly greater than the experimental error in determining the levels of activity of the subsystems.

If one wished to take this musical analogy a little more poetically, one could say that the Hypnotherapist is like the conductor rehearsing an orchestra: the orchestra of subsystems of the Subject. He or she will be bringing up some sections of the orchestra and quieting others. Perhaps the Client's problem is only in one section, in which case it is best if all other sections are stilled and that one section is quietly rehearsed by itself. The tendency of the Hypnotist to repeat suggestions a number of times is akin to the conductor getting one section to run over a little passage several times until it has become smooth.

More lyrically yet, we might observe that just as a conductor's skill is evoking harmony from the orchestra, just so does the Hypnotherapist work to achieve an inner harmony within the mind and heart and body of the Client!

Before we end this chapter we will make a certain important distinction. The above description of a process of a system is a *kinematic* one and not a *dynamic* one. It is a way of noting what *does* happen, and not *why*, in any sense, it does. The distinction is at least that between a kinematic description of the solar system in terms of the changing directions of the planets as seen from the earth, or in terms of their positions relative to the sun, and a dynamic description in terms of Newton's laws.

The orchestral score gives a kinematic description of a process. It tells us what a process is. There is nothing in it that can tell us *why* the music is as it is. It is impossible to *deduce* the remainder of a score from a fragment. We may perhaps deduce certain partial laws in the light of a detailed analysis of it in the form, "Activation of *this* sequence of notes is followed in the next bar by *that* sequence of notes.". But that comes nowhere near explaining the whole. In order to be able to do this we would have to move to a much larger system: the mind of the composer. Within the context of that larger system lie the clues to many of the questions we might ask about the *Why?* of the music. But even that is unlikely to be a large enough system, and we would need to move into the system which incorporates the musical taste of the composer's culture.

The big moral of this is that we cannot expect the most detailed analysis of the processes of an organic system to provide us with anything like a full *understanding* of why they are as they are. In principle there will always be things about them which can only be understood in terms of larger processes of larger systems of which the specific system is a part.

Though this principle may not always be made explicit in this book, it is axiomatic to the approach that whereas a process may be analysed and *described* and *distinguished* by means of looking at subsystems and subprocesses, it is necessary always to look the other way - to the system of which they are a part - to gain anything like a full understanding of why they are as they are. The analogy of the musical work represents this fact. Further remarks on this aspect of systems theory will be found in the chapter on consciousness in Part C.

CONCLUSION

In this chapter we have looked at the notion of a *process* in a little more detail, in order to clarify it. The structure of a system is typically something easy to define and indeed see. The processes are more abstract patterns of change. They have been defined in terms of the pattern of activation of the subsystems. The analogy of a musical score has been used to illuminate the idea. This analogy also draws attention to the severe limitations of an analysis of subsystems when it comes to understanding as opposed to describing processes.

CHAPTER 8

Tests

IN MOST TEXTBOOKS of Hypnosis it is possible to find a section entitled "Tests of Hypnotic Responsiveness" or similar. Within the theoretical approach of this book all such tests are retained as being of potential value, but the interpretation of what they are testing is changed, as follows.

The tests have been evolved in an attempt to answer the question, "Is this person a good Hypnotic Subject?" In this chapter the tests will be seen as answering questions of the form, "In this person, does activation of system A lead readily to activation of system B?".

To illustrate this difference we will look briefly at the tests used in the Stanford University Hypnotic Clinical Scale (SHCS) (Hilgard (1975)).

Test 1. Arms are stretched out forwards, palms facing and about a foot apart. The individual is then told to *imagine* a force attracting the hands together - with options of an imaginary elastic band or an imaginary magnetic force pulling them together. There is then further verbal assertion that the hands will move together.

A person scores a + on the SHCS if, in ten seconds, the hands move to within six inches of each other. That is to say, a positive score is regarded as indicating a good Hypnotic subject.

Now let us ask ourselves what systems are involved in that little experiment. The simplest level of analysis involves the muscular system M, which moves the arms and the system of the imagination I.

Formally we are examining the strength of the interaction:

$$\uparrow I \rightarrow \uparrow M.$$

That is, we are asking, "Does the activation of the Imagination lead to the activation of the corresponding muscles M in this individual?"

However, things are seldom quite as simple as that, and we should at least include in our analysis the primarily verbal system (V) in the brain activated by the suggestion made by the experimenter, so that we are examining the chain:

$$\uparrow V \rightarrow \uparrow I \rightarrow \uparrow M.$$

Now in the SHCS there is a preliminary step of running through a simple five minute "induction" of a relaxation type. But it is important to note that in many people *the process of moving the hands together will happen without any such preamble.*

So what is the point of the "induction"? Does it make any difference?

We can view it in the following way. Scientific method as well as common sense both say that the interaction between any two systems will be seen at its clearest and strongest *if there is no interference from anything else.* You will find it much harder to produce the above response in a man who has a deadline to meet, or in someone who is so concerned with some other matter that the whole business of holding out the arms seems pointless and irrelevant. In such cases other mental systems are very active indeed and these systems can interfere a lot.

One key emphasis of Hypnosis (though not the only one), which distinguishes it considerably from related subjects, is the way in which it involves the exclusion as far as possible of any irrelevant activity, so that any changes are made with the maximum ease.

In the above example of the test of hand movement it is possible, as has been mentioned, for the movement to happen in some individuals with no preamble, but the response will be readier and faster and generally more pronounced if it takes place in a person for whom all other processes are comparatively inactive.

The SHCS makes no attempt to compare responses with and without the preamble or "induction". So there is really no measure of how effective the preliminary procedure is in enhancing the response.

Test 2. This involves asking the Subject to fall asleep and have a real dream. This is not asked in a single sentence but in some gentle sentences lasting for a minute or two. The Subject is then allowed one minute for the "dream", and is then requested to repeat it.

The Subject scores a + on this if an experience comparable to a dream is reported, with evidence of its not being under conscious control.

What are the key systems here? One is that imaginative system which is active in dreaming, which we may again label I. Another is the system of conscious control of our imaginings which we may label C. The characteristic of a dream as opposed to an imagining is that in a dream C is *inactive.* Then what we are testing in this case is the readiness with which the verbal suggestion V of the experimenter can lead to an increase in I with an associated decrease in C, i.e. we are looking at the chains:

$$\uparrow V \rightarrow \uparrow I \text{ and } \uparrow V \rightarrow \downarrow C.$$

From a scientific viewpoint it would have been very much more systematic if the SHCS had *first* asked for a response to a suggestion that the Subject imagine something ($\uparrow V \rightarrow \uparrow I$) and *then* asked for it to have the dreamlike quality of lack of any conscious control ($\uparrow V \rightarrow \downarrow C$). To include TWO processes in the one test is far less informative. A Subject might not respond *either* because there is simply very little ability to produce a vivid imagining *or* because there is very little ability to relax conscious control. To a Hypnotherapist it could be very important to know the difference.

We may note again that although there are some people who can produce a positive response to this test at will, it is again the case that the response can be expected to be far stronger if no other mental systems are active. This is perhaps even clearer in this case, as no one can expect much of a dream-like response in a person who is, for example, preoccupied with hunger.

Test 3. The Subject is invited to return to a happy day at school, with suggestions of being smaller and younger. This is an attempt to induce a form of age-regression.

Various questions are then asked about the memory or experience: "Where are you?", "What are you doing?", "Who is your teacher?", "How old are you?", "What are you wearing?", "Who is with you?"

On this test a + is scored if there is, at a minimum, a feeling of reliving an experience, even if there is still awareness of the present age; but there is also an option of scoring a + if the Hypnotist's assessment on the basis of the answers given is that there has been a "good" regression.

So much for what the designers of the SCHS are attempting. Now let us see what systems are involved in *this* test. The major one is memory, which we will call M. In general, memory is many-faceted. We can remember smells, sensations, feelings, words, fears, actions and so on: any system of the body may have its own memory, and a total regression would involve all these subsystems. At the same time we must notice that memory is organised not only in terms of such systems but also in terms of the time and place at which the remembered event took place. This test clearly involves an attempt to activate in M a particular complex process M_p, which is related to a particular time in childhood and a particular place - school. If we let S be the experimenter's suggestion, then in shorthand we are examining the strength of the process:

$$\uparrow V \rightarrow \uparrow M_p.$$

We may again ask what significance, if any, the initial "induction" has in this test. The general idea is that the recall can very easily be swamped by any current awareness or preoccupation. Consequently if it is possible to reduce all awareness of the *present* to a minimum, it will greatly enhance the awareness of the *past*.

It is perhaps worth noting that the SCHS scheme makes no attempt to enquire if the memories are *genuine*. There is ample evidence that people can fabricate memories without knowing that they are doing so. Thus if we were testing a person in whom the imagination is easily activated, and the "reality testing" system - which normally cross-correlates anything imagined with other memories to check if it is real or imaginary - is easily deactivated, then we could find a good response on this test, but it would not be of memory, but of a day-dream believed to be memory.

Test 4. It is suggested that after the whole set of experiments are over the Subject will feel an urge to cough or clear the throat when the experimenter taps on the table with a pencil. Such a phenomenon is called a post-hypnotic suggestion. The scoring system gives a + if the Hypnotist decides that the Subject's response to the cue of tapping on the table is present, *unless* the Subject says that the response was voluntary.

Now such a phenomenon can happen in everyday life. Take as an example a simple direction such as, "When you reach the corner, turn left." For many, but not of course all, people, the process of turning left (the response) when they later reach the corner (the cue) will be effectively automatic: they might be thinking hard about something else at the time, for example. So, as in all the phenomena of Hypnosis, there is nothing totally amazing about the process of responding involuntarily to a cue in a way dictated by something said at an earlier time.

Let us see if we can again disentangle the main systems and processes tested in this experiment. If we introspect we find that we normally cough in response to a tickle in the throat. But we can also cough without it. This particular experiment would have been more informative if the Subject had later been asked if there was a tickle involved, in which case a sensory system T had been activated, or, instead, there was simply a muscular urge to cough, in which case it was a motor system M that was being primarily activated. The additional system involved in this case is the mental process which is activated by the cue itself, which we will call C.

We should now see that this experiment is actually examining a rather complex process which we can write symbolically:

$$\text{Either } \uparrow V \rightarrow (\uparrow C \rightarrow \uparrow T) \text{ or } \uparrow V \rightarrow (\uparrow C \rightarrow \uparrow M).$$

That is, the process either by which the verbal suggestion can activate a response system in which the cue C will activate a sensory tickle T, or by which the suggestion can activate a response system in which the cue C will activate a motor mechanism M.

It is at once apparent from the notation that the *structure* of this response is different from the others, and this underlines the fact that this Hypnotic phenomenon is qualitatively different from the others. Here V is having to create a totally new system of response. As a result we might well conjecture that this test will be significantly harder than the rest. As a matter of fact this is borne out in experiments, with only one in four subjects (27%) passing this test, compared with around two out of three (60% - 81%) for the earlier tests and two out of five (40%) in the final one below.

Test 5. As part of the process of "waking" the Subject, it is suggested that the Subject *forget* all that has been done or said during the session. A + is scored if no more than two things are recalled.

Now forgetting things is one of the commonest of experiences, so the only unusual thing about such a response is the forgetting of quite recent events - though even that is not so uncommon, as most teachers will attest.

In terms of systems we are again dealing with an aspect of the memory M - in this case a memory M_r of recent events, and the simplest description of the process being examined is:

$$\uparrow V \rightarrow \downarrow M_r,$$

i.e. the effectiveness of the suggestion in reducing the activity of the memory.

The final score a person achieves on this SHCS scale is the number of items on which a + has been scored, and this is supposed to be a measure of "Hypnotic susceptibility".

There has nevertheless been found to be a considerable variation in the percentage of people who "pass" each test, which ranges from over 80% on the moving hands to less than 30% on the posthypnotic suggestion. Moreover some individuals may do better on a statistically "harder" test and poorer on a statistically "easier" one.

I hope that the above discussion has shown that the systems approach to our subject provides a far clearer picture of what is going on in the above tests than is provided by a one-dimensional notion of some kind of "Hypnotic responsiveness", with its simplistic implication that we are dealing with one aptitude.

I hope also that the value of this improved picture will become still clearer as we proceed to see how such tests can be adapted to Clinical Hypnosis or Hypnotherapy.

In such a context we might proceed in the following way.

• *Test* $\uparrow V \rightarrow \uparrow I$, i.e. can the imagination be readily activated?

Method. Ask the person to picture a familiar thing, such as a room in their house. Then enquire if it is a vivid picture. Check by asking detailed questions as to colours, positions of ornaments, etc. If the picture is NOT vivid, then the person may be asked to look again with closed eyes.

The answers to these questions can vary from total vagueness indicating a very poor visual imagination up to a vividness, even with open eyes, scarcely distinguishable from reality. They give a good idea of the ease with which the visual imagination may be activated. (But note the important point, often missed in experimental Hypnosis, that a particular person will be able to picture some things better than others. A fanatical gardener may be able to picture a prize rose with amazing clarity, and yet not have the faintest idea of the furniture in the lounge.)

• *Test* $\uparrow V \rightarrow \downarrow R$, where R represents the reality-testing mechanism.

Method. Ask the person to include in the picture something quite extraordinary, such as a pig flying around the room.

Some people will fail completely on this. Others will picture it readily and happily.

• *Test* $\uparrow V \rightarrow \uparrow M_d$, where M_d is a distant memory, as opposed to a memory of the familiar thing in the first test.

Method. Simply ask how much the person can remember before the age of 10. Follow up with a few questions to establish how vivid the memories are.

• *Test* $\uparrow V \rightarrow \uparrow E$, i.e. how easily an idea couched in verbal terms can arouse a given emotion.

Method. Ask the person to tell you about a very happy or miserable or angry time, with open eyes and no relaxation or other induction. Then ask, "And how do you feel as you tell me?"

The answer to this, together with any signs of emotional arousal during the account, will give a good idea of how easily emotions can be aroused verbally. Actually people seem to be quite good at answering questions of the form, "If we rate the intensity of the original emotion at 10, how strong is that emotion you are now feeling?" The number given is a good measure of the ease with which an emotion can be aroused from the verbal system.

• *Test* $\uparrow I \rightarrow \uparrow E$, i.e. how easily can an imagined situation arouse an emotion?

Method. The eyes may be closed for this to enhance the visual imagination. The person is then asked to *picture* a particular event which aroused a strong emotion - perhaps the same one as above - for a few minutes, without talking about it. Then a rating for the intensity is given. For many people the rating will be far higher than in the previous test, as the visual imagination is commonly linked more directly to emotion than is the verbal system. For others the reverse may be true.

• *Test* $\uparrow X \rightarrow \downarrow IV$, i.e. the ease with which the internal verbal system (IV) can be inactivated by some other system X, which may be the external verbal system, the internal visual system, etc.

Method. Ask the person what they were thinking during the above tests. Answers may range from, "Nothing - I was just listening and picturing what you asked me," to, "I was constantly analysing everything you said, and everything that was happening." Generally it will be much harder to inactivate the internal verbal system of the latter.

• *Test* $\uparrow V \rightarrow \uparrow R$, i.e. the degree to which the person resists suggestions.

Method. Simply ask, "Did you feel any reluctance in any of those tests?"

At one extreme there are people who may say, "Yes, I thought you were impertinent to ask to see my house. I did not want to show any emotion; it is a sign of weakness," etc. At the other extreme are those who will never display any reluctance.

It may be objected that a person may lie in answering these questions. But if the therapist makes it clear that he or she is quite happy with *any* answer - they are being asked in the spirit of diagnosis, not criticism - then there is not a great danger of this.

Further tests may be made in this brief way. Naturally there is no need to test ALL possible systems in therapy. The above have been given because they tend to be important in all cases. Such things as the ease with which actions result from suggestion, like the hand movement one in the SCHS, are not all that likely to be central to the resolution of a problem. But even there note that it is more useful for you clearly to distinguish three approaches. In one you simply repeat, "Your hands are going to move" for a minute and see and ask if there is any response. In another you repeat, "*Picture* your hands being pulled together by a powerful elastic band." In the third you repeat, "You will *feel* your hands filling with an overwhelming desire to move together. They love each other. They want to be close to each other." Different people may respond in quite different ways to these three approaches. You are in this way establishing whether, if you want a motor response, it is better to proceed from the verbal system or to go via the visual system, or via the emotional system.

Notice that all the above have been done with no use of inductions, no mention of Hypnotic states, etc. They are simply establishing a sort of base-line, the way in which the person's mind works readily and naturally. With the above information in hand the Hypnotherapist may move much more swiftly and surely to achieve any particular goal.

We may generally expect that anything that works well at the everyday level of these tests will be enhanced under the conditions typical of much Hypnotherapeutic practice: when interference from competing systems is much reduced by systematically inactivating them. And this can in turn be tested by comparing the speed or intensity of one of these repsonses before and after any given "induction" which changes the pattern of activity of various subsystems.

Finally it is worth remembering that a so-called Hypnotic phenomenon, such as those represented by the SHCS tests, may be produced by some people with great ease and no preamble, while others may only produce it after a great deal of work by a Hypnotist to activate the appropriate response. This is what makes the notion of a Hypnotic state so intangible and elusive. If the phrase "Hypnotic trance" is to have value we must give criteria to determine when a person is "in a trance" and when not. We must therefore apply tests. But any particular test can be passed by some people when they are, by all common-sense criteria, in their normal "state". This is one reason why there has been so little success in reaching an agreed definition of "Hypnotic state", and why this book does not use the notion.

In this context it is worth noting that there *are* scales in existence which are not designed in the context of Hypnotherapy, such as the Creative Imagination Scale of Barber & Wilson (1978). This involves ten simple tests in which the Subject is invited to imagine a number of things and to report on how strong the resulting experience was. Such a test produces results which correlate positively with Hypnotic Responsiveness tests. It can be adapted easily to the present approach by simply attempting to be precise in each case as to what systems are involved.

SUMMARY

Tests are a very important tool in Hypnosis. To be of most value they should be thought out clearly as a way of finding out how easily one system may activate or deactivate another, *in a given person*.

Existing tests of "Hypnotic susceptibility" are generally presented with a far less clear idea of what exactly it is that they are testing (other than the ability to pass the test, of course). They may readily be adapted to test the action of one system on another, however, as has been demonstrated above.

CHAPTER 9

Inductions

THE COMMON MEANING of "Hypnotic induction" is a process which the Hypnotist goes through, the goal of which is "to Hypnotise the Subject". Most books on Hypnosis feature a section on Hypnotic inductions. This amounts to a shorter or longer collection of the author's favourite recipes. Very seldom is any particular reason given for their component parts. It is never clear which parts could be changed without problem. No reason is given for not using other inductions.

As we come to analyse inductions it is useful to bear in mind here the key idea of *goal* or *purpose*. In principle if a person is doing anything consciously and with understanding then the question, "Why are you doing that?" should receive an answer which reveals a goal or purpose.

"Why are you adding sugar to that cake mix, Mummy?" - "To make it sweet, dear."

"Why are you prescribing an antibiotic, Doctor?" - "In order to kill the bacteria which are causing your infection, Mrs. Jones."

If this key question receives answers of the form, "Because it works," or "Because that's the way I was shown how to do it," or "Because I say so," or some other general and vague answer, we can deduce that the practitioner has no real understanding of the *principles* of his or her practice. The greater the understanding, the greater the detail in the answers to, "Why are you doing that?"

If a book on Hypnosis presents a chapter on inductions with no explanation, then the effective answer to our key question, "Why are you doing that?" is no more informative than, "To induce Hypnosis," or "To deepen Hypnosis," or "Because I say so." The lack of real information in such answers should be apparent.

This book is different. It is designed to teach understanding of what is going on. The whole theoretical structure forces the practitioner to think clearly and in detail about what he or she is doing. The question, "Why are you doing that?" should always be answerable in terms of specifying which process or processes in which system or systems the practitioner is at that time attempting to alter. In other words the goals or purposes are much more clear, detailed and definite.

The approach to inductions chosen in this book is therefore inevitably different to the familiar chapter on inductions in other books. There will be constant reference to the particular systems which are being affected. There will be attention to the question of purpose. In this spirit small sections of a variety of inductions will be analysed, as contrasted with the practice of providing total scripts - of which there are unlimited numbers in the literature. No attempt will be made to cover ALL possible forms of induction. The examples are used simply to illustrate the principles involved.

Various things should become apparent as we go along. The most important thing to understand from the beginning is that we are dealing with **complex** processes. Even when an induction seems to be simple, there is very often a great deal happening which is highly relevant but not obvious. If we were emphasising Stage Hypnosis rather than Hypnotherapy this would be even more true, because the stage Hypnotist, like the stage magician, utilises a variety of subtle techniques to make the effects as dramatic and the means as invisible as possible.

Eye Fixation

A common feature of many inductions is a request that the Subject keep his or her eyes fixed: on a spot on the ceiling, on the Hypnotist's eye, on a bright light or on a spinning disc.

Let us try to analyse what this involves. At the simplest level it runs as follows. There is a verbal request from the Hypnotist. It results in a direct voluntary action on the muscles moving the eye. This in turn results in a significant reduction in the amount of visually interesting stimulus received by the brain.

It is a rather commonplace observation that the general level of arousal in a person is related to the amount of external stimulus. We can therefore predict that as a general rule the fixation of gaze, by limiting the amount of new visual information, will result in an overall reduction in arousal.

More briefly we have:

Verbal direction → ↓{eye movement} → ↓{visual activity} →   ↓{arousal}.

That is the central process. But when we come to analyse things clearly in an actual case, it can be seen that there is often far more to it than that. The instruction, "Look at that point" is, in this culture, normally interpreted as, "Look at that point *and do nothing else.*" Consequently there are also the unspoken instructions, "Do not move" and "Do not talk". These, of course, act to reduce muscular activity and vocal activity respectively, which in turn act to reduce the overall level of arousal still further. Practising Hypnotists could ask themselves how much effect an eye fixation instruction would have if the Subject got up, walked around, viewed the spot from various angles, attempted to touch it, discussed it and other matters at length and so on. It should be fairly obvious that the suggestion would have a minimal effect. This is a first example of the fact mentioned above that the most important aspects of an induction may be things that are not explicit in the verbal description at all!

In abbreviated form these additional processes are:

Tacit instruction, "Do not speak." → ↓{vocalising system} → ↓{arousal}.
Tacit instruction, "Do not move." → ↓{muscular system} → ↓{arousal}.

In addition to these we may consider a higher-order system which acts to accept an idea or instruction {Accept}. If the Subject does what the Hypnotist asks, even in the small way of fixing the eyes, it starts to activate this system. In many of the more authoritarian inductions this system is worked on very extensively. There can be a constant stream of small instructions. "Just move around here, would you?" "Now just look at me." "Nod your head if you understand." "Clasp your hands together." "Now just turn to face the audience." The overall effect of such steps in the process is to activate automatic acceptance more and more. We may note that military training was once based very much on a similar process of beginning with obedience on small things. (I gather that mindless obedience is not now rated as highly as it once was in the forces.)

In an abstract form we may represent the activation of the tendency to accept as follows:

$$(\uparrow\{Instruction\} \rightarrow \uparrow\{Action\}) \rightarrow \uparrow\{Accept\}$$

That is, each time the process of carrying out an action in response to an instruction takes place, it reinforces the tendency to accept further instructions. Notice the more complex form of this, which automatically alerts us to the fact that the system {Accept} is of a different order from the others involved.

Eye Closure

The fixation of the eyes is usually a preface to getting them to close. If the *purpose* of this were merely to close the eyes then it *could* be accomplished by the simple directive, with no preamble, "Please close your eyes". Indeed I will often do this, when this is my sole goal.

But many inductions act in such a way that the eye closure is involuntary. What is the purpose of this? On the one hand it may serve to impress the Subject with the "power" of the Hypnotist, and activate a system of belief in him or her. On the other hand it can serve as a test for the Hypnotist of the strength of the process $\uparrow\{Suggestion\} \rightarrow \downarrow\{Eyelid\ muscles\}$.

Let us analyse an involuntary closure. It involves at the minimum the eye muscles (M) and the verbally suggested idea (S) that they are going to close. If we were thinking of such a closure as being of the nature of a test, as in the last chapter, then we would be examining the strength of the process:

$$\uparrow S \rightarrow \downarrow M$$

(the eye muscles are active only in holding the eye open, so their activity is reduced on closure).

Now a reasonably simple way of testing this would be to say to a person, with no prior eye fixation or preamble, "I would like you to be aware of the muscles of your eyelids. Open and close them a few times until you become aware of the slight effort it takes to keep them open. Opening is an effort, closing is a relaxing of that effort. Now, surprisingly, I think that you will find that very soon that effort is going to be too much for you: you will no longer be able to keep your eyes open." Suggestions on these lines may be repeated for up to a few minutes, by which time a person for whom the above chain is strong will in fact have found that their eyes have closed. If, on the other hand, closure has *not* come about, then the Hypnotist may ask questions to see if there is any obvious reason why it has not happened.

In the above example the phenomenon is presented as clearly and simply as possible with a minimum of secondary or concealed factors operating. The attention has been fixed on a particular system - the eyelid muscles. The thought that it will soon be too much effort consciously to control them is given in a non-authoritarian way. The result is observed. I would like you to contrast that process with a more typical approach in Hypnosis.

The more typical process is *first* to ask for eye fixation as above and then, after a little while, to say something like, "Now your eyelids will get heavier and heavier and soon you will be unable to keep them open." In the best cases eye closure will then come quickly.

This *looks* simple, but there is more going on beneath the surface. Notice first that the Subject has been subtly given two contrary directions: to keep looking at the point **and** to close the eyes. This, in itself, can give rise to uncertainty in the Subject. People do not like uncertainty. There is therefore a subtle pressure to resolve the dilemma as soon as possible in one way or the other. How has it happened that the latter wins over the former? Well, the Hypnotist has loaded the dice in one or more of the following ways.

First of all the eye fixation has been arranged in such a way as to activate a natural system which will lead to eye closure. This may be by getting the Subject to look at a point which is high above the normal line of sight, which will quickly strain and tire the eye muscles. There is also a reflex, which leads to eye closure (for the protection of the retina) if the eye is exposed to a bright light, which can be activated if the Subject is directed to gaze at a bright light or object. There is also a reflex to avoid eye contact at a close distance with a relative stranger which can easily be activated by a Hypnotist who comes very close to the Subject and says, "Now just keep on looking me in the eye."

The second point is that the Hypnotist will typically start to mention the heaviness of the eyes *shortly after* some signs of incipient closure are apparent: e.g. a blink or a droop. The ball is already rolling. The Hypnotist gives it a shove.

It is worth adding that there is good experimental evidence that if two events come close together in time and involve different senses, then people find it hard to place them in a correct order. So, if you *say*, "Your eyes will start to blink" straight *after* the eyes have blinked, there is a strong tendency for the person to suppose that they blinked because of what you said! This acts to activate a system of belief that what you say will happen.

On top of this the Hypnotist will be indicating by his tone of voice that of the two options - to keep staring, or to close the eyes - only the latter is what will actually happen. He may, for example, say, "I want you to **try** to keep your eyes fixed on that point," with a subtle emphasis on **try**, indicating that it can be expected to be difficult. But on the other hand he will say, "Your eyes will want to close," in a matter of fact tone which suggests that it is as good as done.

In addition the general patter of the Hypnotist may include the word "sleep", which, by association, tends to increase a sleepy feeling and a heaviness of the eyes. It may be combined with a slight slowing of the voice to a tone which is itself sleepy, which can again suggest a sleepy feeling to the Subject.

Another factor which is very effective is based on our tendency to imitate. It is commonly the case that if a Client has *seen* another going through a given process, he or she will be pre-programmed to do the same. Group Hypnosis utilises this effect, and the Stage Hypnotist is in a position to use it extensively. But there are, very, very few people who have not seen some film or other display in which the Subject's eyes close and he or she becomes immobile and speaks only when spoken to. Consequently there are in effect social pressures on any Subject to copy this.

By now I trust that it has become clearer that, in what appears to be no more than one simple step in an Hypnotic induction, a large number of psychological factors have been evoked which will not be apparent in a typescript at all.

We have seen the following systems implicated. 1) Some physiological or psychological cause of eye closure is activated. 2) The system which determines the order of events is manipulated, to enhance the system of belief that suggestions are being obeyed. 3) Systems which extract meaning from the *tone* rather than the factual content are activated. 4) By association, sleep-like processes are initiated. 5) That complex process whereby we are able, from being babies, successfully and naturally to imitate others may be used.

While bundling all these together may increase the effectiveness and speed of the induction, it is a poor way to increase our understanding of what is happening.

Not only does the conventional way bundle together methods, it also bundles together goals. Let us look at what goals are involved. The following are possible ones. 1) To close the eyes. 2) To demonstrate to the Hypnotist that the Subject's eyelid muscles will respond to suggestion. 3) To reduce the general level of arousal. 4) To demonstrate to the Subject that the Hypnotist can make the eyes close against his or her will. 5) To enhance the belief and confidence of the Subject in the Hypnotist. 6) To meet the Subject's expectations.

I would suggest that for learning and for understanding and for experiment in the field of Hypnosis such a bundling together of goals and processes is far from helpful. Such a bundling may well be the best way of producing the dramatic effects involved in the entertainment field, where speed and drama are important. In a therapeutic context, on the other hand, it is more appropriate in all ways for the Hypnotherapist to have a clear, conscious goal and a clear understanding of what he or she is doing on the way.

Next let us consider what happens if the verbal direction does NOT lead to the expected result: in this case eye closure. This is potentially a big problem for a Hypnotist working in an authoritarian tradition, because it will reduce his credibility, on which he trades a lot. Moreover he cannot readily ask, "Why are your eyes not closing?" because it would again suggest weakness. He is therefore forced to move onto some other technique in the hope that it will succeed where the other failed.

By contrast the more modern Hypnotherapist does not work in such an authoritarian style and can therefore ask questions without losing face. Within the present paradigm the asking of questions arises very naturally because of the way in which we generally want to have a good idea of what is going on.

So what causes can there be for non-closure? One common cause is the existence of a lot of internal verbal activity. The Subject can easily be thinking such things as, "I feel silly," "My neck is hurting - I want to stop this nonsense," "Why is nothing happening?", "I must try hard to fall asleep soon," and so on. All such thoughts will tend to *increase* the general level of arousal. Or, especially if the approach is authoritarian, there may be a strong resistance in many subjects - "I *won't* do what he asks." Or again, there may be a lot of emotional activity: a feeling of anxiety about the situation. This would not necessarily be expressed internally in words, but could arise from a lack of confidence in the Hypnotist (a lack of *rapport*) or, if the Subject is in a reclining chair, associations with being at the dentist's, or just fear of the unknown. Or again, there may be some physical discomfort which is proving very distracting.

How can we tell? There may be some body-language signs which will help, but the easiest way is simply *to ask*. The questions, "What are you thinking?" and "What are you feeling?", "Are you comfortable?" give answers which can be very informative of what is going on. For some reason, rooted in the old authoritarian traditions of Hypnosis, many Hypnotists seem to feel that questions are banned, but in the context of Hypnotherapy the more that we know, the better.

Counting

In many inductions the Subject is given the task of counting silently. This may be from some number in the hundreds down to zero. It may be upwards. What is the purpose of this?

What this activation of a process of counting (C) achieves is to make it very hard for any other internal verbal process (IV) to take place. We cannot speak sentences on two different subjects simultaneously. So IF we are dealing with a Subject in whom there is a lot of internal verbalisation, and particularly if some of this verbalisation is acting to prevent any particular goal that is being aimed at, a task like verbal counting can be very effective.

In shorthand we have:

$$\uparrow C \rightarrow \downarrow IV.$$

What are the problems that might arise with this? The main one is that there seems to be no way of knowing if the Subject is continuing to comply with the instruction. What if he stops counting? A possible answer to this is to synchronise some simple physical movement: a tap of a foot, a movement of a finger, a nod of the head. An elegant way of selecting the movement is to allow the Subject to choose, as follows.

"As you count, I want you to find that part of your body which most feels like moving in time. Keep counting and test the various parts to see which is most responsive. It might be anything. It may be a finger. (*Pause, while Subject tests finger movement.*) It may be a foot. (*Pause.*) It might be your head. (*Pause.*) Perhaps something else? (*Pause.*) Now which comes easiest?" (I wonder if you, the reader, can think of the most natural set of muscles to synchronise with the counting?)

When the Subject has chosen the most natural movement, this can then be made active and synchronised with the counting. As long as the visible movement continues there is then a very good chance that so will the counting.

It is very unlikely that the Subject will hit upon the most natural set of muscles to synchronise with counting, which are, of course, the muscles of the vocalising system! But I do not suppose that one person in a hundred will think of this unless it is suggested. The process of just forming the words with the lips, or even speaking them quietly, is a totally foolproof way of ensuring that the counting is continuing.

It may be argued against speaking the words quietly that by allowing the vocalising system to be active we are encouraging a higher than necessary degree of arousal. Even if this were to be true, the small loss would be more than offset by the gain of knowing that we had the counting procedure firmly in place. But in fact, as has been known since the last century, the brain is actually *more* active in a person asked to rehearse a poem silently than in one allowed to speak it out loud! (James (1950)) That is because there is *active inhibition* involved. We may similarly expect fully vocalised counting to be less arousing to the brain.

I suspect that the only reason one does not come across this idea in the standard texts is that **in the absence of a clear and systematic way of thinking about what we are doing** induction processes are hit upon more or less at random and then copied and repeated by others. We have hit on the idea by the simple process of asking what our exact goal is and then asking how we may be sure that the goal has been achieved.

Visualisation

There are very few inductions without a passage that runs, "Now I would like you to picture yourself.....(e.g. on a hot, sunny beach)..."

The sunny beach is very popular, but other locations may be suggested, such as the deeply carpeted staircase leading downwards, the peaceful cottage with its log fire and so on. The impression given by the books in which these can be found is that the ones printed are particularly efficacious, and can be used in principle for everyone.

THAT IS WRONG.

The indelible memory which imprinted this fact on my mind was of the time when I was using the carpeted staircase induction, only to find that my Client went into a panic! When I stopped to find out why, I discovered that she was claustrophobic. And you can be sure that there are some people who hate lying out in hot sun, or loathe the solitude of a peaceful cottage, and so on.

The moral is that it is wise never to use a visualisation script without checking first with the Subject that it is acceptable. Better still is to ask the Subject to choose a suitable theme, perhaps from a short list.

Let us, again, begin by asking what is the *purpose* of the visualisation? The goals can be varied. At its simplest we may just be trying to find out how readily this pictorial imagination can be activated and in what ways. A related goal is to find out the extent to which visualisation is absorbing, i.e. eliminates other mental processes. A second class of goals can be to arouse certain responses to the visualisation, such as feelings of relaxation or peace.

Now in many inductions quite a few of these goals are all bundled together, and typically no effort is made to discover if any of them have been achieved! The beginner may be assured that the result will be to "induce a light trance", or, at other times, to "deepen a trance", but he or she is given very little way of checking if this is true or not.

Let us see if we can improve on this by proceeding systematically. Some ideas on these lines have arisen in the previous chapter. Another possible approach, given in more detail, is the following.

Start by discovering how readily the Subject can picture something familiar.

"With open eyes I want you to think of a familiar place, person or thing. When you have thought of one, let me know."

When something has been chosen, questions can be asked to establish such things as the clarity of the image, whether colours can be seen, and whether movement can be pictured. These characteristics are functions of different neurological structures in the visual cortex, and so we are actually examining the ease with which these different structures can be activated. Just as there are some people who seem to dream mainly in black and white, so there are people who cannot visualise easily in colour. And I know a photographer who can visualise clearly, but only in still pictures - never in moving ones. Whether his training had led to this characteristic, or whether the characteristic had led him to his profession, I do not know.

As a second step we may then ask the Subject what is the effect of doing the same thing with closed eyes. We may expect it to make the pictures clearer, but the difference is often less than you might expect.

Then we may go on to cover a broader range of subjects. "Now perhaps you would like to let your mind wander to some other place, some other time. It may be indoors or out, castle or cottage, beach or mountain-top. It can be anywhere you want. You can be doing anything you like." After a minute or two of this we may ask, "Now, have you thought of somewhere?" and detailed questions can be asked to establish the details of the setting: in this way we may test its vividness.

Finally we may ask how absorbed the Subject was in the pictures. "Did you notice anything in *this* room while you were doing the picturing?" is a general question which can be asked. You may have moved something, and perhaps tapped gently but invisibly during a part of the visualisation in order to have something to check the answers to this question against. It is also useful to ask, "What were you thinking while picturing?" to establish the extent to which visualisation reduces internal verbalisation.

One great value of the above systematic testing is that it teaches that in many cases what you might have imagined to be a phenomenon induced only by your great skill in using a powerful induction, is something that a particular person does regularly and easily. I recall, for example, one man with an enormously vivid imagination which was capable of placing him at any point inside or outside of the room at will - you may think of it as like a waking out-of-the-body experience.

More generally it can teach how very, very different people are in the way their minds function, and consequently how different your approach is going to have to be in order to achieve useful changes in the different minds.

Having run through the above processes, and IF visualisation is strong, possible further goals are to discover the ease with which the visualisations can evoke other senses, and, perhaps more importantly, feelings.

Thus, for example, if the Subject happens to have chosen a camp-fire scene, it is possible to ask about the sound of the crackling of the fire, or the warmth of the flames on the face, or the smell of the wood-smoke, or the taste of coffee drunk in the great outdoors, or the comfort or discomfort of the place where the Subject is sitting, and finally the feelings - of happiness or adventure - which go with the picture. In this way, which of course seems very natural and pleasant to the Subject, it is possible to discover how readily the image can also activate other internal systems: sound, heat, smell, taste, touch and finally emotions.

If visualisation is NOT strong, it is still possible to run through a similar process, but replacing words like "see" or "picture" with "think", so that we might say, "I am going to want you to *think* of a familiar situation and then *tell* me about it." There are people - poets can be examples - for whom a word is worth a thousand pictures. In this way it is possible to discover which of the above systems is easily activated by words, and to avoid irritating those Subjects who, in fact, find it very hard to picture things, by talking as if they can do so easily.

Let us next ask the question, "What differences are there likely to be between a Subject who has been run through a typical 'relaxing on the beach' induction, and one who has talked about the scene of choice in the above way?"

In both cases we can presume that attention has become focused on internal systems. In both cases we can presume that this has resulted in a reduction of attention to the external environment, but only in the latter are we likely to be certain. In both cases it is presumed that distracting internal verbalisation has been reduced, but in the former we might be quite wrong, while in the latter, because external vocalisation has been encouraged to remain active, we can be much more certain. In both cases it is presumed that the Subject is enjoying feelings of relaxation, but this might be totally wrong in the former case in which the Hypnotist has chosen a scene that *he* finds relaxing. In both cases it is presumed that rapport has been achieved, but in the former (IF it has been accomplished) it is by making the Subject's thoughts keep in step with those of the Hypnotist, where in the latter it has been by means of the Hypnotist pacing the thoughts, sensations and feelings of the Subject.

In brief, then, the approach suggested above will not only achieve all the goals that a good induction is presumed, without proof, to achieve, but will do so more effectively, as well as being enormously more informative.

It is hard to see why vocalisation is encouraged so little in "inductions". Perhaps it is simply a left-over aspect of the traditional, authoritarian approach. It is a commonplace of counselling that talking is, in itself, a relaxing and a helpful process for most people. We should expect that the process of talking about what is happening as the session progresses should also be relaxing, as well as enhancing confidence and rapport.

Hand Levitation

A common "induction" uses hand levitation. The basic process is one in which the Hypnotist does all the talking. The Subject may be invited to imagine a lighter-than-air balloon tied to one finger of one hand. Suggestions are made that this also be felt, and that it will gently pull that finger up into the air. Once that is started, the other fingers and finally the whole hand and arm can be involved in the movement, until it rises to the face. At that point the Subject is usually told to relax completely and "go into a deep trance". The whole process may take some ten minutes.

Let us ask what the purpose of this is. The overt goal is to induce a non-voluntary movement of the hand and arm. So at the simplest we are trying to establish the possibility and ease of the process:

Verbal direction → ↑{involuntary system} → ↑{arm muscles},

where we are being vague about exactly what involuntary system is mediating the muscular response.

Possible secondary goals are to reduce most other mental activity as a result of focusing on the movement; to impress the Subject with the power of the Hypnotist; and to test how easy it is to induce analgesia. This third point arises because in order for the rising of the arm to feel involuntary, sensations of tiredness in the arm must be unavailable to consciousness. (Try lifting your arm consciously over a period of minutes and feel the ache.)

Note that although this process is normally presented as an "induction", there is *no discernible difference in the result* if the whole thing is presented on the lines of, "I would like to test a certain response," followed by the request to visualise the balloon, etc. This underlines yet again the problem that supporters of "Hypnotic states" have in trying to establish any difference between such a hypothetical state and the result of such a straightforward process. The theoretical approach of this book avoids this completely.

Although there is no strong reason why the image of the balloon should not be used in the above, it is perhaps easier and more informative to be more flexible. Erickson (1981) is known to have approached this phenomenon by asking the Subject to rest his or her hands lightly on the legs and then to look at and pay close attention to the fingers. He would then ask the Subject to look out for *any change* in any of them: of feeling, or warmth or position. When something was reported, he would then build on this to produce more change and then still more. (The feedback loop involved in this way will be emphasised later in the book.) The great advantage of this non-dogmatic style is that it allows question and answer in the process. As we have seen, a Hypnotist who asks questions of the Subject can gain a lot more information about exactly *which* processes are active than one who simply gives directions and hopes that the direction is being followed.

We might ask *why* a therapist would be interested in this Hypnotic phenomenon: why specify that particular goal? The most common reason is the following. In evolutionary terms the vocal system is a newcomer when it comes to communication. Gestures and movements of various kinds have a much more ancient history. Now, as we shall discuss in more detail later, in certain people some mental systems can become detached from the vocal system. In some cases this means that the person is effectively not consciously aware of some process or processes in the brain. In others it is milder, and the person simply feels unable to speak about them. We probably all know men who seem to be "out of touch" with their own feelings, for example. And in cases of trauma, memories of the experience can be "repressed", i.e. not consciously recalled.

In cases of this kind, it may nevertheless be possible to establish a connection between that hidden subsystem of interest (H) and a muscular movement (M), which does NOT proceed via the verbal or conscious or even visual systems. If we can interpret the movement, then we have a channel of communication with that hidden system.

Now a common muscular process to be used for this signalling is the movement of a finger. Consequently IF a Hypnotherapist has, as a goal, the establishing of a connection with H, it can be a useful preliminary to test for finger levitation. The presumption is that if the process:

$$\uparrow V \rightarrow \uparrow \{\text{involuntary system}\} \rightarrow \uparrow M,$$

i.e. a verbal instruction can lead indirectly to the motor activity without passing through the normal voluntary system of movement, then the process:

$$\uparrow H \rightarrow \uparrow \{\text{involuntary system}\} \rightarrow \uparrow M,$$

i.e. an activation of the motor process by the hidden system, also bypassing the normal voluntary system, is also easily possible.

Logically, the one need not imply the other, because V is quite distinct from H, but they do have in common the bypassing of the voluntary system, and so the test is some kind of pointer and also a preparation.

Incidentally the process of using a muscular system for communication in this way is commonly called Ideo-Motor-Signalling (IMS). More on this is described in Chapter 19 on indirect questions.

We see again the importance of thinking clearly about goals here. The simplistic Hypnotherapist may use a hand levitation as part of every induction he does, for no other reason than that he has always used it. A more systematic Hypnotherapist will activate that particular system of response only when it lies on the path of his projected therapy.

But notice then that, with the particular goal of communication with H in mind, the systematic Hypnotherapist is likely to proceed yet more precisely as follows.

Suppose that H has to do with a hidden fear, and we want to find out more about it, via a non-verbal channel of information. We could proceed on the following lines.

"When people start to feel frightened they usually have characteristic ways of responding. Some will cry, others will clench their fists, others may start to tap their feet as if getting ready to run away, others may feel a need to turn their heads away, others may frown: there is no *one* way. Now I want you to think of something that you find a bit frightening and then notice which parts of your body respond."

Of course the first response may be something that cannot be easily seen, like a flutter in the stomach: in which case the Hypnotherapist can accept that one, but ask also for another, which involves visible movement.

When a movement has been chosen, then we have found a muscular system which is readily activated by the emotional process of fear. It is therefore one of the most promising candidates for a channel of communication. It could be possible to waste large amounts of time trying to use finger movement in an individual whose natural response to fear is to "freeze" all the major muscles, while at the same time the eyebrow muscles might be tightening up very readily in response to that same fear! Once a channel has been obtained it can be used more and more freely, perhaps in the way outlined below.

"I am just going to talk about some things that people can be frightened of. I do not want you to feel any fear, and should you start to get uncomfortable, I want you to ask me to stop. While I talk your eyebrow muscles (*if these are the channel discovered*) will be telling me how you feel, without you having to think about it at all." The Hypnotherapist can then gradually talk around possible areas of fear, simply noting when the non-verbal response gets stronger, in a simple game of Hunt the Thimble. The closer he gets to talking about things that really arouse fear (whether consciously or not), the more the muscles signal that he is getting "warmer".

In this section we have looked at a few items from inductions, and expanded on the principles involved at great length. The intention has been to show how the systems approach to our subject leads to a far clearer idea of the goals of such processes, and how it generates an ability to reach specified goals more quickly, more surely and more confidently. There has, of course, been no attempt to analyse all possible inductions. On the contrary it should be apparent that in the spirit of this approach **the same "induction" will never be used twice**: the precise approach depends so much on the response of the Client that it must be different for each person.

It should, however, now be possible for the reader to look at ANY "induction" process and start to analyse it in a similar way. The key questions are the following:-

1. What processes of which systems are involved?
2. What are the possible goals of this "induction" in terms of those processes?
3. How could each goal be achieved more simply and directly?
4. How can it be verified that each goal has actually been achieved?

This last question is of great and general importance, I believe. The great advances in knowledge in recent centuries have come about as a result of demanding that statements be verifiable NOT simply by a reference to an "Authority", but by reference to fact. The motto of the Royal Society of London is *Nullius in verba*, part of a Latin quotation which may be freely translated as, "We do not take anybody's word for it." Just because someone has said, "This process leads to a deep Hypnotic trance," it does not mean that it will work for you or with every Subject, or indeed at all, as it stands! It may well be, for example, that the person who wrote those words was using some very important, but not verbal, process as part of his induction, of which you are unaware.

To proceed blindly, with no certainty that the changes which are happening are what you think is happening, is foolishness. Verification is the cornerstone of science and of sure progress in all things. A bricklayer does not lay the next layer of bricks without checking that the previous layer is correctly placed.

I hope that any student of Hypnosis will go away and test what I have said by trying out, with the above questions in mind, many components of many "inductions" many times on a variety of people, and in that way build up a very good foundation of understanding of how each part works. This approach of mastering the component part of a skill is fundamental to most expertise.

CONCLUSION

"Inductions" as viewed from the systems viewpoint are more precise and more flexible and more accurate than the traditional "scripted" approach.

They can be more precise because they are built around a firm structure of detailed goals in terms of specified changes to specified systems.

They are more flexible because the approach lends itself to modifying and tailoring the processes to the personality of each individual Subject.

Finally they are more accurate in that the systems approach encourages continual verification that all is going as it is supposed to: which allows corrections and adjustments to be made as necessary.

Conclusion of Part A

BY THIS STAGE it is expected that the newcomer to the field will have picked up a reasonable overview of Hypnosis.

In addition it is hoped that all readers will have become familiar with the systems perspective.

PART B

Introduction to Part B

THE NEXT AND CENTRAL part of the book takes the ideas which have been presented in Part A and develops them in the context of Hypnotherapy. This is, in brief, a three-stage process of finding out what problem a Client has, planning how to solve the problem and finally making the changes necessary to achieve this goal.

In the course of doing this the virtues of the organised "Morganic" approach to thinking about what we are doing will become yet more apparent, and will reveal not only the dynamic basis of many problems, but also give more insight into the way in which many Hypnotic processes work.

The ideas which are presented here do not exist, to the best of my knowledge, in any other book on the subject. The whole question of diagnosis in Hypnotherapy and deciding on the best approach is NOT one which seems to have received a great deal of attention in the literature. Gibson & Heap (1991) exemplifies the best current thinking on Hypnosis in therapy, and is required reading for anyone training in Hypnotherapy. But it retains, as an unspoken assumption, the common idea that problems should be classified in the medical manner by symptom. Although they observe that different approaches will be made to different patients with similar symptoms, they give little in the way of guidance as to why one should use one approach rather than another. The book also avoids giving any categorical definition of Hypnosis, while leaning (p.1) to the idea of a "state of Hypnosis".

By contrast this present book is evolving a robust and extensive theoretical view of the subject. This view in turn provides an approach to diagnosis which is both more informative, involving as it does an analysis of the *dynamics* of the problem, and also far better at prescribing what should be done.

CHAPTER 10

The Process of Hypnotherapy - Stage 1:
Elements of Diagnosis in Hypnotherapy

NOW THAT WE have established some of the principles of Hypnosis it is time to look at the specific field of Hypnotherapy, which is our goal. We will discover that forming a clearer idea of what we need to achieve in therapy will help to clarify the kind of Hypnotic processes we need to use. We have already seen a little of this at the end of the last chapter, where we have chosen to modify an item from a standard Hypnotic "induction" with an eye on its therapeutic purpose.

The key word in the chapter title is "diagnosis": the "determination of the nature of a problem". It may be thought that this is not a matter that needs discussion. Panic attacks are easily diagnosed by their symptoms, sleeplessness is simply an inability to get to sleep, a headache is a headache: where is the problem?

We may begin to understand why this is not sufficient by considering the advice that appears in many people's writings: "You should not simply treat the symptoms." What does this mean? It means that it has often been found that a headache, let us say, is simply a sign of some deeper problem which, like an iceberg, is 90% concealed from sight. If you remove the symptom then all that happens is that some other symptom will arise in its place. In practice then, Hypnotherapists will generally look deeper than the presented symptom before doing anything.

However the *way* in which this should be done is nowhere explicitly given in any detail. (Though this, I repeat, is not to say that it is not done by practising therapists. It has not been written much of because of the absence of a theoretical framework within which to do so.) The following should begin to make the whole matter of systematic analysis of problems in the context of Hypnotherapy much more understandable, accessible and effective.

The starting point of all Hypnotherapy is a Client saying, "I have a problem." And the goal of therapy is that same Client being able to say honestly and happily, "I no longer have that problem." (It is to be understood that this is not achieved by means of brushing the problem under the carpet and that it is not achieved at the expense of introducing a new and perhaps worse problem.)

Between those two statements lies a **process of change**. It is a process which is facilitated by the therapist. In order to do this with maximum effectiveness the therapist must first understand the nature of the problem and then help to make appropriate changes.

This chapter is devoted to answering the question, **"How does the**

Hypnotherapist begin to understand the nature of the problem?"

Notice that problem-solving happens in many professional contexts - medicine, engineering, business consultancy and so on - and in each there is going to be an initial phase in which the professional is asking questions in order to grasp the nature of the problem. The actual questions asked will vary from speciality to speciality, but the answers received will gradually characterise the problem more and more precisely. It is important to notice that to a large extent the questions are determined by the kind of tools which the professional has. A doctor, for example, has a limited number of medicines and procedures at her disposal: a diagnostic session is therefore going to be biassed towards simply determining which is the most appropriate one.

Since the tools of the Hypnotherapist deal, as we have seen, with altering the functioning of a very wide variety of internal systems in a naturalistic manner, it follows that during the diagnostic phase *the questions will be aimed at finding out which systems are involved and what functional processes involving them need to be changed.*

The emphasised words are of central importance, and are not to be passed over lightly. Notice how this definition of the diagnostic process is rooted directly in our basic concept of Hypnosis as a manipulation of the processes which various subsystems undergo. Notice how clear the goal of diagnosis is. Notice that the goal is to get a real idea not merely of a static symptom, but of the dynamics of the whole process of which the symptom is merely a part. Diagnosis in Hypnotherapy is *finding out which systems are involved and what functional process or processes involving them need to be changed.*

The bare bones of this process of diagnosis can be represented by a series of questions, the key ones of which will now be described.

Q. "What is the problem?"

Q. What process C is the central one for the Client? What system does it involve?

In asking verbally the question in bold type, we are aiming to get information which answers the question in italic type.

As examples we may find answers such as, "I blush," the central system in which is the capillaries of the face, and the troubling process is a dilation. If the answer is "I panic," then the central system can be thought of as part of the limbic system in the brain, and the central process that of arousing systems in the body which would be active in a "flight or fight" situation.

Of course the particular process which is the symptom does not arise in isolation, so the next couple of questions explore the preceding and resulting events.

Q. "What is happening just before the problem starts?"

Q. What system P (for precursor) activates C?, or in shorthand

$P? \rightarrow C.$

In practice this question stands for a whole series of questions, since many Clients have never thought their problem through in this way. "I blush in front of people" may be what is believed to be the truth, but in fact it may be that blushing only happens in front of members of the opposite sex who are found attractive, or with people who are felt to be in authority, or in conditions where guilt is felt and so on, or it may be only when the sufferer has thought to himself, "Oh dear, I hope I do not blush here!" In these cases the answers to our technical questions would be, respectively, an arousal of a sexual or inferiority or guilt or an internal verbalisation system. In the case of smoking the answers may turn out to be, "My mouth feels very dry", "I get a tickle at the back of the throat", "It is like a voice saying, 'Have one'", in which cases the precursors seem to involve the salivary glands, the sensory system and the internal verbalisation system respectively.

Of course in many cases there will be *several* answers to this question. The immediate precursors to smoking may well be boredom *or* stress *or* a cup of coffee, for example.

In the above, the answers to the question have mainly related to *internal* systems. It must not be supposed that this is the only class of possible answers. The answers given may relate to external precursors which may involve people or things - "When the boss shouts at me", "When the chlorine in the swimming-pool gets up my nose". Of course we may work from such answers to discover what system in the Client is responding to such external stimuli, but it is important for us to bear in mind the possibility that the best way to tackle the problem may be a purely practical one: to change jobs or wear a nose-clip.

When we have a clear idea of immediate causes of the problem symptom we should also find out what happens as a result of it.

Q. And what happens afterwards?

Q. What systems R (for resultant) does the process C affect in turn? Or in shorthand,

$C \rightarrow R?$

Although it is obvious that the precursor of the symptom is important, it may not be quite so obvious why the resultant is, so here are two primary reasons.

There are times when the result of C is a reward of some kind: heroin can lead to an ecstatic high, or at least to the relief of the craving; a headache may lead to a day off work or at least some loving attention; obsessive cleaning late at night may result in avoiding unwanted sex and so on. It is an elementary principle of psychology that when an activity is rewarded the behaviour tends to be reinforced, i.e. the whole pattern is more likely to be repeated.

In other circumstances the result may not be a reward, but can still have the result of reinforcing the pattern. For example, a common result of stammering is an increased conviction that stammering is inevitable. This conviction feeds back into the next social occasion and increases the chances of stammering happening again.

As a result of a first-order application of our first two questions, we should know P^1 and R^1, such that:

$$P^1 \rightarrow C \rightarrow R^1,$$

but there will often be a value in asking the same questions repeatedly to discover earlier precursors and later resultants, until we have a single causal chain describing a long process of which the symptom is only a part:

$$\ldots \rightarrow P^3 \rightarrow P^2 \rightarrow P^1 \rightarrow C \rightarrow R^1 \rightarrow R^2 \rightarrow R^3 \rightarrow \ldots$$

In practice we may well discover a number of such processes. There are many roads that pass through Rome, there are many sentences which contain the word "love", there are many activities which involve an increase in heart rate, and there will in general be many processes of which the symptom is part.

Typically, in order to determine the patterns above, the Client is referring to memories of occasions when the problematic central symptom C arose. Indeed it is often necessary to listen to accounts of a number of different episodes in order to distinguish factors which are an essential part of the problematic processes and those which are incidental. Useful questions to ask in order to clarify the nature of the key processes are:

Q. **And when else has C_s happened?**
Q. **What did the different occasions have in common?**
Q. **Can you recall the <u>first</u> time C_s happened?**

In many cases, of course, the first time is of great importance as it set the pattern of the process which has been followed with only small variation ever since.

At times the first occurrence has been consciously forgotten, and then a very careful analysis of the current process will often enable one to determine what the original experience is likely to have been. Let us suppose that as a result of questioning it is found that the central symptom in a man is that of a panic attack; that a common factor in triggering off the attack is the sight of a bearded man; and that a common effect of the panic is a gagging reaction and some nausea; and that this has been current since the age of three. Then one possible explanation is that as a child the Client was forced to perform fellatio on a bearded man at that very early age. This provides a hypothesis which can be explored by means of further questions: **it is very risky to suppose that the assumption is true without rather more evidence than the above.** If four or five other aspects of the problem also fall into place when this hypothesis is adopted then its likelihood is increased.

But it is important to note that the appropriate attitude to take to such an hypothesis is to look for evidence that it may be *wrong*, rather than confirmatory evidence that it is *right*. Thus evidence that the man's fantasies and sex life are perfectly normal would cast doubt on the theory, for example. If we were to discover that the man *also* has the same panic reactions in hospitals, and further questioning revealed that he had been in hospital when he was two with a throat problem, then we have a second hypothesis, which is that the phobia was initiated by a bearded doctor examining his throat too roughly. If, alternatively, we found that the panics could also arise at times when the Client is sitting at a table on a formal occasion, the roots may have to do with his father (we would have to check if he wore a beard at the time) *forcing* him to eat at an early age.

Hypnotic techniques could then be used to provide further evidence in ways that will be described later. In some cases it is useful to regress the Client to the time of the original experience and to allow it to be relived and the associated feelings to be expressed. Such an expression of emotion is termed abreaction. However, it is worth realising that in many cases symptoms reduce or disappear purely as a result of the *understanding* which can be achieved by means of the above analysis, which has more of the flavour of Sherlock Holmes than Sigmund Freud.

In dealing with such phenomena it is important to be careful about the language we use. It is easy and common to say that a problem was "caused by" an early trauma. But this sense of cause is not the same as that implied by the use of "→" which is that of a direct or immediate cause. In fact we should analyse such situations in the following way.

Trauma → {Memory trace at a non-conscious level}.

Current stimulus → ↑{Memory Trace} → ↑{Associated responses}.

This is not to split hairs. The above analysis can be of central importance since if, using Hypnotic techniques, we *alter the memory trace in certain key ways*, we can dramatically improve the response to current stimuli. Put more bluntly, people are affected NOT by the past but by what they remember (consciously or subliminally) of the past. We cannot change the past, but we can change memories.

Returning now to the above line of questioning, we have seen that it results in a linked chain of processes, with precursors leading to the symptom which in turn has its resultants. Now consider how this chain could end.

We have the following alternatives. A chain may have open ends lying either inside or outside the person, or the chain may close and form a loop. An example of a chain which starts outside a person is one in which the initial process is that of being shouted at. The process will end outside the person if it leads to hitting or vomiting. It will end inside the person if the last clear resultant is something like a headache or muscle tensions. The chain may start inside a person if, for example, the first clear precursor is a recurrent thought of self-hatred, or some recurrent feeling or physical symptom.

The distinctions above become of value when we come to the next stage in our work, which is changing the situation. It is a commonplace that a ventilated emotion tends to dissipate harmlessly, i.e. an external end to the chain is less of a problem to the individual than an internal end. And the approach to solving a problem will generally be quite different according to whether the primary cause is some quite definite factor in the external environment or some internal process.

The third alternative, which is that the chain may close to form a loop, is of enormous importance. Such loops are very, very common. In colloquial language they are called vicious circles and are often recognised as such by the Client.

Let us look at some simple examples. A man has a slight tendency to blush. But he is embarrassed about blushing. The embarrassment results in more intense blushing. We have a vicious circle, which in a short form can be expressed as:

$$\uparrow\{\text{Embarrassment}\} \rightarrow \uparrow\{\text{Blushing}\} \rightarrow \uparrow\{\text{Embarrassment}\},$$

or $\uparrow\{\text{Blushing}\} \rightarrow \uparrow\{\text{Embarrassment}\} \rightarrow \uparrow\{\text{Blushing}\}.$

It does not matter which item we start with when we are defining loops: a loop has no beginning and has no end.

Other examples arise in many contexts: sleeplessness can lead to an anxiety (about lack of sleep) which in turn leads to sleeplessness; a sickness at the thought of food can lead to a fear of starving to death which can lead to an increased feeling of sickness; the pain of muscle tension can lead to mental worry which can lead to yet further muscular tension; an asthmatic attack may both be caused by anxiety and provoke anxiety, in which case a vicious circle can exist; acid production in the stomach can both be prompted by stress and (because of its discomfort) cause stress; perhaps simplest of all we have the fact that the feeling of fear can itself be fearful, though a more careful analysis of this will usually show that there are two parts to the system - the emotion of fear and the mental process which says, "This feeling is dangerous".

The general pattern that runs through the above and many other complaints that a Hypnotherapist will see is that of:

$$\uparrow\{\text{Fear/anxiety}\} \rightarrow \uparrow\{\text{Symptom}\} \rightarrow \uparrow\{\text{Fear/anxiety}\}.$$

Many things can be both a cause and a result of fear, and hence create vicious circles. The consequences of a feeling of fear are many - we have already met them in the "fight or flight" responses. Typically the heart rate increases, breathing becomes faster and shallower, blood is diverted to brain and muscles and away from intestines and skin (though the face is a common exception to this), muscles tense, there may be a tendency to evacuate stomach and bowels, there is sweating, speech tends to be inhibited, the mind races and so on. The exact pattern varies from individual to individual, but if any of these effects is regarded as itself being dangerous or a problem then the above vicious circle becomes established.

A very important part of the diagnostic process is to establish whether or not there is such a vicious circle, which we will later describe as an internal increasing positive feedback loop.

Such vicious circles can exist not just in the individual human being but in other organic systems too. For example, if we find that a problem chain is ending in another person - a spouse, for example - then by changing focus we may consider our primary system to be the couple, which has two clearly defined subsystems - the partners - which we may label A and B. The action of crying by A may lead to violence in B which leads to an increase of crying in A: a vicious circle.

This example is quite important because it reminds us that we should generally not stop our analysis at the boundaries of the individual. Very many problems have to do with the individual's reactions to and actions on others.

One of the beauties of the current systems approach is that we can use precisely the same language and shorthand and diagnostic approach in dealing with processes within the individual, *and* processes within the family which involve the individual *and* processes within the society which involve the individual.

We may find for example that the presented problem of a headache is part of the following loop:

$\uparrow$ {The boss's anger} $\rightarrow$ $\uparrow$ {resentment in man} $\rightarrow$ $\uparrow$ {headache} $\rightarrow$ $\downarrow$ {job performance} $\rightarrow$ $\uparrow$ {boss's anger}.

In such a case we have a vicious circle where the most potentially useful system to change has little to do with the system where the symptom appears. Instead we should be focusing on the sufferer's methods of dealing with authority and anger from others. If the man can stand up for himself - be more assertive without being aggressive - then the repeated doses of resentment will be avoided and the whole vicious circle will wind down.

Or we might have a typical situation in which the presented symptom is what the sufferer may call paranoia - the feeling that people are thinking in an unpleasant way about him. (This is not the strict clinical definition.) But as a result of that feeling he may start to scowl at people, to skulk into rooms and perhaps to mutter under his breath, as a result of which people *will*, indeed, start thinking unpleasant thoughts about him: a vicious circle is established.

In such a case the Hypnotherapist might choose to work on the *thoughts* about other people or the *feelings* of paranoia or on the *behaviour* which is maintaining the circle.

The question of how to choose the most appropriate point to start to change a circle will be left until another chapter.

I hope it is clear that the diagnostic procedure outlined above goes a long way to avoid the criticism, "You are only treating symptoms." In fact, the criticism might with more justice be aimed at large areas of contemporary medicine, particularly when it comes to treating the vast range of anxieties, panics, depressions, etc. which are becoming an increasing proportion of the doctor's case-load as the specifically organic illnesses are being controlled more and more. The diagnostic process in Hypnotherapy is detailed and should in principle reveal *all* factors involved with a presented symptom, and will therefore *never* be dealing with it in isolation as the doctor all too commonly is.

The above process of establishing the causal chains - the dynamic patterns - involving the presented symptom is clear, though of course the results can be very different in different cases. I would suggest that diagnosis is not complete until the picture that emerges from such an analysis is complete and satisfactory: that it accounts for all the known facts.

But what if this does not happen? What if no chain arises? What if we cannot find any causes? Then, I suggest, we have *prima facie* evidence that the problem does not lie in our field, but in that of someone else. We are then in a similar situation to the doctor who, having applied all his tests (which are simply a technical form of asking questions), cannot find a cause for the ailment. He is then likely to think of the problem as being psychological. If we can find no clear cause-and-effect chains then we should equally be thinking, "This is physical," and sending the patient back for another opinion. (In the UK people normally take problems first to their General Practitioner and only later to a Hypnotherapist, because the former consultation is free.)

We might also consider referring the Client to another specialist. For example, although *in principle* we should be able by means of our diagnostic scheme to discover if there is a dietary cause for a problem, it is outside our expertise and so it is unlikely that we will know the precise questions to ask in order to establish the dietary cause. Equally although we should in principle be able to decide if the cause is an allergy, or perhaps some poison in the environment, it will depend on asking the right *detailed* questions, and the right questions will again be best left to specialists.

I hope that these few remarks will go a little way to explain why it is not necessary for an experienced and intelligent Hypnotherapist also to have a full training in medicine any more than it is necessary for a General Practitioner to have a full training in Psychotherapy. (Though I would strongly recommend that each of these specialists should acquire a basic, sound and relevant familiarity with the other field.) Each has a collection of diagnostic questions designed to establish the causes of a given complaint which is treatable by his or her methods. Each, with practice, learns to recognise when the answers do not add up to something that is capable of being treated by the means to hand. Each then learns to pass the patient on to someone who might have a better chance. Of course each may make mistakes, but I hope that these paragraphs may at the very least moderate the view that a Hypnotherapist commonly attempts to "suggest away" any symptom with no regard for possible physical or psychological causes, and hence makes things worse. This is far from the truth. This is not to say that "help" cannot be misguided: we only have to consider the consequences of Thalidomide or of the indiscriminate use of the Benzodiazepines (Diazepam, Valium, etc.) in the sixties to see that mankind may easily take what appears to be a step to improve things and succeed only in creating greater problems. But it should be clear that the systematic approach to Hypnotherapeutic interventions presented explicitly here leads to a high level of awareness of possible problems and to a minimising of any dangers of an ill-considered intervention.

SUMMARY

The first stage of diagnosis is to establish the existing dynamic patterns. Generally this will mean discovering chains of precursors and resultants of the central, presented problem.

One very common and important pattern that can emerge from this analysis is that of a vicious circle (an increasing positive feedback loop). At times these circles involve larger systems such as family or society.

In considering those chains which do not form circles (open chains) it is useful to note if their ends lie within or outside the individual.

The diagnostic process ensures that the symptom will NOT be seen in isolation.

The failure of the diagnostic procedure to reveal a dynamic cause for the complaint suggests strongly that the Client should be sent to other specialists for their opinion.

CHAPTER 11

Feedback Loops - an Introduction

IN THE LAST CHAPTER we met the notion of a vicious circle. This chapter will deal with various forms of loop, of which the vicious circle is only one example.

In this chapter P^1, P^2, etc. are all labels for processes undergone by certain systems which will not be explicitly mentioned.

A **loop** is a compound process with N identifiable subprocesses P^1, P^2, ... P^N, which will be represented in the general form:

$$\updownarrow P^1 \to \updownarrow P^2 \to \updownarrow P^3 \to \ \ldots \ \to \updownarrow P^N \to \updownarrow P^1.$$

Loops can be discovered by starting with any process and then, by finding precursors and resultants, creating a chain until the process at the beginning and the process at the end are the same.

Notice that the change in activity of each component process of the loop may be an increase or a decrease. We will therefore end up with a loop having one of the following four forms:

1) $\uparrow P \to \ldots\ldots \to \uparrow P$

2) $\downarrow P \to \ldots\ldots \to \downarrow P$

3) $\uparrow P \to \ldots\ldots \to \downarrow P$

4) $\downarrow P \to \ldots\ldots \to \uparrow P$

1) When an increase in the activity of P leads via a chain of other processes to a further increase in the activity of P, we will call the compound process **an increasing positive feedback loop**.

2) But when a decrease in activity of P leads to a further decrease, we will call the loop a **decreasing positive feedback loop**.

3) and 4), in which an increase in activity leads to a decrease or vice versa, will be called **one-sided negative feedback loops**. The form 3) tends to prevent the activity of P getting too great, and form 4) acts to prevent it getting too small. A **two-sided negative feedback loop** is one in which *both* of 3) and 4) hold:

$$\uparrow P \to \ldots \to \downarrow P \to \ldots \to \uparrow P.$$

Notice that positive and negative have no emotional overtones. P may be a favourable process, which creates happiness, or an unfavourable one that leads to misery. But we would still see it as a positive loop if a change leads on to the same kind of change, and as a negative loop if a change in it leads to a change of the opposite sign.

The science which deals with such feedback loops is Cybernetics, the foundations of which were laid by Norbert Weiner and others in the 1940s (Weiner (1948a,b)). Another phrase which is used for the science is that of Control Theory.

At the present stage of the science of Hypnotherapy we are dealing with these processes in a *qualitative* way, but should we ever get to a stage of research in which a *quantitative* description of " $A \rightarrow B$ " can be given, then we will have access to a great deal of established mathematical theory which will integrate our science with many other related ones.

Examples of Feedback Loops

1) We have seen a number of examples of increasing positive feedback loops in the last chapter. Such loops are one of the important causes of problems. But here we will consider their application in the simple Hypnotic phenomenon of hand levitation which we have already met briefly when looking at "inductions".

Practising Hypnotherapists will be aware that when they begin to suggest that a finger will rise into the air, nothing happens. Several minutes and many suggestions may pass before there is the slightest movement. During that process the Client will typically be thinking, "Nothing is going to happen," and there is a lot of doubt. But once there has been the slightest movement, which we may label $\uparrow F$ (an increase in the activity of the finger muscles), it leads to a decrease in the doubting mental processes ($\downarrow D$). The positive suggestions of the Hypnotherapist therefore gain ground ($\uparrow P$), and these in turn lead to a greater movement of the finger ($\uparrow F$). Hence we have the increasing positive feedback loop:

$$\uparrow F \rightarrow \downarrow D \rightarrow \uparrow P \rightarrow \uparrow F.$$

In practice we find that an initial movement soon becomes much bigger and it can take as little time to get the entire hand and arm levitated up to the face as it took to get a single finger to move a fraction in the first place.

It can at times be useful to give Clients a "picture" of feedback loops, to help them to understand things. The following is one picture.

"I wonder if you have ever been in a hall with a Public Address System which has started to give off that high-pitched whistle? You know what is happening, of course. The microphone is designed to pick up sound. It passes the sound to an amplifier, which makes it louder. It is then passed on to the loudspeakers which spread the sound into the hall.

"Now if the loudspeaker is too close to, or is facing, the microphone, we have trouble. The trouble is that the microphone then picks up the sound from the speakers. This is then amplified further so that very quickly the mike is picking up a louder sound. This is amplified in turn, making the speakers still louder. The whole thing quickly gets out of hand until it reaches the limits of the system, and you get the terrible whistle.

"Now in *you* we might see the symptom as being the sound from the speakers. You noticing the symptom is like the mike picking up the sound. You worrying about the symptom is like the amplifier making things worse, because in you the worry is in fact directly causing the symptom.

"The problem can easily be solved by turning the speakers away from the mike, or putting them further away (helping you to take less notice of the symptom). It is also helped by turning down the amplification (reducing your feelings of anxiety)."

Other examples of increasing positive feedback loops arise in many places. A good learning process, for example, is often characterised by the following loop:

$$\uparrow\{\text{skill}\} \rightarrow \uparrow\{\text{satisfaction}\} \rightarrow \uparrow\{\text{practice}\} \rightarrow \uparrow\{\text{skill}\}.$$

In other words, if a person gets satisfaction from the exercise of a skill, it will motivate actions which will lead to a further increase in the skill.

Most GROWTH phenomena in a biological setting involve increasing positive feedback loops. Thus the growth of a bacterial infection is described by the simplest of all loops:

$$\uparrow\{\text{bacteria}\} \rightarrow \uparrow\{\text{bacteria}\},$$

i.e. if, in a given environment, the activity of the bacteria increases - basically as a result of the bacteria multiplying - then the increase will in a short time result in a still further increase, as the increased numbers also multiply. Such a process of growth tends to increase very rapidly (technically the growth is exponential) until it reaches a size in which other factors become important. These will typically act to limit the growth in a way which can often be recognised as a negative feedback loop.

2) **Decreasing** positive feedback loops are often of importance when we come to discuss the resolution of a problem. They may arise naturally and can lead to a spontaneous solution to that problem.

As a simple example, suppose that a person has a phobia about something that has been growing worse for years under the influence of an increasing positive feedback loop. The more fear (F) is *felt* on meeting the object that triggers the phobia, the more that object is *thought* of as fearful (T), but the more it is thought of in that way, the more terrifying it will be felt to be. ($\uparrow F \rightarrow \uparrow T \rightarrow \uparrow F$)

Now suppose that some progress can be made *by any means whatever* - tablets, Hypnosis, acupuncture, advice... - in reducing either the feeling of fear or the thought that the object is terrifying. We may generally expect that a reduction in the fear will lead to a reduction in the thought that the object is fearful, and that a reduction in that thought will tend to reduce the actual fear next time. IF that is in fact the case we have a decreasing positive feedback loop:

$$\downarrow F \rightarrow \downarrow T \rightarrow \downarrow F.$$

The activity of each process thus gradually decreases until they both drop to zero (an activity cannot be negative). In other words if we can once get a noticeable improvement, things will then continue to get better under their own momentum.

A Hypnotherapist is in an excellent position to make the initial improvement because he is in a position to make improvements in both component processes of the loop. He may reduce the emotion or the thought or both, and often in a very specific way.

By contrast the medical approach to such phobias is the rather general one of supplying the sufferer with some form of drug which induces a generally more relaxed state. This may reduce the feeling of fear, and the decreasing positive feedback loop may then work as above. However, the very thought, "It is so bad that I had better take my pill," tends to increase rather than decrease the perception of the object as a fearful thing, and after a while the activity of pill-taking can become involved in the whole process.

Initially we may have $\uparrow${Pills} $\rightarrow \downarrow${Fear} $\rightarrow \downarrow${Worrying thoughts} $\rightarrow \downarrow${F}, which leads to the initial decrease. But we also have the secondary effect $\uparrow${Pills} $\rightarrow \uparrow${Worrying thoughts} which typically becomes more and more important as the initial levels of fear drop a little. It practice then it is quite common for the general level of activity of both fear and perception of fear to drop the first few times a pill is taken and then to start to pick up again under the influence of $\uparrow${Pills} $\rightarrow \uparrow${Worrying thoughts}. But the old increasing feedback loop is still there waiting to take effect, so that the increase in the thought of "This is fearful/bad" will again lead to an increase in the fear felt. Typically when this starts to take hold again, the sufferer acts in one of two ways. One way is to say, "These pills do not work - I will give them up." The problem then quickly returns to its previous level, or even a bit more because, "It *must* be bad if the pills can't help." The alternative is to increase the dose. But all too often this simply leads to the same process as before: an initial improvement followed by a subsequent rebound.

This example illustrates the care one needs to take in analysing the nature of the feedback loops involved in a problem.

Some other examples of decreasing positive feedback loops are as follows. A person might, quite naturally, grow out of a habit of nail-biting as a result of the loop $\downarrow${biting} $\rightarrow \uparrow${satisfaction} $\rightarrow \downarrow${biting}, which will lead to the nail-biting activity dropping to zero. There is a good chance that when a Hypnotherapist is asked to eliminate any activity, then a decreasing positive feedback loop for the symptom will be instituted.

As another example, which illustrates that decreasing positive loops can also cause problems, consider a poor student who has become trapped in the loop ↓{studying} → ↓{confidence in ability} → ↓{study}, which can cycle until he or she gives up studying altogether and loses all confidence in his or her ability in that area.

This example underlines the fact that whether a positive feedback loop is increasing or decreasing is not the most important thing. Indeed a positive loop can be increasing for one system involved and decreasing for another, e.g.:

↑A → ↓B → ↑A

is increasing for A but decreasing for B, so we should properly always use phrases like ".. is an increasing positive feedback loop *for A*".

The ultimate reason for the distinction between increasing and decreasing as applied to loops is that the activity of a system cannot drop below zero: there is therefore a strict limit to how far down the activity can go. On the other hand there is no such strict limit on how *high* the activity can go: it may be limited by resources, but that limit is often flexible and changeable. In principle the number of individuals in a species (e.g. of domestic chickens) can be indefinitely large. On the other hand there is a definite and final lower level: which the dodo has attained.

This remark is often very relevant to feedback loops involving organic systems, and distinguishes them from feedback loops which often arise in inorganic systems, in which variables are more commonly capable of taking negative as well as positive values. The other difference is that in inorganic systems the effect of a reduction in the activity of a system is generally equal and opposite to the effect of an equal and opposite increase. We have noted that in organic systems there is generally an asymmetry between the two cases.

3) **Negative** feedback loops are of great importance in all biological systems. It is such loops that provide **stability**. They are how **homeostasis** - the preservation of relatively constant internal conditions in a changing environment - is achieved.

The word stability can be used in a static or dynamic sense. The static sense of stability is represented by the picture of a milk-bottle standing either on its base or on its top. It is not moving in either case - it is stable - but is more easily disturbed in the latter case: it is less stable on its top. Dynamic stability is more like the stability of a cyclist. She is constantly moving, constantly correcting for slight wobbles on one side or the other. (Look at tyre marks in snow: they are never straight; the track of the front wheel is always crossing to and fro across the track of the back wheel.) The cyclist is never still but will never fall off. In many ways she is *more* stable than the milk-bottle, because she has more power to correct for any disturbance.

For all of us even the process of standing involves negative feedback loops. If we lean forward a little this activates a sense of imbalance via the mechanism in the inner ears, which in turn activates the appropriate muscles at the legs, feet and elsewhere to create a backward movement. It will often happen that this results in overshooting the mark. We then start to sense a backward lean, which activates an opposing set of muscles and starts a forward movement. Simultaneously the system of balance is monitoring and correcting for sideways movements in a similar way. The net result is a dynamic stability.

The maintenance of body temperature involves similar loops. If the temperature increases, it activates such systems as increased sweating, whereas if it drops, it can activate an increase in metabolic rate and shivering, which tend to increase the temperature again. Shorthand for two of these processes is:

$$\uparrow \text{Temperature} \rightarrow \uparrow\{\text{Sweating}\} \rightarrow \downarrow \text{Temperature}$$
$$\downarrow \text{Temperature} \rightarrow \uparrow\{\text{Shivering}\} \rightarrow \uparrow \text{Temperature}.$$

Notice again the way in which increases and decreases in temperature activate *different* systems: this is quite common in biological systems. We will commonly see asymmetrical double-sided processes like:

$$\uparrow P \rightarrow \updownarrow A \rightarrow \downarrow P \rightarrow \updownarrow B \rightarrow \uparrow P,$$

where A and B are different processes or even processes of different systems.

In fact the entire internal economy of the body depends crucially on such loops at all levels to maintain and sustain life. The relative constancy of blood-sugar levels, of oxygen levels, of white cell levels, of fat levels, together with our ability to execute any action, say any word or concentrate on any thought depend on the existence of negative feedback loops which will prevent any great departure from the required level or process.

Feedback loops exist at other levels also. If you watch two people in conversation you will observe negative feedback loops regulating their physical distance apart. If this distance gets a little small, one or other will initiate movement in order to increase it. But if the gap gets too large there will be a movement to close it. The result is a fluctuating distance about some average value.

More generally the stability of a family or relationship will generally be maintained by means of such feedback loops, so that in any problem which features relationships it is important to look out for relevant loops.

In the market-place the price of goods is kept relatively fixed by means of negative feedback loops. A simplistic example of this is as follows. If the price rises, demand drops ($\uparrow P \rightarrow \downarrow D$). If the price drops, demand rises ($\downarrow P \rightarrow \uparrow D$). But a drop in demand will commonly induce the seller to reduce prices ($\downarrow D \rightarrow \downarrow P$) in order to increase sales and so to maintain profits, while an increase in demand will encourage him to increase prices ($\uparrow D \rightarrow \uparrow P$) in order to benefit from it. We therefore have a double-sided negative feedback loop:

$$\uparrow P \rightarrow \downarrow D \rightarrow \downarrow P \rightarrow \uparrow D \rightarrow \uparrow P$$

which tends to keep the price within bounds.

Against this background we will now look at the specific ways in which negative feedback loops are of importance in Hypnotherapy.

The first and *important* point is that IF a problem has not disappeared spontaneously after a period of time THEN **there is a very high chance of it being maintained by some negative feedback loop**, which may be internal or external.

As an example consider the dynamics of the following alcoholic problem. As a result, it turned out, of childhood sexual abuse a woman hated sex when she got married. She could only tolerate it if she was drunk. After a while it followed that IF she were to stop or even reduce drinking, her husband would perceive her as being in a "worse" state and consciously or unconsciously encourage her to drink again. ($\downarrow$ {Drinking} → $\downarrow$ {Sexual activity} → $\uparrow$ {Husband's discontent} → $\uparrow$ {Drinking}.)

As another and classic example from the annals of Hypnosis we may consider the famous case of Mesmer's treatment of the young woman Maria Theresa Paradies, who had been blind from an early age. She was also a gifted pianist and musician. There are various accounts of this case in circulation, but the main features are the following. Mesmer had some good initial success. But then, to his amazement, the parents objected very strongly and removed her from treatment. Then:

> "The logic is that Paradies [the father] began to anticipate serious embarrassment if Maria Theresa was saved from blindness. Her music already suffered from the improvement of her eyes. Partial sight made her nervous at the piano; nervousness made her hit the wrong keys, and the deterioration of her playing made her more nervous. It was a vicious circle from which she could not hope to escape except after long, arduous experience - if then. Meanwhile she would cease to be the accomplished, petted star of the concert stage with a handsome income of her own. She might lose the pension granted by the empress [her godmother] in consideration of her blindness. She would then become a half-crippled burden on her parents." (Buranelli (1975))

Clearly there were quite a few consequences of an improvement in sight which were unfavourable to Maria Theresa and her family. The natural result was to react against the improvement, and to return to the *status quo ante*. In short a negative feedback loop was revealed.

The outcome of the case was that her parents took her home from Mesmer's house where he had been treating her, and the condition of her eyes promptly deteriorated again. In outline the pattern was the one-sided negative feedback loop:

$\uparrow$ {Sight} → $\downarrow$ {Playing} → $\uparrow$ {Parental fury} → $\downarrow$ {Sight}.

However, this story has an ending which should be a caution to all therapists.

Mesmer was furious that *his* cure should have been undermined. But what of Maria Theresa? How did her life proceed?

She went back to her concert life and was a great success in Paris and London. She was so good that Mozart wrote a composition especially for her, the Concerto in B Flat Major. In other words the lack of sight did not blight her life, and might indeed have made it in many ways more fulfilling. Music may well have been all the more beautiful as a result of there not being any visual distractions. She would have had servants to do all the boring, practical things in life. She had music and friends and fame. Was life so very bad? We should beware of thinking that the improvement of a particular symptom by *our* technique *must* be the best thing for the Client.

FOR THE CLIENT THE LIFE AS A WHOLE IS THE MOST IMPORTANT THING.

So if there is a negative feedback loop involving the symptom *we should consider what function it serves and whether it is of value to the Client*.

In fact the great blessing that Mesmer gave Maria Theresa was a relief from the other, truly agonising treatments which had caused her enormous pain. Before Mesmer went to work the family might have thought that it would be better to have a sighted daughter and so went on trying to bring about a cure. The effect of Mesmer's treatment would, no doubt, have been to make them realise that the regaining of her sight would *not* be the great blessing that they had imagined, so they dropped all other treatment as well.

The common existence of negative feedback loops in life is one of the things that makes the Hypnotherapist's task so much harder than that of the Hypnotist. It is one thing to make a change, even a dramatic change, in the functioning of some subsystem of a human mind or body. It is another to make it stick: to ensure that it will survive the pressures that so commonly exist to make things return to the way they were before. It is easy enough to plant a rose in a desert: keeping it alive is another matter.

So we have noticed that when a problem has remained in existence for some time, there is a very good chance that it is being maintained by a negative feedback loop which will tend to return things to the status quo, after an intervention by the Hypnotherapist. But a good Hypnotherapist will not only recognise and deal with this, but also realise that if he or she is to institute a new practice or habit, then the simultaneous introduction of a negative feedback loop to stabilise the change is often very necessary.

Thus it is very little use making a suggestion for increased motivation (M), for example, and expecting it to remain in force indefinitely. True, it might well have an effect for a while, but what happens when the motivation tends to drop, as it will sooner or later? It might be more lucrative to have the Client return for a "booster", but is it the best professional practice? It would be better to work on establishing a loop so that $\downarrow M \rightarrow \ldots \rightarrow \uparrow M$; i.e. the very fact of the motivation dropping should trigger off some other system which will lead to renewed motivation.

As an example, it is common for a drop in motivation to lead to an increase in guilt, which leads to self-blame, a drop in morale and yet further loss of motivation ($\downarrow M \rightarrow \ldots \downarrow M$), a decreasing positive feedback loop. In fact the lack of motivation may, on analysis, have been found to be a simple result of trying to do too much all at once. If we then institute the rule that a drop in motivation MUST be responded to by spending some time in a recreational way, then in due course, as the systems which have become exhausted are refreshed, motivation will rise again. That is to say, we have instituted a negative feedback loop $\downarrow M \rightarrow \uparrow \{recreation\} \rightarrow \uparrow M$, to replace, if we have done things well, the old decreasing positive feedback loop $\downarrow M \rightarrow \uparrow \{guilt\} \rightarrow \downarrow M$.

So here we have an example of a beneficial negative feedback loop, to emphasise the fact that the words positive and negative are not the same as beneficial and harmful.

Let us look at another example of the usefulness of looking for a negative feedback loop to maintain a change, this time when the primary system is a couple. Let us suppose that they are arguing; they have been to counselling; they have taken the good advice on board; they argue less frequently; so they get on better; so they need to argue less. In short the intervention has started off a beneficial decreasing positive feedback loop for the quarrelling.

Whether this has a good chance of *surviving* will depend on whether the counselling has also managed to establish a negative feedback loop to cope with any future *increase* in quarrelling, such as might be triggered off by job problems, in-law problems, etc. The question is, "How will the couple react to an increase in quarrelling?" If no attention has been paid to this problem, then a small increase is all too likely to escalate as before to the point where counselling is again sought. If the counselling had been good enough, it should have instituted an automatic process which would have limited the quarrelling. As a very simple avenue, possible to the Hypnotherapist, a post-hypnotic suggestion might be used to ensure that on the cue of a quarrel one of the partners will behave in a new way, which might be as simple as to go for a walk, and thereby defuse the situation before emotions get out of hand. Erickson is reported to have got one couple to stand in the bath to have their quarrels! A common result of quarrelling in the nude might perhaps be predicted.

SUMMARY

We have learned to recognise different kinds of feedback loops which arise within the framework of complex biological systems. They are intrinsically neither good nor bad.

Increasing positive feedback loops are typically involved when we see growth. At times we may be working to prevent such loops, if they are detrimental; at other times to encourage them, if they are beneficial.

Decreasing positive feedback loops are characteristically involved in the elimination of the activity of some system. Again we may at times be trying to establish such loops or to eliminate them.

Negative feedback loops are characteristically involved in maintaining things the way they are. (But a double-sided negative feedback loop may lead to instability, as is shown in Chapter 25.) Again we may be eliminating or instituting such loops.

THE NATURAL FUNCTIONING OF THE MIND AND BODY IS MAINTAINED BY NEGATIVE FEEDBACK LOOPS. The same is also true for social groupings and most dynamically stable organic systems.

It is central to successful Hypnotherapy to recognise the overwhelming prevalence and importance of these classes of loops in determining the way in which we work. It is even more important when we come to try to make effective and long-lasting changes.

CHAPTER 12

The Process of Hypnotherapy - Stage 2:
Consequences of Symptom Reduction

IN CHAPTER 10 we considered the first step in the process of analysing the problem in terms of the various processes involved. The consequence of looking for precursors and resultants by means of various questions then led to one or more causal chains involving the problem symptom. A particularly important form of such a chain was then called a vicious circle, but now that we have analysed loops in more detail it will be called a positive feedback loop.

We may note that in some cases the above diagnostic process is, in itself, therapeutic. Three reasons for this are as follows. First, it provides the client with an opportunity to talk about the problem to a sympathetic person. Now whether it is an instinct, or a pattern from childhood, it is certainly the case that for many people (though not, of course, all) the following process is deeply ingrained: $\uparrow$ Distress $\rightarrow$ $\uparrow$ Talk $\rightarrow$ $\downarrow$ Distress. In fact studies have shown that there is no measurable difference in the improvement of patients who have been through a process of psychoanalysis and comparable patients who have simply talked to a sympathetic listener (Shapiro & Shapiro (1982)).

A second reason is that the very questions asked in Stage 1 will have forced the client to think more clearly about the problem, and in many cases this will in itself make it seem less intractable.

The third reason is that the process of diagnosis will often provide an answer to the question, "Why? - *Why* is this happening?" For many people a greater part of the distress which arises when something feels wrong results from not knowing the answer to this question. In such people there exists an internal process of the following form: $\uparrow$ {Discomfort} $\rightarrow$ $\uparrow$ {Search for cause}. Now if no cause can be found the search continues, and continues and continues, often turning up wilder and wilder ideas as to what can be wrong, and creating increasing levels of unease. Such people have often been helped enormously in a medical context by a doctor who will simply give a name to what is wrong: "You are simply suffering from Interrogitis." "Thank you, Doctor. You have set my mind at rest - I thought it was far worse." The point is that even if the name is meaningless, this pseudo-answer can be enough to stop an endless search which was in itself a prime cause of distress.

People who *understand* what is happening are generally able to cope far better that those who don't. This even applies in situations like operations, in which the patient has no control over the situation. Studies have shown that those who are told what is going to happen seem to feel less pain post-operatively, need less medication and on average leave hospital three days earlier! (Egbert et al. (1964))

However, in general we will *not* find that the process of obtaining a clear picture of the dynamics of the problem will in itself solve the problem. We must next focus on the question of the removal of the symptom. But it is a cardinal rule of good therapy that **symptoms must not be treated in isolation.** This is easy to say, but you will seek in vain if you seek any other book which will explain exactly how this rule can be carried out. This is not to say that good modern therapists DO treat symptoms in isolation, simply that the *absence of a good theoretical foundation for Hypnosis* has made it impossible for their practice to be codified. We have already done a lot of the work of seeing a symptom in context by establishing the chains which feature an *increase* in the activity of the symptom. But, as we started to see in the previous chapter, it can be as important, if not more so, to examine chains which involve a *decrease* in the activity of the symptomatic system.

This chapter then will focus on the question, "What will happen if a symptom is reduced?"

Notice that this is NOT a question that comes all that naturally to the mind. If we have a "problem" we do not naturally look beyond its removal. It takes quite a lot of mental discipline to think, "What would happen if these headaches went?" because they seem so obviously a problem. It does not naturally occur to us to think that their removal might lead to worse things. But our notation and approach automatically train us to think in this new way.

Some of the relevant questions to the Client which can be used are the following:

Q. Let us imagine that the central problem C were to go away: what else would change?

Q. $\downarrow C \rightarrow$?

Q. In particular can you think of anything which would be likely to make it get worse again?

Q. Is there a negative feedback loop ($\downarrow C \rightarrow \ldots \rightarrow \uparrow C$) maintaining the problem?

As was mentioned in the last chapter, there will very often be such a loop involved and, if there is, it is very important indeed to discover what it is, because such a loop will tend to act to prevent any change. In the case of Miss Paradies, the fact that her professional career was in several ways *harmed* by having sight was something that Mesmer had not anticipated and led to a negative feedback loop.

Another useful question in the hunt for the negative feedback loops is:

Q. Can you think of any small benefits that C leads to?

The point here is that the Client will have labelled C as a "problem", but has failed to realise that a consequence of C may actually be of some benefit. Such a benefit will reinforce the process C, which will be more likely to happen again: i.e. a negative feedback loop will exist.

Suppose, for example, that a person is doing something from a sense of duty - visiting in-laws, having sex, going to work, etc. Suppose also that there is some "problem" - migraines, nausea, quarrels, etc. - which has as a natural consequence the avoidance of the duty. Then, although the Client will almost certainly NOT have made the connection at a conscious level, there is a very good chance that the benefit gained from the "problem" process is at least partly responsible for maintaining it in existence.

In such a case it will probably not be enough simply to work on reducing the activity of the central process, as it will lead to an increase in the unpleasant duties, which will simply tend to reactivate the old pattern again:

$$\downarrow C \rightarrow \uparrow \text{Duties} \rightarrow \uparrow C.$$

Although the questions above are simple in principle, it must not be supposed that the process of finding the answers to them is necessarily a quick one. It will often be necessary to activate the Client's imagination in quite some detail and for some time in order to get full answers to them. There is a natural human tendency to pay more attention to things that are wrong than to things that are right. There is a natural human tendency to suppose that somehow the removal of a perceived problem will lead, as in the fairy stories, to, "... and they lived happily ever after." It is seldom *that* simple.

In some cases the only way of discovering the consequences of a reduction in the problem will be to go ahead and start to reduce it, and see what happens. The fact that we have thought about the questions above prepares us for the possibility that after a period of improvement there may well be a relapse, which will not therefore take us by surprise, as Mesmer was taken by surprise by the case of Maria Theresa. Instead we will welcome it as possibly providing a fuller answer to why the problem continues to exist. This reason can then be tackled.

As another example, a Client may be suffering from a lack of self-confidence. In theory she and her family want this to improve. But when the change actually begins to take place and they realise that as a consequence of her increased confidence she will say "No" to them some of the time, they may well start to resent it and act in such a way that they demoralise her again.

The pattern is simply:

$$\uparrow \{\text{Self-confidence}\} \rightarrow \downarrow \{\text{Compliance}\} \rightarrow \uparrow \{\text{Family discontent}\} \rightarrow$$
$$\uparrow \{\text{Family annoyance}\} \rightarrow \downarrow \{\text{Self-confidence}\},$$

i.e. a negative feedback loop.

If such a loop exists (and the above pattern is very common) the

Hypnotherapist will *have* to take account of it and modify the approach accordingly. An obvious step which can be taken is to restrict rather clearly the particular actions of a more confident Client to those which meet with approval, at first. In this way we can create a more firm basis for later change.

Notice the contrast between the above approach and that of the naïve Hypnotherapist who might simply suggest, with all the power which suggestions can have in certain Clients, "You will become super-confident. You will be totally confident. Nothing will get you down." The very generality of this is such that the Client is left to his or her own devices when it comes to expressing this confidence. There is little guarantee that others will like what happens for long. It is almost certain that *someone* will resent it and act against it. Since this new-found confidence has no real roots in behaviour or experience it will quickly wither in the blazing heat of someone's reactive anger, and the whole thing will die, leaving the Client more demoralised than before. "It is easy to plant a rose in the desert: keeping it alive is another matter."

Indeed even as I am writing this, there is an episode on the television series *Neighbours* in which a young man, Brett, has gone to a Hypnotherapist for help with his lack of confidence with girls. He has been given the phrase, "I can do anything!" which has given him a great *feeling* of confidence. But he has been given no detailed directions on *how* he should attract the girl of his choice, Debbie, and has gone for a "super-cool" approach - leather jacket, sunglasses, cigarettes and showing off on his bike - which is not only totally alien to his personality, but a total put-off to Debbie also. When he falls off the bike in an ignominious heap, we see at the same time the inevitable collapse of such an ill-considered application of Hypnotic suggestion!

When we have answered the question $\downarrow C \rightarrow ?$, i.e. what happens *later on* in the chain if we reduce the activity of C, we also need to look at the *earlier* processes as well, to see what their effect is if C is removed. The point here is that it is an everyday observation that if the habitual consequence of some feeling or action is thwarted, then some other consequence may follow instead. For example, in animals and mankind we see *displacement activities*. There may be a desire to attack which is thwarted by fear, so the energy which is ready to go into the attack is displaced into some other channel. The animal may paw the ground and a man may thump the desk.

In general terms we need to know what the precursor will lead to if its effect on the central process is blocked. If the precursor of smoking is a feeling of anger, what will the anger lead to if smoking is prevented? Violence? Family rows? Overeating? It is important to have some idea of this, for it is very bad therapy if the result of removing the original problem is an even worse one.

In order to clarify this we need to ask questions like the following.

Q. What other things does it (the precursor) lead you to do/feel/feel like

doing?

Q. What has it at times led to in the past?

Q. $P^I \rightarrow$? What other resultants of the precursor P^I exist?

Remember that there are generally many complex processes which can involve a particular subprocess. We have already sought to find all the process chains which contain the central process C. Now we are looking for all the chains leading on from P^1. We may end up with several. Suppose that we have as a precursor of C an increased feeling of anger A, then we may discover the following resultants of ↑A:

$\uparrow A \rightarrow \uparrow C \rightarrow ... ;$

$\uparrow A \rightarrow \uparrow \{\text{Shouting}\} \rightarrow ...;$

$\uparrow A \rightarrow \uparrow \{\text{Squash playing}\} \rightarrow ...;$

$\uparrow A \rightarrow \uparrow \{\text{Stomach Acid}\} \rightarrow ...;$

$\uparrow A \rightarrow \uparrow \{\text{Desire to sell (in a salesman)}\} \rightarrow ...$

If these are the primary ones then we can be pretty sure that if the connection ↑A → ↑C is somehow removed, then one or more of the other four processes will happen. One of these has no redeeming features as it can lead to ulcers rather directly. The shouting may or may not be advantageous: we would have to follow the chain a bit further to discover the consequences. If it were to be properly orchestrated it might be neutral or even advantageous. The other two should lead to a healthier body and a healthier bank balance respectively. The job of the Hypnotherapist is then to ensure that simultaneously with removing the effect of ↑A on C, one of the two (or three) *favourable* connections is selectively enhanced, so that the overall result is beneficial to the Client. If the removal of C leads to an unfavourable resultant of A, then this will act to increase the motivation to return to C again. Thus many people have returned to smoking because the simple elimination of smoking from the chain:

$\uparrow \{\text{Anger}\} \rightarrow \uparrow \{\text{Smoking}\}$

has led to the alternative process:

$\uparrow \{\text{Anger}\} \rightarrow \uparrow \{\text{Distress of spouse}\} \rightarrow \uparrow \{\text{Spouse insisting that smoking be renewed}\} \rightarrow \uparrow \{\text{Smoking}\}.$

This is another example of the homeostatic properties of negative feedback loops.

For another example suppose that the presented central symptom S is over-eating. In response to the questions answering ? → ↑C let us suppose that we find that there are many causes as follows:

$\uparrow\{\text{family rows}\} \rightarrow \uparrow C$

$\uparrow\{\text{boredom}\} \rightarrow \uparrow C$

$\uparrow\{\text{feeling unloved}\} \rightarrow \uparrow C$

$\uparrow\{\text{worry about ailing parents}\} \rightarrow \uparrow C.$

In a case like this there will probably be still more such chains leading to overeating, but we will take just these four for simplicity. It should be clear that we have a complicated case on our hands, because we need to know the answer to $\uparrow P_1 \rightarrow$? for *each* of the four precursors above. What will our Client do after a family row if she does not eat? What will she do if she is bored? What will she do when feeling unloved? What will she do when she thinks about her parents? If we *did* use a Hypnotic technique simply to block the over-eating, then we might find her going into a deep depression, having an affair, taking to drink, gambling or even developing an illness herself.

In such a case then it will be worth synchronising a slow change in the eating pattern with other changes designed to improve each of the above chains. If we were to find that the family rows were rooted in financial worries, then it might be worth putting effort into giving her the confidence to get a job. This would have as side-effects a reduction in boredom and a greater feeling of being appreciated (if not loved). We might also find that channelling some of the desire to eat into the pattern of seeing the parents and cooking them a very nice meal in which she would join, would both help her to feel that she was doing something for them and reduce any secret worry-binges. We might suggest that joining some club in which she would find herself appreciated - ideally something active as well - would simultaneously make her feel less unloved and help to lose weight. Although it may take time to work through all these possibilities, it is time well spent *because the result is permanent beneficial change.*

As an analogy imagine that we are in control of a water system of streams and rivers. To solve a flooding problem downstream we may try damming a river. But this will generally have effects upstream as well. What is going to happen to the waters running down to the dam? They have to flow *somewhere.*

If the engineer does not plan a safe path for them, then they will either build up until they could even destroy the dam, or find their own path, which could easily be just as disastrous. (Of course engineers are never as stupid as that.) But in the same way if *we* ignore precursors in making changes to the primary system, we may enjoy a temporary success but then find the whole work completely destroyed by the power of those precursors either forcing the original symptom to return for lack of other outlet, or forcing another outlet which may well be far worse than the original symptom. Our careful analysis of the problem is a very necessary way to avoid such problems.

Perhaps at this stage some readers are thinking that this all seems rather complicated. They might then remember the analogy of the problem of changing an ecosystem. If you start to mess around with one species then it has effects on a large number of others, both up and down the food chain, and therefore indirectly on most of the other species involved. We no longer live in times when it is acceptable to say, "You have a problem with species C? Fine. We will simply exterminate it by means of chemical X or prey species Y." This has led too often to worse problems. An ecologist has to propose a detailed and convincing case for the proposed change, and this involves FIRST analysing the existing food chains upwards and downwards in a great deal of detail.

In the same way we should analyse the existing causal chains involved in the various mental, emotional, practical and social processes which are connected to the problem, directly or indirectly, if we hope to make an "ecologically sound" organic change for the better.

In fact the systematic foundation which we have established has made it quite easy to work our way around even very complicated problems without getting lost. Let us summarise in our shorthand the questions asked so far to emphasise this point.

It really amounts to the repeated asking of the simple questions, $\updownarrow X \to ?$ and $? \to \updownarrow X$, i.e. "What resultants are there of a change in the activity of process X?" and "What are the precursors of a change in the activity of process X?"

Step 1 was based on establishing the causal chains involving an increased activity of the central process C, by asking the two questions:

$$? \to \uparrow C \to ?,$$

which led, by repetition, to a collection of chains involving $\uparrow C$, each of the form:

$$\ldots \to \updownarrow P^3 \to \updownarrow P^2 \to \updownarrow P^1 \to \uparrow C \to R^1 \to R^2 \to R^3 \to \ldots.$$

Of particular importance was the discovery of feedback loops involving C.

Step 2, which we have met in this chapter, was based on two questions which illuminate what would happen if we succeeded in reducing the activity of process C:

$$\downarrow C \to ?,$$

which will tell us what the resultant will be if we succeed in reducing the activity of C; and:

$$\updownarrow P^1 \to ?,$$

which will tell us what the resultant of P^1 is likely to be if the activity of C is reduced. The first of these will very often lead to the discovery of a negative feedback loop for C, which is very important in maintaining a problem, or causing a relapse, depending on how you look at it. The second is rather more likely to reveal alternative problems which could arise if C were eliminated.

The only other question which focuses directly on the central process C which we can ask within our formal structure is:

$$? \rightarrow \downarrow C,$$

i.e. what immediate precursors to a decrease in the activity of C can we find?

This question is, of course, very important. It brings us to the key issue in treatment which is the question, **"HOW are we to remove the problem?"** We will treat this in the next chapter.

But before we finish this chapter it will be noticed that although the dynamic structures revealed by the systematic analysis on the above lines are, in this book, primarily applied to the systems of importance in Hypnotherapy, they are **of much wider applicability**. We have already noted that sound ecology goes through the same process. If S is some species of interest, then sound ecology involves finding all the factors that are involved in either increasing or decreasing the numbers (and hence activity) of that species. The analysis again involves a repeated asking of what causes or results from a change in the activity of a given species or (more generally) from a change in the non-organic environment.

The same process could, and should, be used by a businessman who wants to make changes in the functioning of a company, to ensure that the change is advantageous and efficient. There *may* be (I am not an expert in the field) Management Consultants who step into a business, make a few dramatic changes which produce immediate positive results and then leave, without thinking through any negative feedback loops involved. We may then find a year or so later that things are worse than before.

As an imaginary example: suppose that the expert brings the company into profit by cutting costs in a way that involves a great loss of personnel. In six months he brings it back into profit. But a natural consequence is that morale will drop and uncertainty rise in the remaining workforce. Even if it is the case that only the less productive personnel were sacked, there will be a tendency for the remaining, better people to look for other jobs. Within twelve months this could come about: quality will drop; a little later this will result in a drop in sales. The collapse of the emaciated company is only too likely: and all because the probable consequences were not thought out. The better approach would have been to anticipate this, and work hard to ensure the continuing morale of the people remaining.

Notice that although the disastrous final consequence was a result of the consultant's poor analysis, superficially it looks as if the consultant did well, and that it was his absence that led to the poor results! Poor Psychotherapy can look the same.

We have already noted examples of this in family therapy, which further underlines the fact that the theoretical approach in this book can be applied to all organic systems, not simply the human mind, which is our primary concern in this book.

SUMMARY

In this chapter we have examined the important therapeutic principle that a symptom should not be treated in isolation and spelled out HOW this can be done in a systematic way by thinking through the consequences of reducing a symptom. It is important to note that this involves looking not only for any direct consequence of a symptom reduction, but also for the indirect consequence of what the precursor leads on to if not to the symptom.

CHAPTER 13

Making Changes in Hypnosis

THE PREVIOUS CHAPTER led us up to the point in the therapeutic process at which we have a particular change in mind. It is now necessary to spend a little time looking in more detail at some rather important principles underlying the creation of change in the fields of Hypnosis and Hypnotherapy.

In previous chapters we have touched on the importance of positive feedback loops in Hypnotherapy in creating problems and of negative feedback loops which prevent the problems from disappearing. In this chapter we will be looking at the other side of the coin: we are looking at the ways in which these feedback loops and their manipulation is CENTRAL TO UNDERSTANDING HOW VERY MANY HYPNOTIC TECHNIQUES WORK.

It is worth remembering that our primary tool is sound waves of minimal energy. (The power involved in ordinary conversation is around 10 microwatts, i.e. one *millionth* of the power of a *ten*-watt bulb. Most of that acoustic energy goes into imperceptibly heating up the room, and only a very small fraction will hit an eardrum. An ear can in fact respond to about one *million millionth* of the acoustic power of typical conversation: one *million million millionth* of the power of a ten-watt bulb! Remember that when anyone says of a remark, "How illuminating!") Somehow we have to use this minute amount of energy to create large-scale changes in the functioning of a human being.

This can only be done in one way: by amplification. Consequently we are, in the field of Hypnosis, dealing constantly and at many levels with **the problem of amplifying changes**.

We will see in this chapter that the primary mechanism for amplification is the *creation of a positive feedback loop*. Closely related to this is the *removal of a negative feedback* mechanism that is limiting an existing positive feedback loop.

Let us start by emphasising the extent to which we can power a change by introducing increasing positive feedback loops.

The atom bomb works because the greater the number of neutrons flying about in a lump of uranium, the greater the number of uranium atoms which disintegrate as a result of a collision with a neutron. But the greater the number of disintegrations, the greater the number of neutrons flying about, since each of these uranium atoms (of the rare 235-isotope variety) releases several neutrons as it decays. In shorthand:

$$\uparrow\{\text{neutrons}\} \rightarrow \uparrow\{\text{splitting of uranium atoms}\} \rightarrow \uparrow\{\text{neutrons}\}.$$

This simple process forms a powerful increasing feedback loop which leads to the well-known mushroom cloud, provided only that the lump of uranium is not so small that too many of the neutrons escape from it before they get a chance to hit an atom.

Anyone familiar with the workings of a laser (Light *Amplification* by Stimulated Emission of Radiation) will realise that there is a similar process at work there. Without explaining the terms in detail: the greater the number of photons of light in the laser, the greater the number of excited atoms which are stimulated into emitting further photons, which in turn leads to the stimulation of yet more atoms until nearly all of the atoms have decayed from their initial excited state, and all the photons emerge in step. In shorthand this is:

$$\uparrow\{\text{photons}\} \rightarrow \uparrow\{\text{emissions}\} \rightarrow \uparrow\{\text{photons}\}.$$

In common parlance we may call such increasing positive feedback loops the "bandwagon effect": the more people who get on the bandwagon, the more other people are drawn to get on, and so on.

It is sometimes also called the "snowball effect": you picture a large snowball rolling down a snowy hill, growing larger and larger as it collects the snow it passes over. The bigger it gets the more snow it collects, which makes it still bigger, and so on. (People tend to use "vicious circle" when they do not like the result and "bandwagon effect" when they do: but both are positive feedback loops, and may be either increasing or decreasing in terms of activity.)

The bandwagon or snowball effect can be seen at all levels of the universe. We have seen it in lasers and atom bombs. We may also see it in the condensation of intragalactic dust to form stars: the more dust collects into one place, the greater its gravitational force to attract more dust, which increases the combined mass, making it possible to attract more dust, and so on.

In economics the more successful a product is, the cheaper the unit cost, which makes it possible to advertise more widely and sell at a lower price and attract more customers, which allows a further reduction of the unit cost and so on until the market saturates. We have the increasing positive feedback loop for sales:

$$\uparrow\{\text{Sales}\} \rightarrow \downarrow\{\text{Cost}\} \rightarrow \uparrow\{\text{Sales}\}.$$

Once you see the pattern, it becomes visible all around you at all levels.

In our field we have already seen increasing positive feedback loops being involved in the creation of problems such as blushing:

$$\uparrow\{\text{expectation of blushing}\} \rightarrow \uparrow\{\text{blushing}\} \rightarrow \uparrow\{\text{expectation}\}.$$

Now we are going to emphasise the fact that the active creation and utilisation of such loops in order to amplify change is one of the primary

techniques of Hypnosis and Hypnotherapy.

An example that has been cited already is the simple Hypnotic phenomenon of hand levitation. From the moment that there is the slightest movement in the hand, the feedback is clear: the perception of movement leads to an increase in the expectation of movement, which in turn leads to more movement:

$$\uparrow\{\text{movement}\} \rightarrow \uparrow\{\text{expectation}\} \rightarrow \uparrow\{\text{movement}\}.$$

In a similar way a slight sleepiness in the Subject can be amplified by the Hypnotist who creates a loop:

$$\downarrow\{\text{arousal}\} \rightarrow \uparrow\{\text{thought, "I am sleepy"}\} \rightarrow \downarrow\{\text{arousal}\}$$

which, as long as it is maintained, will lead to decreasing arousal or increasing sleepiness. I have written this in terms of arousal rather than sleepiness firstly because it is closer to our principles of working as closely as possible with the notions of activation. The second reason for this example is to demonstrate a *decreasing* positive feedback loop, to revise the fact that it is the adjective *positive* which is the key one when we are trying to amplify a change. The primary difference between a *decreasing* and an *increasing* positive loop for a given system is merely that in the former the change is limited by the fact that the activity of the system cannot be less than zero. In the latter case any limits will be imposed by other considerations, such as the effects of other systems.

An "induction" routine will often contain repetitions, such as, "Your legs will feel heavier and heavier ..... heavier and heavier ... heavier and heavier", to be followed a few minutes later by, "Your legs are now still heavier ... heavier and heavier." Here again we have a procedure which has been found empirically to be effective in producing the required effect, but the mechanism passes without explicit comment in most books. This is not to say that practitioners are not aware of what they are doing: it is more that there is no established theoretical framework in which to express it. With the language and notation we have developed we can throw into high relief the fact that the repetition is part of the process of establishing a feedback loop. The first mention of heaviness will establish an *expectation* of heaviness; after a while a slight heaviness will normally be *perceived*; once this happens, it will increase the *expectation*, which will in turn increase the *perception*. The task of the Hypnotist is simply to draw attention repeatedly to these two systems while they build each other up systematically.

If you were to turn back to look at the list of characteristic Hypnotic phenomena in Chapter 2, you would find many simple phenomena that can be produced in a great number of people **with no other "induction" than the establishment of a direct feedback loop between the phenomenon and the expectation of the phenomenon.**

It is really a very worthwhile practice for anyone training in Hypnosis to attempt to create these phenomena with *no* preamble or induction by simply establishing positive feedback loops in a fully alert and conscious individual. Such groundwork gives an excellent insight into what a great part of our subject is about.

As another example, the question, "I wonder if there is a small grain of sand in your shoe at this moment?" establishes a mild expectation that there might be. This tends to amplify the response of any nerves in the sole of the foot. If we keep on asking the question there will generally come a time when one small group of nerves happen to fire more than average. This will reinforce the expectation that there might be something there. This leads in turn to a greater amplification of the messages from those nerves, relative to the others, in an attempt to find out if there really is a grain there. But this makes it seem as if there *is* something there, and so the expectation is amplified still further. Within a few minutes this feedback loop will increase to the point where there is a clearly "hallucinated" grain in the shoe. It is perhaps even easier to create an itch in the nose in a similar way.

We may note *en passant* that the above process is very similar to that which is current in the hypochondriac, whereby the expectation of a symptom leads to small signs of the symptom, which build up the expectation and so on.

The common form of loop which we are meeting here is the simple:

$$\uparrow\{\text{expectation}\} \rightarrow \uparrow\{\text{perception}\} \rightarrow \uparrow\{\text{expectation}\}.$$

Note that the idea that *belief* is an important factor in Hypnosis is common. What this normally fails to take into account is the fact that a belief which is not accompanied by some evidence confirming the belief will tend to wither away: only those which seem to be confirmed by experience are retained and strengthened. In shorthand we have:

$$\uparrow\{\text{confirmation}\} \rightarrow \uparrow\{\text{belief}\},$$
$$\downarrow\{\text{confirmation}\} \rightarrow \downarrow\{\text{belief}\}.$$

It is mainly when we have a situation in which a belief produces its own confirmation that a positive feedback loop is established which leads to a deeply entrenched belief. We have the phrase, "a self-fulfilling prophecy" to describe such beliefs. Once they are fairly established they become unshakeable.

So, to put things in another way, ANY of the simple phenomena we have listed may be produced with absolutely nothing in the way of "induction" other than creating a self-fulfilling prophecy by the fixing of attention on an appropriate loop involving the phenomenon and the expectation of the phenomenon for long enough for the loop to become established.

In cases where they cannot be established, the most likely cause is one of the following. a) The attention of the person has wandered. b) The person has been able actively to entertain the belief that nothing will happen; when nothing happens, that belief becomes stronger; this ensures that the phenomenon is less likely to happen and we have a positive feedback loop - but of the opposite kind to that desired. c) There is simply not enough amplification as we go around the loop to produce a significant effect.

We have already seen that the traditional tests of "Hypnotic responsiveness" are far better understood as a way of testing how easily one system may activate another. But it is very often the case that one system will not naturally activate another enough for our purposes, so that the effect has to be amplified. In this chapter we see HOW a typical Hypnotic procedure of creating a positive feedback loop is used to *amplify* a small effect into a large one to create the dramatic effects we associate with our field.

In the chapter on tests, feedback loops were not emphasised, because at that stage in Part A such things had not been described. It should now be possible to understand why a professional Hypnotist or Hypnotherapist may get far more dramatic effects than are readily achieved in a laboratory test under "standard" conditions. The former can tune a feedback loop far more accurately to the individual Subject. The latter, who is using the same tape-recorded approach for each potential Subject, will be less likely to activate the strongest form of feedback loop in each.

It should also be clear now that the simple idea that it is straightforward to establish how easily one system acts on another was a little naïve. We can now distinguish the ease with which one system can activate another directly from the ease with which it can do it when an increasing positive feedback loop has been called into play.

In an abstract form we now distinguish between the case in which we are merely examining, for two systems A and B, the strength of:

$$\uparrow A \rightarrow \uparrow B$$

and the case in which B also acts on A and so we are examining:

$$\uparrow A \rightarrow \uparrow B \rightarrow \uparrow A.$$

Even if at times it may be hard in practice to distinguish between the two, it is important to bear the distinction in mind.

In the practical context of Hypnotherapy the advantage of thinking about and working towards the creation of increasing positive feedback loops to amplify our efforts leads to a great increase in efficiency. IT IS EQUIVALENT TO THE DIFFERENCE BETWEEN USING POWER TOOLS (WHICH AMPLIFY EFFORT) AND HAND TOOLS.

You may now be beginning to understand why the Hypnotherapist has more power to change a person than other therapists. **It is through having learned skills which can now be more clearly seen as highly rational, scientific and practical: skills in using the intrinsic systems of mind and body to create positive feedback loops to power change.**

Next we will take a look at the other side of amplification: the elimination of negative feedback elements which prevent a positive feedback loop from taking off. In a nuclear reactor an explosion is prevented by the introduction of rods of a moderating material which absorbs neutrons. If there is the slightest danger of over-heating, these rods are pushed in a little further to absorb some of the extra neutrons and the reactor is dampened down a bit. We have the negative feedback loop:

$$\uparrow\{neutrons\} \rightarrow \uparrow\{moderator\} \rightarrow \downarrow\{neutrons\}.$$

The brain relies very heavily on the use of such negative feedback loops to inhibit activity. The action of an enormous number of the neurons in our brains is to *inhibit* the action of the thousands of neurons that they are in contact with. If it were not for this fact, every neuron in the brain would soon be firing in an orgy of unco-ordinated activity as a chain reaction of mutual excitation took place. There would be massive hallucinations of all kinds: visual and sensory, ecstatic or agonising; frenetic activity of the muscles, and so on. I suppose that to experience such a thing would be not unlike feeling an atom bomb exploding in the brain.

Most of the peripheral nerves of our bodies are continuously sending messages inwards towards the brain. But most of them fail to activate any conscious response most of the time. Somewhere along the line they pass through a subsystem which at that time prevents the message from being passed on.

An exactly analogous process is visible in human organisations. At any given time many customers may be complaining about a product to salespersons. In many cases the complaint is actively prevented from going further. In the rarer case it gets passed on to a manager, where it may again end. If it happens to be a particularly serious complaint it may get up to the Managing Director's Assistant, or even, but only very rarely indeed, to the Managing Director. At each level we are seeing an *active* process of preventing the message getting any further. This is, in fact, necessary to the good organisation, since if the MD had to handle every complaint in person he or she would have no time for anything else.

In the task of picking up a pencil, the action is a result of the amplification of the minute amounts of energy involved in thinking of the task into the much larger amounts involved in contracting the muscles of the fingers. But there has also to be a continuous process of monitoring the contraction and limiting or controlling it to make it a useful one.

These simple examples illustrate the principles which run through the organisation of our whole bodies and nervous systems. On the one hand we need processes of amplification, and on the other hand we have to be able to prevent them getting out of hand. The eye can multiply the effect of a few photons of light falling onto a few cells in the retina until a very large proportion of the entire cortex is activated. (Suppose that you are lost at sea in a small boat and have just seen the merest flicker of light from a lighthouse.) But on the other hand we need to be able to control these amplification processes or they will get out of hand. If *every* few photons were enough to trigger off activity in the entire cortex it would be totally overwhelming.

The important ideas that we want to emerge from these examples are first the general one, of the complex and extensive network of amplification and control systems which is involved in all our thoughts and actions, which is the essence of cybernetics. The second, and specific, idea is that amplification can be achieved not merely by creating some form of increasing positive feedback loops but also by *reducing* the activity of a process which is limiting the action of an already existing amplifying loop.

As some further simple examples of this consider first a simplistic picture of rabbit numbers in the wild, which are limited by the number of predators in a negative feedback loop of the form:

$$\uparrow\{\text{rabbits}\} \rightarrow \uparrow\{\text{predators}\} \rightarrow \downarrow\{\text{rabbits}\}.$$

We can therefore increase or "amplify" the rabbits by eliminating the predators, since (at least when there is enough food) the system of rabbits is naturally self-amplifying:

$$\uparrow\{\text{rabbits}\} \rightarrow \uparrow\{\text{rabbits}\}.$$

In society, criminal activity is limited by police activity. The elimination of police activity would lead to an increase in criminal activity.

In some marriages many kinds of activity in the wife are limited by the husband. If the husband dies we may see a dramatic increase in his widow's activity in those ways, once she has passed through a period of grieving.

In many adults an inclination to playing the fool is usually limited by social convention acting through higher brain centres. If we incapacitate those centres with drink, or eliminate the normal social conventions by calling the situation a "fun party" or a "hypnotic show", then we can quite easily see a dramatic increase in the playful activity.

I hope that these examples are enough to illustrate the principle: IF we have a system A whose activity is being limited by the activity of a second system B, THEN a reduction in the activity of B will lead to an increase in the activity of A. This is obvious when you start to think about it.

We may now look back at the idea presented in Part A, which was that a general feature of many Hypnotic procedures is the gradual reduction of the activity of most systems, with the exception of the one or two of interest. We presumed there, on grounds of common sense, that this reduction in the activity of the majority would tend to increase the activity of those few left active.

Now we can see a little more of the reason behind this. The general reduction of activity will almost certainly blanket off all those systems which acted in such a way as to inhibit or moderate the activity of our key systems of interest. These are left free then to act to their fullest extent.

There is a good chance that by eliminating all other species of animals but one herbivorous species in an ecosystem, we will find that this one, with no predators and competition left, will start growing exponentially.

There is a good reason to suppose that if we send on holiday all other departments in a factory, *especially the quality inspectors*, then we will be able quite easily to get an increased output from a remaining production department.

There is a good reason to suppose that if we can switch off most mental functions, including those which resist suggestion and monitor behaviour (self-consciousness), then we might easily induce a totally uninhibited (in most senses) activity from the Subject - as can happen in stage Hypnosis.

In brief, we can now see more clearly the rationale of another of the characteristic procedures of Hypnotherapy which distinguishes it from other therapies: the inactivating of the majority of internal systems. The reason is that this can be expected to remove the effect of systems which are acting to limit change, and hence allow required changes to take place under the influence of a positive feedback loop.

We are now in a position also to see why this may not always work. We might, by this global switching off, also switch off systems which *activate* the one of interest: the Subject is then too sleepy to respond at all. (The workforce may simply down tools and play cards.) Or systems which are vitally involved in the proper action of a key system may be switched off and the result can be dangerous. (The absence of safety personnel may quickly lead to dangerous practices and an accident.)

The moral of this is that whereas it may at times be helpful to follow the practice common in contemporary Hypnotherapy of aiming (it would seem) at rather generally low levels of activation other than in the key system, the more accurate analysis and approach recommended here is far safer and more effective. If we have done our diagnostic analysis fully and properly we start, ideally, with an awareness of the part played by all related systems. Some may increase and others decrease the key activity. And we should be aware of the consequences of changing any of them, and in this way know just which ones it is useful and advisable to work with.

Finally we will look at an application of the principles of this chapter which is very important in the context of Hypnosis, since it deals with those areas we may call rapport and suggestibility.

In most people an early tendency to trust others is gradually limited by the creation of a *learned* ability to doubt. In the child the tendency is for every idea presented to be accepted, provided only that it can be grasped. Notice the incongruity of the following dialogue.

Mother: "Look at that nice doggy. See, it is white."
Child: "No, Mummy. You are not necessarily right. We have no evidence to

establish whether it is nice or not, and it may be black or brown as well as white: we know only that it is white on *this* side!"

Such replies can *only* come at a later stage in life, after the child has learned to analyse, criticise and doubt. These are *active* processes that some people learn and develop more than others. Notice also that we generally learn them more in some areas than others. The philosopher, who may be ruthlessly analytical of his colleagues' statements, may be like a babe in arms in the hands of a car salesman.

If we let A be the process of Accepting an idea, and R denote the learned system of Resistance to accepting a new idea, which is a mixture of doubt and self-assertion and self-protection, then it is the nature of the relationship that the greater the resistance, the less the acceptance:

$$\uparrow R \rightarrow \downarrow A.$$

The Hypnotist will therefore often be trying to reduce the inhibiting effect of the resistance - the critical, analytical reactions - in order to increase the acceptance of his or her suggestions.

How does he do this? Typically by means of a feedback loop! We thus see the two themes of this chapter brought together in the one example. On the one hand we plan to activate a useful system - that of Acceptance - by means of decreasing another system which is holding it in check - Resistance. On the other hand we will see that this is typically not achieved in one step, but as a result of a feedback loop:

$$\downarrow R \rightarrow \uparrow A \rightarrow \downarrow R$$

which is a positive feedback loop which is increasing for A and decreasing for R.

This abstract formula had better be illustrated by an example. Generally the persuasive speaker, Hypnotist or not, will use the procedure of starting with an idea for which there will be automatic acceptance, such as, "Now, I think you will agree with me when I say that you seem a very sensible person?" The acceptance of this statement will reduce the resistance a little. Why? Because we cannot *always* have R active. We have learned that if we trust a person - which amounts to discovering that what he says is in agreement with our ideas - then we gain by reducing our resistance to other ideas. As a rule of thumb we therefore start with a fairly high resistance and lower it on every example of agreement and raise it on every example of disagreement.

Because the resistance is reduced, the next suggestion will then be accepted a little more readily. It might be, "But as a sensible person you will know that some people suffer from closed minds like tortoises?" This can also be accepted easily, which will in turn reduce the resistance. This can then be followed up with a more direct action to reduce the resistance still further, such as, "But I am sure that you are not like them. *You* will certainly recognise the importance of having an *open mind."* Again, with the reduced resistance, this can be accepted, and the way is becoming open to stronger and more questionable statements, such as, "Now, I have your best interests at heart, and when I say that *this* car is going to transform your life, I know that you will not be like one of those tortoises and dismiss it out of hand, but will really examine the advantages." And so on.

The above is clearly a manipulative process: it is not being recommended! It is mainly mentioned to illustrate the fact that the nature of the process is a feedback loop. Creating rapport is a process. It takes time. And it involves the amplification of small changes.

These facts are also true for the Hypnotist's task of developing rapport. As an example consider the following process which might be used on stage. "You probably wonder if you will be hypnotised tonight?" This will usually get a "Yes" response. (The good Hypnotist, like the good salesman, will be looking for responses - a "Yes" or a nod of the head - to verify that there has been acceptance at each stage.)

"So do most people. Now, are you prepared to co-operate with me to see if we can find out?" (This is an easy statement to accept, so resistance drops a bit, reducing in turn its inhibiting effect on acceptance.)

"Now just face the audience. That's fine." Here we have an example of a trivial request to which the potential Subject cannot object, but the acting out of it means that the idea of moving has been accepted, and the Hypnotist is a small step further on. I have seen cases in which the Hypnotist does a lot of little adjustments in this spirit: "No, if you could just move along a bit. No, back a bit. That's fine. Now give a big smile to anyone you know in the audience." And so on.

The accepting of these seemingly trivial suggestions generally reduces the resistance to all other suggestions, whether of actions or ideas. It is really quite immaterial what the suggestions are: the important thing is that they are accepted, so that the loop is travelled a few more times. It is then correspondingly quicker to get another loop started, such as the loop involving the expectation of eye closure and the acting out of it. But the achievement of the eye closure loop will further act through the Resistance-Acceptance loop to reduce the resistance still further, and so on.

This underlines the dynamic and loop-like nature of what is involved in quite a central aspect of stage Hypnosis. At least one professional Hypnotist is explicitly aware of this fact (McKenna (1993), p. 28), though he gives only a little detail of HOW it is done.

In Hypnotherapy the way in which resistance is reduced is generally different. In part, I suspect that this may be due to a difference in the personalities of those who choose to work on stage and those who work in therapy. The latter are going to be primarily carers, which tends to correlate with a rather low level of authoritativeness and a comparatively low-key personality. The former have to be quite extrovert and tend to like to dominate a situation, so that an authoritative style is rather congenial to them.

In any case the Hypnotherapist, who will still be operating (typically with great sincerity) the loop:

$$\downarrow R \rightarrow \uparrow A \rightarrow \downarrow R,$$

will tend to do it in a slower and more relaxed manner. She will establish an atmosphere of trust by empathising with feelings and agreeing with statements. Responses such as, "I know how bad you must be feeling", "It must be terrible for you", and so on are quite as good at reducing resistance as the methods we have seen above, and far more appropriate to the therapeutic environment.

I find a not uncommon pattern in therapy is for the Client to come with what seems to be a small problem. I then deal with that as well as I can. Then, seemingly out of the blue, a totally new problem is presented, which is often far larger. We might start with nail-biting, and end up with childhood sexual abuse, for example. The process is clear: the client is simply testing me on the first item. If he or she is satisfied at that level that I make sense, can be trusted, etc., then it seems possible to proceed to a larger and more sensitive matter. This approach is totally understandable. It is what I would do myself. It is an example of the above positive feedback loop.

The above loop process of reducing the inhibiting effect of resistance may be called achieving rapport, however it is established. In general, note that the process is very much richer and more complex than has been indicated above, for the potential Subject or Client will be responding not only to what is *said*, but to a great variety of other things such as the tone of voice, the nature of the eye contact, smiles or their absence, bodily gestures and so on. Something of this complexity has been hinted at in the chapter on Inductions. Consequently resistance will generally only reduce if ALL the signs are in agreement with the expectations of the person. A look in the Hypnotist's eyes which is interpreted as being shifty, or a note in the voice which seems to indicate insecurity or hostility are quite as able to increase resistance - reduce rapport - as a statement which is thought to be false. People tend to be very sensitive to insincerity and any lack of consistency in the messages they perceive.

It is for this reason that I would not recommend a conscious *striving* for rapport in Hypnotherapy. It is one thing to recognise the nature of what is happening, and thereby to recognise where you may be going wrong. It is another to be forever operating a system mechanically; by rote; following rules.

In the end it seems to me that the only rule is that the Hypnotherapist should be honest and sincere. If you do not sincerely wish for the well-being of the Client, then the chance of any success is greatly reduced because something of this will show up in the way you speak or act, and in most cases it will simply induce resistance to anything else you say or do. To attempt to bluster through a feeling of having slipped up, for example, will be disastrous.

Sincerity and honesty are the central virtues needed in order to build up rapport. If you have these then your body language will be consistent with your speech and your intentions. If, on the other hand, you are trying to follow the handbook, *Ten Gold-Plated Techniques for Creating Instant Rapport*, by I. McConn, the chance of there arising a discord between some of these aspects of yourself is great, and the chance of a good and lasting rapport with all Clients is low.

The moment a discord is sensed, the resistance R to accepting what you say will rise quite dramatically, breaking the loop. This will tend to result in a denial (D) of your next statement. If you press the point, the resistance will rise still further and we are well on the way to establishing the loop:

$$\uparrow R \rightarrow \uparrow D \rightarrow \uparrow R,$$

which is the dynamical form of a quarrel!

It is because of this that there can be as many styles of Hypnotherapy as there are styles of people. Extroverts and introverts will tend to have opposite styles, for example. But each is acceptable, as long as it is consistent:

> This above all: to thine own self be true,
> And it must follow, as the night the day,
> Thou canst not then be false to any man.
> - *Shakespeare, Hamlet I. iii. 75.*

So we have seen in this centrally important example that in order to increase acceptance we have had to work to reduce the activity of the system of resistance, and have done so via a suitable direct loop.

Let us look at a few other examples of this same pattern in the field of Hypnosis.

In many people there is a natural tendency to daydream - to visualise freely - from time to time. In such people this process is actively suppressed by the need to pay attention to things or people in the surroundings. If we therefore act to reduce the system of active attention to surroundings in such people, the daydream will naturally emerge.

In anyone who has had a busy and rather stressful day, there are definite messages of fatigue being sent from the body to the brain, but these are typically being actively ignored (as we have seen messages to the Managing Director being ignored: "Don't bother me now. I'm busy!"). We may readily "induce" a feeling of tiredness in such a person by simply *reducing* the activity of these suppression systems. The words, "Now, just listen to what your body is telling you," may be enough to do this.

In problems in which some memory is *actively* prevented from coming clearly back to mind by some defensive system because it was so painful (see later chapter on dissociation), then the inactivation of the repressing system will lead to the activation of the memory. This should not, of course, be done without experience of how to handle the resulting expressed feelings.

These few examples are representative of very many more in which we amplify by removing the effect of a controlling system. But notice that although it is easy to say, "remove the effect of a controlling system", that is itself a change that is unlikely to come about by simple *diktat*. Normally we will need to establish a positive feedback loop to turn a slight reduction of the controlling effect into a larger one, as we have seen in the case of rapport.

We may now put the message of this chapter another way. The image of Hypnosis which has the Hypnotist giving a single order which is obeyed gives a misleading impression. The essence of so many Hypnotic practices is that, far from being as simple as flicking a switch, **they involve complex dynamical processes which demand repetition for their effectiveness. They involve repetitive processes which build towards the desired outcome.**

A picture to have in mind is a child on a swing. She builds up height by means of many small synchronised extra pushes. Before she has the knack of it she cannot get anywhere.

A business grows, **not** all in one bound, but by a steady round of increasing sales and feedback in a particular market.

Products are NOT usually designed perfect. There is a loop in which a change is evaluated, then improved and then evaluated again. It was how the Wright brothers learned to fly. It can be how a car is rocked out of the mud, slowly building up momentum.   Repetition. Repetition. Repetition. Repetition in order to establish loops which will build up a significant change. Repetition (with slight variation) in order to establish positive feedback is central to Hypnotic phenomena, as it is to so many organic processes. Repetition in this book is by design: a significant change of mind generally requires repetition.

SUMMARY

It is not generally going to be the case that simply suggesting a change will produce it, nor that reducing the activity of all other systems will automatically increase that of the one of our choice. We have now added to these simple ideas the more powerful one that the body and brain are full of systems that can be turned into increasing positive feedback - amplifying - loops which can enhance the activity of any particular system very powerfully indeed.

In the fields of both Hypnosis and Hypnotherapy the use of powerful positive feedback loops is a central and distinguishing feature.

We have also noted that in some cases there will exist natural processes of amplification that are held in check by a negative feedback process. In such cases it is indeed the case that a reduction of the activity of the one process will lead to an increase in activity of the other.

These two principles have been illustrated in the key matter of creating rapport.

CHAPTER 14

The Process of Hypnotherapy - Stage 3:
Planning a Change

BY THE TIME we have completed the first two steps of diagnosis we should have
a clear idea of the dynamics of the problem: we should know what systems are
involved. Some of these are important when the central system becomes active; some
of them are important when it is reduced in activity (and may act via a negative
feedback loop to increase it again.) With all this information in mind we are in a
position to begin to consider the strategy of how things are going to be changed for
the better.

The claim of Hypnotherapy is that it IS possible for the therapist to intervene
and to change things for the better. It is a well established fact that Hypnotic
techniques CAN change things. We have just seen in the previous chapter HOW
many of these changes are effected.

In this chapter the focus is more on the question of what *exactly* we should
be aiming to change. The simplest approach is to find an answer to the question:

$$? \rightarrow \downarrow C,$$

i.e. is there a system which has as a direct result a reduction in the problem process?

The simplest answer to this is, "If we activate a system of belief in the Client
that the symptom will disappear, then it will!" This is the hope and belief of many
who come to a Hypnotherapist for help. And in many cases this will work.

A case in which it *should* always work is one in which our earlier steps have
revealed that the only chain involving C is C itself and the thought (T), "C will
happen to me", and has the form:

$$\uparrow T \rightarrow \uparrow C \rightarrow \uparrow T,$$

i.e. a simple increasing positive feedback loop in which the more the Client thinks
that a problem will arise the more it happens, and the more it happens the more he
or she is convinced it will happen again.

If, in such a case, we can replace T by the thought $T_1 = \{$"C is going to stop
happening"$\}$, then we will institute the loop:

$$\uparrow T_1 \rightarrow \downarrow C \rightarrow \uparrow T_1,$$

which is a positive feedback loop which is increasing for T_1, which therefore gets more and more ingrained, and decreasing for C which therefore gets less and less active until it disappears.

An example of the above loop might be provided by a case of stammering in which the belief, "I stammer" leads to stammering which reinforces the belief. In that case a Hypnotherapist could have a dramatic success if the old idea could be replaced by the new one, "I do not stammer". In practice, it would not be best to start with that suggestion for the following reason. There is a high chance that the old pattern will NOT be totally eliminated immediately, so that although the Client would be free from stammering for a few days, a stammer might start a little later. But if this were to happen it would immediately tend to replace the new thought by, "I am stammering again," and we are back into the old loop. It is therefore better practice to suggest a thought on the lines, "I am stammering less and less". This will establish a loop in which the less the stammering, the stronger the conviction that it is improving, which will feed back into reduced stammering, and so on. Then, at a second stage, the thought, "I do not stammer" can be introduced.

This example reinforces the idea we have observed, which is that Hypnosis is so very often about *amplifying* small changes into larger ones by means of a positive feedback loop. Here we are amplifying a small improvement into a greater one.

The recognition of the fact that what a person repeatedly thinks or believes can have the most profound effect on the whole of the mind and personality and feelings and body is one of the traditional cornerstones of Hypnotherapy. The emphasis on this fact is one of the features that contributes to distinguishing it from related disciplines. The trouble is that if this idea is made the *sole defining* characteristic of Hypnotherapy it can lead to the excessively simplistic view of things which amounts to the idea that Hypnotherapy consists solely of "placing the person in a trance", and then suggesting that the problem will disappear. Practising Hypnotherapists will have discovered that things are not always *that* easy, without perhaps being always clear about why it sometimes works and sometimes does not.

We have seen that such an approach *will* almost certainly work if there is only a simple feedback loop of the above form involved in maintaining the problem, and if the suggestion is appropriately worded. But it will often *not* (except perhaps for a short time) if the situation is more complicated.

Notice that the way in which we have diagnosed cases should make it clear when such complications exist and therefore when direct suggestion of the above form is almost certainly NOT the only treatment needed. We will have analysed all the causal chains involving C. In many cases these will be open-ended (e.g. blushing may be a direct result of "friends" making fun of the blusher in a deliberate attempt to arouse it) or involve other factors such as deep emotional responses. In such cases there is no guarantee that the simplistic approach is going to work and the exact way to tackle the problem is going to be less obvious and direct.

The central question for the Hypnotherapist in these more general problems is, "*Where* is the intervention going to be focused?". At times this may still be on the central system C, but it will often be on related systems.

As a simple example, Erickson is on record as having treated insomnia NOT by focusing on sleep at all, nor on the belief that, "I suffer from insomnia," but by putting his effort into establishing a new pattern of behaviour, which is that if sleep does not come then the sufferer should get up and polish floors for hours (Gordon & Myers-Anderson (1981) pp. 149-150). Let us see how this works.

A typical insomnia problem involves an increasing positive feedback loop:

$$\uparrow\{\text{Arousal}\} \rightarrow \uparrow\{\text{Anxiety}\} \rightarrow \uparrow\{\text{Arousal}\}.$$

In the simplest terms, Erickson has focused on the result of an increase in arousal and instituted:

$$\uparrow\{\text{Arousal}\} \rightarrow \uparrow\{\text{Polishing}\} \rightarrow \downarrow\{\text{Arousal}\}.$$

He relies on the empirical fact that spending hours polishing in the middle of the night is in fact physically tiring, to produce the resulting lowering of the level of arousal. In this way he breaks the original positive feedback loop and creates a negative one. After this is repeated for a few nights, arousal will lead simply to the thought that polishing is on the agenda, which is such a tiring thought that arousal will drop until sleep supersedes: the "problem" is then over.

Another example, from my casebook, involved blushing. The basic process was the typical one for blushing: an increasing positive feedback loop of the following form:

$$\uparrow\{\text{Feeling of embarrassment}\} \rightarrow \uparrow\{\text{Blushing}\} \rightarrow \uparrow\{\text{Embarrassment}\}.$$

This stops being a positive feedback loop if we create a different resultant of the increase in blushing. In this case, which involved a man who had recently been promoted and so felt rather insecure in his new position, it was suggested that he feel and express anger as a result of the onset of blushing. He was to raise his voice and perhaps thump on the desk. It was explained that *any redness would then simply be interpreted by others as a sign of anger*. This would make him feel less embarrassed. He was quite happy to do this. We then had the new process:

$$\uparrow\{\text{Embarrassment}\} \rightarrow \uparrow\{\text{Blushing}\} \rightarrow \uparrow\{\text{Anger}\} \rightarrow \downarrow\{\text{Embarrassment}\} \rightarrow \downarrow\{\text{Blushing}\}.$$

This constitutes a negative feedback loop for the blushing and embarrassment. Once he had repeated this process a few times in real life he had no further problem. People responded quite well to his anger by backing off a bit and this gave him enhanced confidence in his new position, and so he seldom felt embarrassed at all, and if he ever did then he knew how to cope with it.

In choosing anger as a suitable resultant we may be guided by the notion that in the male at least, blushing can often be the result of suppressed anger. I have known a number of cases in which a young man had once freely expressed his anger, and went red in the face while doing so. Then, for one reason or another, he started to suppress the anger. Then the same redness remained, but now the associated feelings were of humiliation or embarrassment. In such cases the above intervention simply restores an earlier pattern of behaviour, but in a controlled way.

Although the point will not always be laboured, such a change should NOT of course be implemented without *checking the consequences of the change* in the way in which we have checked for the result of reducing the central symptom in Chapter 12. An increase in the expression of anger will affect people close to the Client. We would have to ensure that they will not react so strongly that the anger is again inhibited, i.e. that there is not a negative feedback loop for the anger of the form:

$$\uparrow\{\text{Anger}\} \rightarrow \uparrow\{\text{Reaction}\} \rightarrow \downarrow\{\text{Anger}\} \rightarrow \uparrow\{\text{Embarrassment}\}.$$

We should also ensure that the expression of anger is kept within bounds, which is why a banging on the desk and raising the voice are *specifically* suggested. A general suggestion - "You will express your anger" - might lead to actions for assault!

In the above examples then, the focus of the intervention has NOT been on the presented symptom, but on other aspects of the loop involved.

Notice that no claim is being made that those are the ONLY ways of tackling the above problems. The problem of insomnia may be tackled in many ways. A common one is to give the sufferer a suitable tape which, typically, activates a non-rational part of the mind. This might be a generic, "Imagine yourself on a desert island" script or a more specific, "You like walking. You are now going to imagine yourself on an old familiar walk, and follow it every foot of the way..."

In this way we plan to *inactivate* the system of verbal thought which is so often involved in keeping the person awake, and instead to *activate* the daydreaming system, which at night can change so readily into normal dreams and hence sleep.

Note that the choice between the two approaches - the polishing or the tape - can be made on the basis of deciding whether the arousal has more to do with an active mind or an active body. If the arousal is more in the muscles, then Erickson's approach is likely to be better. If it is more in the (verbal) mind, then the tape may be the better choice. This illustrates the way in which a clarity of analysis of the systems involved in a problem leads to a clarity of understanding of the best approach to resolving a problem.

Blushing may likewise be tackled in many other ways. Simple suggestions that, "You will grow out of it" may be enough in a given case, particularly if the cause is a simple loop of the kind met at the start of this chapter.

Again the choice of the better technique will depend on our underlying analysis of the systems involved. If we have analysed a suppressed anger then the first method has clear advantages. If we have discovered an immature self-image - that criticism activates a childlike response - then the second can be recommended. Again notice that **the approach is not determined by the SYMPTOM, but by the TOTAL PROCESS**.

The difference between the skilled workman and the novice is often not that one can and the other cannot do the job, but rather in the quality and efficiency that the former brings to the job. A bookcase can be made in many ways, including holding it together by knocking nails in with a screwdriver. A Client's problem may be cured by many Hypnotic techniques, some of which are equally bizarre and liable to produce a result that could collapse in a short time. However, a professional Hypnotherapist should be constantly striving to achieve the best, smoothest and most efficient results.

In order to do this we study very carefully the person we are dealing with as well as the particular problem. In earlier chapters we have described a systematic way of approaching the analysis of the problem. Some examples of interventions have now been given. We now move on to see how we can proceed in a systematic way to plan possible changes, with a view to choosing and implementing the best.

The central difference between this process and the diagnostic process is that it is synthetic rather than analytic - it involves divergent rather than convergent thought, or lateral as opposed to linear thought. There is no ONE way, as we have seen above. Consequently there is no precise linear description of a process which is guaranteed to determine the best method of change for a given therapist and Client.

However, we can lay down some general principles to guide the creation of therapeutic interventions which will bring us as close as possible to such a description. The process is not, however, linear, but a loop. (They are everywhere!)

Step 1. Focus on a particular part (P) of one of the causal chains involving C. (This may be a named subprocess, or the link between two named subprocesses.)

Step 2. Think of a number of interventions (I) which can affect P in such a way as to lead to a reduction in the activity of C. (The more the better.) *This step is the creative one.*

Step 3. Of each intervention ask, "How easy is this likely to be with this Client?"

Step 4. Of each intervention ask, "Does there exist a negative feedback loop which will act to eradicate the effect of this intervention?"

Step 5. Of each intervention ask, "Will the change that this intervention introduces create new problems?"

Step 6. Return to Step 1 and consider intervening at another point until all possible points of intervention on each chain have been examined.

As a result of going through the above process the Hypnotherapist should end up with a short list of possible interventions which will have the desired result of achieving a permanent improvement in the central process C, with no harmful side-effects, and which are (comparatively) easy to implement. It then remains simply to choose the better ones and to start making the changes.

That makes it sound very easy. Sometimes it is!

It does, however, leave open the question, "How on earth can one think of interventions out of the blue?" There are various answers to this. The first answer is that they are seldom created "out of the blue". A practising Hypnotherapist will have acquired an extensive list of possible ones from his or her training, reading and experience. An excellent source-book of Erickson's interventions (which tend to be more innovative than most) is Hanlon & Hexum (1990), but other books, journals, seminars and discussions with other practitioners can give the Hypnotherapist a familiarity with a wide range of approaches. With this background a "new" intervention is seldom more than a modification of an existing one.

The second answer is that the intervention may be "revealed" by the process of listening intelligently to the Client during a certain amount of open-ended discussion. If, as an example, it is found that a woman has trouble stopping herself eating the snack foods that all children love, while being quite firm with her own son in those matters, then it does not take too much lateral thinking to think of instituting the following resultant of eating such food: "You must be fair. Every time you indulge the little-girl-in-you with ice-cream, etc. *you must give your son exactly the same.*" Notice that, as in the above examples, we are not seeking directly to change her eating habits, which were the central symptom, but rather introducing a change in the resultant. Since she has in fact tried very hard to reduce the eating directly *with no success at all*, we may presume that a direct attack will not be too successful. On the other hand this indirect approach, which still allows her to eat as much as she likes, will soon lead to the amounts being moderated by her motherly concern that it is not going to be good for her boy.

Equally, if while we were thinking about the precursor, we discovered that she mainly ate in that way at times when she felt alone in the evening because her husband spent all his time renovating cars, and we *also* discovered that she quite liked working on machines herself, then the following thought is obvious: "What if she were to be able to join him in the garage in some way at any time she felt that urge to nibble?" In just such a case things got a lot better when the husband bought an old car for *her* to renovate with him.

Notice how unique such a prescription must be! There can be very, very few women for whom an eating problem can be solved by their husband buying them a wreck to renovate! Yet, in this one case, it was a strategy which will improve the marriage, reduce her weight and improve her confidence (when she is able to drive her own car around), and all without further dependence on "therapy"! That is elegant. It is specific.

The ancient story of the Procrustean Bed comes to mind. Procrustes offered hospitality to passing strangers in the only house on a road through a wild land. But his standards of hospitality were demanding indeed. He only had one bed, but he was determined that every traveller should have a bed which fitted him perfectly. The solution? If the traveller was too short, Procrustes would stretch him on a rack until he was long enough. If he was too short, Procrustes would lop off whatever overlapped the ends.

Some therapies have a limited number of resources and have therefore to fit the patient to the remedies, rather than fitting the remedies to the patient. In reality many a General Practitioner, through no fault of his or her own, is limited to prescribing one of a limited number of drugs to deal with a very wide number of cases where there is no clear organic malfunction but some disturbance of emotional balance, or sleep, or digestive processes, and so on.

Systematic Hypnotherapy, far from being a non-scientific option, is in many ways a *more* scientific one than is open to the GP. It is aware of the complexity of the dynamical systems with which it deals. It diagnoses not in terms of simplistic, static, symptomatic categories but in terms of the precise dynamic processes involved, which may include external as well as internal systems. It has a great flexibility and there are an enormous variety of changes it may institute, so that over the range of problems to which it is best suited, it is in a far better position to fit the bed to the patient rather than the patient to the bed.

Now it may be thought that the types of interventions mentioned above, e.g. getting a woman to feed her son the same treats as she feeds herself, or getting her to work with her husband, are not *Hypnotic*. But notice that these, also, are changes in *thoughts and/or habits*. And it is NOT always the case that habits or thoughts can be changed simply as a result of saying that they could be. We will often have to bring to bear the full power of suggestion, amplified in the ways we have outlined, to start and maintain such a change in thought or habit. In this way, an actual session will often proceed in what looks a fairly normal way, with relaxation, visualisation, etc., but with the goal of changing one of the new, indirect processes rather than by a direct attack on the central or presented problem. Nevertheless such a method can often be a lot faster and more efficient than the direct attack because of its intelligent use of the real dynamics of the person's personality.

When it comes to implementing the above central process of determining the possible approaches to change, remember that, as in diagnosis, it is NOT being suggested that the Client be asked questions in a systems-oriented language. It is both common sense and courteous to talk in a language familiar to the Client, and the answers to the questions involved will normally be obtained as a result of informal conversation.

Thus we will *not* normally ask,

Q. How easy do you think it will be to change X?

But we might say something on the lines of,

A Client with a similar problem found it very helpful to do Y,

and then simply note the response from the Client. Clients will typically relate such a remark to themselves appropriately.

Equally we will certainly not ask,

Q. Does there exist a negative feedback loop involving I?

But we might conversationally say,

Of course, I have known cases in which a change in .... has led to an improvement in .... but unfortunately this led to ..... happening and this in turn started the problem up again.

The exact details would be provided from some known case which had points of similarity with the case in hand.

This will get the Client thinking on such lines and if there are any such consequences which they can envisage, then they can easily be prompted to speak of them. There is a fair chance that in this way any obvious feedback loops will be detected.

Or we might ask,

Q. I wonder if you could spend a few minutes visualising in detail what would happen if we could arrange for .... to happen? Do you think it would improve matters?

This question is rather more likely to answer the question of whether making the change could lead to new problems. But this question and the last could yield information both on the existence of negative feedback loops and on the existence of other problems if a change were to be implemented.

There are many other questions and approaches which can speed up the search for the most efficient points of intervention. For example we have:

Q. Have there ever been times when the problem has got a bit better? If so, what seemed to do the trick?

Q. What do *you* feel would help to remove the problem?

These will often give a lot of insight into a possible solution. Suppose, for example, that a woman has got slimmer each time she had a boyfriend. If the nominal problem is "weight" then it would seem that a promising line is to find out why she does not now have a boyfriend, and perhaps overcome that. There might, for example, have been a disastrous relationship breakdown which has led to a reluctance to try again. If this obstacle can be removed then she could again find a boyfriend and the weight would then reduce of its own accord. On the other hand there may be a feedback loop in such cases, which may be the main reason she does not have a boyfriend:

$$\uparrow \{\text{Weight}\} \rightarrow \downarrow \{\text{Confidence}\} \rightarrow \downarrow \{\text{Going out}\} \rightarrow \downarrow \{\text{Male company}\} \rightarrow \uparrow \{\text{Weight}\}.$$

In that case we may have to work on several factors at the same time: some confidence boosting, some encouragement to go out to a suitable place, some seeking male company, and some weight reduction.

The second question is valuable because the Client is seldom stupid or ignorant, and will have thought hard about the problem. The fruits of this thought are valuable, even if not perfectly correct. If the presented problem is panic attacks, and the Client thinks that it has to do with an assault eleven years ago, then he is probably right. I once had a Client with a strange skin condition - a redness on one side of the face - that a Harley Street consultant had given various names to, but been unable to stop. She herself connected it to a statement that her sister had made to her as she was sitting in front of the fire: "If you sit as close as that your face will stay red." Working on the assumption that the Client was right led to a removal of the problem.

It can also be useful to ask,

Q. What is it that you would like me to do?

This *might* get an answer like, "Swing a pendulum in front of my eyes, send me to sleep and I will wake up without the problem." Such an answer is not to be ignored: it is either going to have to be integrated into the procedure which is used or a very good explanation of why it is not will have to be provided. Otherwise there is going to be a strong reaction in the Client of the form, "*This* is not what I expected. It will not work!" which is going to make everything much harder. If, in such a case, there is an obvious reluctance to change the preconception then it would be advisable to use a pendulum to begin with and in time to send the Client to sleep. Notice that paradoxically this means a real sleep, from which there is a strong sense of awakening, since this is what is expected, despite the fact that the Client will have seen Hypnotic Subjects on stage and screen changing from a sleep-like appearance to a wakeful appearance with no sign of thinking that they have been asleep! Of course there will almost certainly be other and more useful interventions made as well: a simple piece of practical advice may be the most important thing done in the session!

Of course if we held a traditional, simplistic idea of Hypnosis then it could be objected that a piece of advice has nothing to do with Hypnosis. But within the present theoretical framework the central theme is the changing of key mental processes. If a new thought process can be accepted without doubt then it is irrelevant whether this was achieved as a result of a complex ritual or a simple totally convincing statement.

At other times the answers to the last question can clarify the goal. It may be that a person suffering from a chronic pain, which seems at first to be the central problem, does NOT expect it to be removed, but rather hopes to be able to sleep soundly in spite of it, or to be able to be less frightened of it, or simply to reduce it to manageable proportions. In such cases the focus of intervention is likely to be different according to the different goal.

There is no end to the questions that *might* help to throw up the piece of information needed to help to decide on a smooth and efficient intervention. I suppose that it is experience that gives the practitioner more and more of the ability to hit on the right questions earlier in a session as the years pass. Many of these are asked directly, but there are also many indirect ways of finding out the answers to questions. This last point is covered in the chapter on Indirect Questions in Part C.

In this chapter the process of planning the best way to intervene has been outlined. Deeper understanding is, I think, only possible as a result of the reader attempting the analysis in particular cases. This is easy for those already in practice, who have ample opportunity and should find it stimulating and easy, since it should simply involve tightening up in a clear and precise way what they are already doing. To trainees it should be the basis of training exercises: without which it will remain rather abstract. To the intelligent reader it should give a good understanding of the *kind* of thought processes involved. This last class of reader, who is unlikely to apply any of this work in Hypnotherapy, might nevertheless find that further insight can be obtained by trying to apply this method of thinking to analyse any problem found in daily life which involves others. For remember that the approach is general enough to be applicable to *any* organic system, which includes your family, or social or work group.

SUMMARY

Hypnotherapy deals not only with processes of change, but with practices which are themselves processes. An important such process is planning an intervention. This process has been outlined in a simple way which can be summarised as follows.

For *all* possible points of intervention in the relevant causal chains, ask the following questions:

- How can it be changed?
- How easy is the change?
- Will it result in a relapse because of negative feedback?
- Will it result in any other problems?

This mental process will lead in time to a collection of the better ways of intervening, which will form the basis of treatment.

CHAPTER 15

Therapeutic Interventions and Reinforcing Changes

NOW THAT we have covered in outline the first two stages of therapy - Diagnosis and Planning - and we have also learned more about some of the powerful ways in which Hypnosis acts to institute change, we are ready to move on to the third stage, which is the therapeutic intervention itself.

It should be clear now that there are going to be as many different results of the first two stages as there are Clients. That is why it is important to emphasise PRINCIPLES, rather than simple rules-of-thumb. It would be impossible to list all the conceivable different combinations of causes and symptoms and interacting factors which could arise. But, as we have seen, it IS possible to outline *principles of approach* which can enable us to form a very clear picture of the dynamics of each particular case.

In many instances, I find, there is really very little work involved in the intervention at all, by the time the really hard work of understanding the dynamics of the problem and of possible interventions has been done. Because the optimum point of change has already been determined there is no waste of effort such as can happen when the therapy is directed in the wrong way.

It will often happen, for example, that the processes of diagnosis and planning a change will come up with some simple suggestion that the Client accepts enthusiastically and has no problem in implementing. In such a case the session looks from the outside as if it is simply counselling or possibly a form of mild psychotherapy.

In rather more instances it may still be the case that the Client happily accepts an idea at a superficial level, but that more time will have to pass before it is naturally woven fully into the fabric of life. In such a case the use of Hypnotic techniques can accelerate this process. Practising therapists will know how to do this in detail. An example of such a technique is sometimes called "future pacing". In this the Client is taken through a typical process, such as is indicated in the earlier chapters in this book, with a view to inactivating distracting mental and physical processes and activating feelings of confidence and the detailed visualisation of situations in the future in which the desired change or changes will be naturally incorporated into life. (But notice that we may well have already done a little mild "future pacing" as a part of the process of checking out the change for any problems which might arise as a result. In such cases there may be little need to do more, if the Client has a naturally strong involvement with what he or she is imagining.)

In other cases, in which an emotional change is involved, it may well be that the questions and answers involved in the diagnostic and planning stages will themselves begin to activate emotional systems, such as suppressed grief. In that case, also, it may be that little extra work is needed, and the session may again look like a session of psychotherapy.

But there are advantages in again handling things more precisely by means of techniques which fall within the field of Hypnotherapy. There is, for example, another well-known technique for dealing with traumatic material which goes like this. The trauma may have been induced by, for example, a severe accident, or sudden bereavement, or an assault. (It is not ALL sexual problems.) The memory of the incident is cut off from consciousness by an automatic mechanism which is there to prevent excessive distress.

Now the beauty of the typical Hypnotic approach is that it is possible FIRST to activate a very strong feeling of calm detachment, and THEN to activate the imagination in a detached way such as to show the events in question on a TV screen, or as happening to a third party. In that way the *information* about what happened is absorbed consciously without great distress. Once that has happened, and the fact that the event *can* be thought of *without* overwhelming distress has been discovered, the whole thing becomes far less of a problem. Typically it will then be possible later to allow a certain amount of controlled crying or other natural expression of feeling to become activated until the whole matter is cleared up.

The dynamics of such processes can be characterised in terms of a subliminal memory, consciousness, the emotional system and a mechanism which can inhibit the connection between the memory and the conscious mind.

In shorthand then we have the pattern:

$$\uparrow\{\uparrow\{\text{memory}\} \rightarrow \uparrow\{\text{consciousness}\}\} \rightarrow \uparrow\{\text{emotion}\} \rightarrow \uparrow\{\text{inhibition}\} \rightarrow$$
$$\downarrow\{\uparrow\{\text{memory}\} \rightarrow \uparrow\{\text{consciousness}\}\}.$$

That is, we have a strong negative feedback loop which prevents the process of conscious recall of the memory, since whenever this process starts it activates a strong emotion, which in turn activates the inhibitory process which stops the recall continuing.

If we look at ways of changing this loop, in the way suggested in the chapter on planning, then the above method, which is to work on the system {emotion} and prevent its activation, is an obvious way of preventing the loop operating. We might have considered trying to prevent the activation of the system {inhibition}, but this would, in itself, lead only to a sudden recall which would lead to violent emotion. This would be dramatic and might make the therapist feel pleased at obtaining an "abreaction". However it is not to be recommended, as it does nothing to ensure that the remembered material is in any sense come to terms with. It is quite possible that the experience will simply confirm the feeling that the memory is NOT to be approached, since it is so distressing, and the inhibitory mechanism will grow stronger after a while, and be reinforced by a fear of therapy, so that nothing will have been gained.

Similarly to work directly on the element $\{ \uparrow \{memory\} \rightarrow \uparrow \{consciousness\}\}$ in the loop and to attempt to enhance it directly by forcing the memory through to conscious recall could lead to an excessive expression of emotion which will potentially lead to the same problem. That is why the normal approach is the one suggested above: working first to moderate the emotional response.

The above examples bring our attention to that part of our subject which may be called detailed technique. Every trade or profession has its particular techniques, which its members pick up with experience, reading and contact with others in the same field. We have here seen "future pacing" and the use of an imaginary TV screen to convey information from one subsystem of the mind to another without evoking strong emotion. But there are countless more.

It is not the purpose or intention of this book to list all such detailed techniques. Remember that this is not a training manual. Neither am I introducing any "Holy Grail" type innovation in technique. All I am attempting is to make clear the principles involved in what we are doing, in order that we may think more clearly about it and do it better.

I am therefore going to take as read (in other books) all such detailed techniques which can be used to implement changes in the field of Hypnotherapy and focus attention on one principle of overwhelming importance. The fact that there is little conscious awareness of this principle makes it all the more important.

This principle that should be emphasised as being central to effecting effortless interventions is the value of establishing **positive feedback loops** to power the change. We have seen such loops being used in inducing simple Hypnotic phenomena. We will now be looking at their typical forms in therapy.

Let us begin by looking at an elementary example. It is a fact that many people pay disproportionately greater attention to things that are getting worse, and too little to things that are getting better. Consequently, even if their mood is lifting as a result of some form of therapy, they scarcely notice it, but notice instead only the times when there is no improvement. This naturally limits any improvement and will usually occasion a relapse.

One possible Hypnotic intervention is to remedy this by changing the balance and instituting the habit of consciously noticing any improvement. But an awareness of improvement will generally lead to an actual lifting of mood, which will again be noted and thus a positive feedback loop is instituted.

If we let M be the actual mood, and A an awareness of an improvement in mood, then we will have instituted the increasing positive feedback loop:

$$\uparrow A \rightarrow \uparrow M \rightarrow \uparrow A \rightarrow \uparrow M \rightarrow \ldots$$

Consequently if we can only change the balance of paying attention from "worse" to "better", there can be steady improvement in all things. And things will go on getting better and better, without our needing to intervene in detail in all ways.

This principle was involved in the success earlier this century of Émile Coué, who went around the world promoting his ideas on the value of positive thought: ideas which he encapsulated in the saying, "Every day and in every way, I am getting better and better and better." He encouraged people to repeat this saying over and over again until it became a part of their philosophy of life.

In many people it had a lot of success. The expectation of improvement will often lead to actual improvement. The fact that this idea has NOT transformed the world shows that things are not quite as simple as that. In particular, I wonder if you can spot the inevitable negative feedback loop which will act on the practitioner of Couéism? Let us suppose that it works to begin with, and the use of the maxim leads to improvement. That will, of course, encourage the person to continue, and so improvement will increase. But continuous growth is simply not possible for anything or anybody. Sooner or later the growth will slow or stop. There will be problems that resist the maxim, such as toothache, or a wife leaving to marry a man who is less self-confident but needs her more as a result (in fact more like the man she married before Coué took a hand!). In any case there will come a time when a man relying entirely on the maxim will find that it no longer has any effect. If anything, since things are deteriorating, it will seem that repeating the maxim leads to the deterioration. He will lose faith in it. He will stop using it.

A not dissimilar loop lies behind those frequent small advertisements: *FOR SALE - Exercise bike, hardly used.* For the first few days after an exercise bike has been bought we have:

$$\uparrow\{\text{exercise}\} \rightarrow \uparrow\{\text{feeling of well-being}\} \rightarrow \uparrow\{\text{exercise}\}.$$

But soon the exercise has been increased to a level where fatigue sets in and we have:

$$\uparrow\{\text{exercise}\} \rightarrow \uparrow\{\text{fatigue}\} \rightarrow \downarrow\{\text{feeling of well-being}\}.$$

The common immediate reaction is to increase the exercise in the hope of reinstating the original loop and so increasing the well-being again, but now, of course, it simply leads to more fatigue and so to still less well-being, so within a short time the whole thing is given up in disgust.

By contrast to Couéism the introduction of the principle of simply *altering the balance* between the amount of attention paid to improvement as opposed to deterioration, or to good as opposed to bad, has much more chance of instituting a slow but steady positive feedback loop which can lead to continuing improvements in different areas. It does NOT depend on continual improvement for its maintenance. It expects *some* setbacks, but notices improvements more.

If you want a phrase to encapsulate the change we want, it can be found far back in time, before Coué. It is the simple, "Count your blessings."

I would suggest, tentatively, that the happy people I know tend to adopt this attitude, while the unhappy ones do not. What does your experience suggest?

Another example of the use of increasing positive feedback loops lies in teaching. As my father, a teacher, first told me, "The important thing is to set tests in which they do well from the beginning. This leads to confidence and self-esteem. That in turn leads to better performance in the next test, which can therefore be a little harder." This is an increasing positive feedback loop. The corresponding decreasing positive loop would set in if the tests were too hard: confidence would drop; performance would drop further, even on the same difficulty of test, and things would steadily deteriorate.

The important psychological concept in this context is that of *reinforcement*. If a rat in a common experiment in a psychologist's laboratory performs some required action, such as pressing a lever, it finds that it gets a small amount of food. The food increases the possibility of its again pressing the lever. The food is called a *positive reinforcer* of the action. If, on the other hand, every time the rat goes into a certain area of its cage it gets an electrical shock, then the frequency with which it will go there is reduced. An electrical shock is termed a *negative reinforcer* for that activity.

In shorthand we may summarise these in the following way. Let A be some process of some system in the rat. (In experiments this will usually result in some clearly visible action such as pressing a lever, or moving towards or away from something.) Then if we let PR denote a system in the rat that responds to a Positive Reinforcer (e.g. the digestive system) and NR denote a system which responds to a Negative Reinforcer (e.g. the pain system), then we have in shorthand:

$$\text{either } \uparrow A \to \uparrow PR \text{ or } \uparrow A \to \uparrow NR$$

(courtesy of the experimental psychologist), while:

$$\uparrow PR \to \uparrow A \text{ and } \uparrow NR \to \downarrow A$$

because of processes which have evolved in animals which ensure that it repeats actions which lead to food etc. while reducing those that lead to pain etc.

We therefore find an increasing *positive* feedback loop for A when there is *positive* reinforcement:

$$\uparrow A \to \uparrow PR \to \uparrow A,$$

but a *negative* feedback loop when there is *negative* reinforcement:

$$\uparrow A \to \uparrow NR \to \downarrow A.$$

For a typical student, doing well in tests is in itself a positive reinforcer to study in that subject. Conversely doing badly is a negative reinforcer.

As a general rule someone who habitually notices *only* when things are getting worse is getting *only* negative reinforcers. This is likely to end up with depression and total inertia. In order to improve the condition of such a person we will have somehow to introduce the habit of noticing improvements in order to get some positive feedback when things get better, which will then enable the changes leading to those improvements to be reinforced.

These examples illustrate the important principle that **in establishing a change for the better in a therapeutic context we need to institute increasing positive feedback loops** just as surely as we have used them in inducing simple Hypnotic phenomena. If we fail to incorporate positive reinforcing factors, then any change is all too likely to lapse. If we *have* introduced them, then any small change in the right direction will continue to grow stronger.

There is a very important distinction to make here. In an Hypnotic process the Hypnotist is in a position to provide reinforcers. In the context of establishing feedback to maintain a therapeutic change it is *life* which has to provide the reinforcers. Within a session a Hypnotist may say things like, "Very good. You are doing well." But any therapy is only successful when the Client no longer needs such affirmations because *life* is saying, "You are doing well," and reinforcing the changes made.

To this end we will be on the look-out for positive reinforcers which life can offer the individual Client. Of course such reinforcers vary from person to person. One useful question to ask in the search for positive reinforcers is the following.

Q. Can you tell me what things in life give you greatest satisfaction / pleasure / happiness?

If, as a random example, someone gets a great satisfaction out of tidiness, then to tie in the prospective change to an increase in tidiness gives it a positive reinforcer which will in turn create an increasing positive feedback loop. Thus we might help such a woman with certain emotional problems NOT by talking about *control* which is a rather more masculine concept, but by thinking in terms of how to keep her feelings, like her hair and dress, *tidy*. (This would also imply *attractive*.) Then, any step in the direction of dealing more effectively with her feelings would get the lovely positive feelings which go with *tidiness*. This would then be a positive reinforcer for the changes being introduced.

Quite a lot of Milton H. Erickson's successes are based on finding a small but very effective intervention that leads, in time, to the elimination of the problem. The frustrating thing, I found, is that while I admired Erickson's approach, he never wrote anything which enabled me to determine HOW he arrived at a particular choice of intervention, or HOW he knew it was going to work. Consequently I might find myself applying one of his techniques in what *seemed* a similar case, but to no avail! I realise now that I was mistakenly looking for a similarity in *symptoms* where I should have been looking for a similarity in *dynamics*. Now that I focus on the dynamics more than the symptoms, in the way which is described in this book, I find that his work makes much more sense and it is easier to begin to emulate him in effectiveness.

Another question which can be useful in the hunt for reinforcers is:

Q. What, to your mind, would be the greatest benefit of this change?

Suppose, as a rather obvious example, that the Client wants to lose weight, then it can be very important to know how the benefit will be most appreciated. Is it in being able to buy smarter clothes? Is it in feeling fitter? Is it in looking slimmer? Is it in feeling more sexually attractive? And, if so, for whom? Is it in simply seeing a different number on the scales when weighed?

In these different cases we might well be able to use some aspect of the desired result as a reinforcer of a useful change. In the first example we might institute the habit of window shopping for an ideal wardrobe, with an eye to looking for items which can be bought and worn at steps along the way to the ideal weight. In some cases it is then hardly necessary to specify exactly the changes in lifestyle which are necessary to achieve the change, any more than it is necessary in biofeedback training to specify *how* the blood pressure etc. is to be controlled. The feedback in either case can be enough to reinforce any improvement, provided it is quick and clear enough. In the present case every small reduction in weight leads to the reinforcer of a new article of clothing, which leads to continuing the actions which led to the weight loss, which leads to more clothes, and so on.

In the second case, where the desire is to feel fitter, we might link any eating to some exercise, as when Erickson got a woman to run around the house after every slice of toast. In this way we are more likely to produce real fitness which will reinforce the improvement.

If the goal is to feel more sexually attractive in general, then we might focus on the question of how to *eat* in a sexy way. The Client might be directed to watch films, paying special attention to *how* actresses eat so as to increase their attractiveness, and then to imitate them.

Notice that we will then have broken the identification of eating as being somehow connected with being NOT sexually attractive, and instead connected it to BEING sexually attractive. There will therefore be a reward of the desired kind every time she eats in the new way. Since, in practice, this new way will not be gluttonous, we will have the foundations of a useful positive feedback loop.

If there is a compulsive need to see a change on the scales we might manage something on the following lines. The scales had better be accurate. This means finding one of those precise ones which measure to the nearest ounce. Suppose that there is one in town in a pharmacy. We would then work to establish the rule that the person must WALK to the shop each time, and make a note of his or her weight to the nearest ounce. If luck is on our side this could mean a twenty-minute walk every day at least. This will tend inevitably to reduce weight; the resultant loss will act to reinforce the habit of walking; and we have a nice gentle positive feedback loop:

$$\uparrow\{walking\} \rightarrow \downarrow\{weight\} \rightarrow \uparrow\{walking\}.$$

These examples should be enough to show how the discovery of a potential reinforcer can suggest ideas for the establishment of a suitable positive feedback loop which will lead to the desired result. Another way of looking at this is to note that a search for positive reinforcers can throw up ideas for potential changes at the crucial, creative Step 2 of the process of determining possible changes.

The advantage of using weight loss as an example is that it should be obvious it is a *process* which *takes time*. This is really the characteristic of all Hypnosis and Hypnotherapy, which is unfortunately masked by the tendency of the Stage Hypnotist to present Hypnosis as having to do with instantaneous changes of state. This leads people to suppose that it is possible instantaneously to have excellent memory or unshakeable confidence or what have you.

Let us take another characteristic problem for which a feedback loop is useful: phobias. One of the standard psychological methods of overcoming a phobia is that of progressive de-sensitisation. Let us see how this works with an example. Suppose that the fear of water is so great that it is impossible to learn how to swim, because even going to the pool arouses anxiety. The solution to the problem involves first sitting on the edge of the pool until the anxiety subsides. **Then feeling pleased with this progress.** Then standing in very shallow water until the fresh anxiety subsides. **Then feeling pleased with this progress.** Then sitting in very shallow water until the fresh anxiety subsides. **Then feeling pleased with this progress.** Then walking in up to the knees until the fresh anxiety subsides. **Then feeling pleased with this progress.** And so on.

Each fresh stage arouses some anxiety, of course, but it is impossible to maintain that anxiety forever, and so, provided that there is no impatience and no pressing on too fast, each level of anxiety *must* fade away.

The abstract pattern describing this process is:

$$\uparrow(depth\ of\ water) \rightarrow \uparrow\{anxiety\} \rightarrow \uparrow\{slow\ perception\ that\ there\ is\ no\ danger\}$$
$$\rightarrow \downarrow\{anxiety\} \rightarrow \uparrow\{\textbf{pleasure in progress}\} \rightarrow \uparrow(depth).$$

The feeling of success is *very important*, since this is the *positive* reinforcer which makes the loop a *positive* one. If this is not instituted, the sufferer is inclined to be forever thinking, "I *am* stupid! Fancy being scared of the water, at *my* age!" So that instead of being pleased at being able to sit in the water without anxiety, he or she is feeling bad because no one else has to do that. They therefore provide themselves with a *negative* reinforcer, and so enter a negative loop which soon discourages them from continuing.

I have known cases of individuals who have been "treated" for their phobias by psychologists who seem to have learned the process of progressive desensitisation by rote, with no understanding of the nature of the loop they are supposed to be instituting. They have neglected the central importance of the reinforcer, with the result that each step has been taken with increasing reluctance, and the "cure" failed.

A similar method may be used to eliminate a phobia in the context of Hypnotherapy. The main difference is that the Client is usually taken through the stages by means of an enhanced visualisation rather than in reality. This has the advantage that there is little problem of self-consciousness - as there often is at the real pool. Various Hypnotic techniques can also be used to instill confidence and, which is often of great importance, to deal with memories of some early disaster which may have initiated the phobia. But it remains of importance to ensure that each small improvement results in great satisfaction when the Subject tries things out in real life. Remember: Life must provide the Reinforcer. Consequently we need to ensure that satisfaction will be felt with each step of progress.

After these examples it should be possible to see the principle involved fairly clearly. The good Hypnotherapist will always be trying to arrange that any change made in the consulting room will be *amplified* or *reinforced* by the Client's environment: "Life must provide the Reinforcer."

This attention to environment is what is sometimes denoted by the adjective "holistic", but it should be realised that the customary antithesis between "holistic" and "analytic" does not hold in the context of the present theory of Hypnotherapy, which clearly incorporates a great deal of analysis of the systems involved, but does not limit itself to *internal* systems, but rather includes *external* ones in the environment as well. Consequently it may also be termed "holistic".

This attention to arranging for reinforcement by the environment highlights a certain important ethical and professional point. We have noted that many elementary Hypnotic phenomena are evoked by means of reinforcement by the Hypnotist. If things go beyond that, and deeper and more personal changes are reinforced by the personality of the Hypnotherapist, then we have danger of the Client becoming almost addicted to the Hypnotherapist. If the *only* place the changes are reinforced are in the Hypnotherapist's office, then the Client becomes subtly conditioned to return again and again.

One advantage of the "Morganic" approach is that it forces us to consider relevant external systems, and the ways in which they affect the problem. We are forced to ask what the resultants of changes are. We are forced to look for negative feedback from the environment which could actively eliminate an improvement; we are forced to look for aspects of the environment which will provide positive feedback to change. We cannot restrict ourselves to the cosy little world of { ⇕ Therapist ⇔ ⇕ Client}.

For an equivalent analogy consider again the management consultant who restricts himself to analysing the behaviour of a business *with no reference to the market in which it operates!* Any businessman should see how futile this can be. An organisational structure which works excellently in one market such as insurance, would be of doubtful value in the world of entertainment or a high-tech, high-innovation field like computers. Moreover any change which does not result in a positive reinforcer - increased profits - from the market is going to be thrown out quickly. Organisational changes which lead to increased profits will, however, generally get reinforced with no further work by the consultant.

Now it might be objected that the Hypnotherapist cannot control the Client's daily environment. And in the simplest sense this is, of course, true: the Hypnotherapist does not leave the consulting-room. However, when you start to think about it, it IS possible to alter the Client's effective environment, as a result of changing the Client's behaviour.

Suppose, for example, that there is a young man who is miserable because he does not have a girlfriend, and would like the confidence to get one. It might be very clear that since he spends all his spare time at home or with an elderly uncle there is no chance, even if he *were* more confident, of meeting someone. In this case we might simply look to give him enough confidence to take him to a place where he will inevitably meet suitable girls. This changes his effective environment. With only a little luck, nature will then take its course and he will need no more "therapy".

In many cases it is possible also to change the behaviour of people around the Client by means of changing the behaviour of the Client in their presence. As a very simple example, suppose that someone complains that everybody at work hates him, and it also turns out that he has a habit of scowling all the time. If we can get the scowl removed - perhaps on the pretext that it indicates tension and we will remove the tension - then, human nature being what it is, those around him will perceive him as a much more pleasant individual. They will therefore start to act in a more pleasant way. This will encourage him to smile more and scowl less. This will make him seem more likeable. And the loop will continue to power the change.

There may be some readers who, at this stage, will be objecting that some problems are deeper than this. Indeed they can be. It might well be the case that in the last example the scowling is a result of some deep emotional wound which will need some examination. But remember that within this systematic approach we do not attempt even to change a scowl without running through the diagnostic process described in chapters above: looking into the question of the systems with which it is involved; what arouses it; what are the associated feelings; what were its origins; what would be the consequences of change. In fact, therefore, the scowl may be the very door that we need in order to enter the area of the deeper problem. On the other hand, it may just be a habit of no great significance other than that it has become involved in an external loop in which the more he scowls the less people like him, and so the more he scowls. If it is the latter it should be comparatively easy to change it. If it proves to be very hard, then we may well suspect that there is more to it, and a careful analysis should reveal what that more is.

When we start we do not know how much of the problem process is internal and how much is external. The diagnostic process is general enough to provide the answers to this, as we follow up the causal chains involved. If the chain is purely internal then, as in the chapter on the use of positive feedback loops in Hypnosis, we will be looking to internal positive loops to power the change. In order to achieve this end we may well be enhancing changes via a positive feedback loop involving Client and therapist. If, on the other hand, the world external to the Client is playing an important part in the problem then we may well need to change *that*. This we can do indirectly, using changes in the Client's behaviour to produce the required changes. This will in turn involve us in making certain internal changes, and we are back to powering these changes with positive feedback loops. And these may start with a process like a typical induction.

Turning again to our Consultant analogy: he or she must first determine the large-scale changes that need to be made, looking, as the Hypnotherapist does, for ones that are relatively easy, will be viable, and will not be harmful. Such changes will generally be made with the external environment in mind. Then he or she will have to get down to the nitty-gritty of making the specific internal changes which may be necessary in, say, the accounts department. It is at this stage that he or she *seems* to be working hardest: that is the point where people *see* the changes. But in fact the most important work is his or her understanding of the larger scale: an understanding which is invisible. It is also the understanding which is hardest to teach - and the understanding which pays best.

Most books on Hypnosis teach the simple techniques for making local changes. We have seen that many are no more than establishing simple feedback loops involving the change and the expectation of the change. They are easy to learn. Most students can pick them up within weeks. But that is not Hypnotherapy. In much of this book, by contrast, the higher-order skills of changing a person as a whole, with a clear understanding of the interactions of the individual with his or her environment, have been emphasised. Nevertheless when the skilled Hypnotherapist gets down to work, the first *visible* sign of work may well be the same early familiar steps of many an "Hypnotic induction": "Now, I would like you to sit comfortably and fix your eyes..."

SUMMARY

When we come to making a change it may be very simple, and involve only an internal adjustment. In that case the change can be powered by internal positive feedback loops. Some examples have been given of such loops in the context of therapy.

We have noticed the importance in this context of looking for *positive reinforcers.*

More generally in Hypnotherapy, however, we are making changes which affect and are affected by the Client's environment. It is very important then to ensure that any changes are reinforced by the environment outside the consulting-room. In other words we look to create positive feedback loops involving the Client's environment to support and enhance the change.

It is important to notice that it *is* possible to change the Client's environment via changes in the Client's behaviour. At its simplest, this might mean simply introducing the habit of going to new places, wearing new clothes or treating people differently so that they in return behave differently.

SUMMARY OF PART B

IN PART B we have seen the simple notions of systems and their activities and interactions, which we started with in Part A, develop into very powerful tools of thought for understanding much that happens in the fields of Hypnosis and Hypnotherapy.

The whole area of diagnosis has been transformed from something that was at best a listing of symptoms into a clear and logical procedure for defining the nature of the dynamics of the systems involved. (And organic systems are nothing if not dynamic.)

The feedback loops which have emerged naturally from the same approach have been seen to be not only fundamental to the functioning of most organic systems, but also central to the nature of very many of the most common Hypnotic procedures.

Positive feedback loops have been seen to be *responsible for* very many of the common problems presented to the Hypnotherapist, but also to provide one of the more powerful tools for making changes to *eliminate* problems.

Negative feedback loops have been seen to be essential for the *preservation of valuable processes* in organic systems; but equally they can be responsible at times for *maintaining a disadvantageous* one.

We have seen that the process of diagnosis leads on naturally to a systematic way of generating changes, and a way of thinking systematically about those changes to ensure both that they are permanent and that they do not cause further problems.

Furthermore it should be clear that the principles developed ensure that we neglect neither any important internal aspects of the problem, nor any important external aspects. There is built into the thinking an automatic "analytic" element, and an equally automatic "holistic" element.

It is hoped that practising Hypnotherapists will see how this way of thinking makes explicit and rigorous what most of us have been doing for years.

It is hoped that the non-specialist will understand in a deeper way what Hypnotherapy is all about: that it is NOT the domain of charlatans and showmen; NOT simply a matter of waving a watch, sending someone to sleep and having them wake up "cured"; NOT totally dependent on a belief that it will work. It is, rather, at root a very practical, logical and scientific approach to changing (for the better) the functioning of a wide range of mental, emotional and habitual systems in the human being.

It should also be clear that the same approach and principles can have application in broader fields such as families or organisations, or indeed medicine. The use of a diagnostic procedure based on the dynamics of the systems involved rather than static symptom clusters would seem to be an advance in many other fields.

Cautions

1)   Throughout this book there are many examples which are chosen for their illustrative value: they are therefore simple. In real life things are generally complicated. This means that we may end up with *many* causal chains and *many* loops, which may link together in very much more complex ways than have been indicated here. Note also that even in the simpler cases it can often take many sessions to make useful, permanent changes.

2)   Be aware of the fact that a particular causal connection between systems may well hold only under particular conditions. For illustration, whereas blowing on a small fire can easily put it out, blowing on a large one can fan the flames. Forcing oneself to go into mildly fearful situations can reduce the anxiety felt. Forcing oneself into highly fearful situations on the other hand can produce a very strong phobia.

3)   Do not imagine that the principles alone make an expert. Training and experience are essential, as in other professions.

4)   No matter how well someone understands the *theory* presented above, it will be of limited use unless it is combined with a good share of humanity: an ability to understand and empathise with our fellows from all backgrounds and of all temperaments.

5)   Do not imagine that I will be applying the formalism in a rigid way in the course of a session, though I may subsequently write down the dynamic structure as part of the case notes. Just as a composer hears music in his head and only subsequently puts it on paper, so I grasp the dynamics in my head in a rather abstract way, and only later consign it to paper.

6)   It is not being suggested that the theoretical framework developed here is *complete*. I think that there is still a lot of work to be done to tighten up the exact notions used (though a step towards a tightening of the definition of activity is given in Part C), and in the recognition of significant dynamic patterns and of the functioning of the many systems with which Hypnotherapy is involved. In the above only the simplest patterns have been described. It is being claimed only that the framework provides a relatively rigid foundation on which such further work can proceed.

PART C

IN THIS PART of the book the chapters deal with a variety of different themes which are largely disconnected from each other, though all relate to the theory developed in Parts A and B. They may be read in any order, or skipped.

The first three of these can be broadly seen as expanding on important aspects of Hypnotherapy.

The next three are there to relate the "Morganic" approach to Hypnotherapy to important associated fields, namely experimental work, family therapy and other forms of psychotherapy.

The final four chapters take a more detailed look at some very important theoretical concepts and constructs.

A summary of each is available at the front of the book in the list of contents and, in a different form, at the end of each chapter.

CHAPTER 16

Dynamic Rebound and Paired Systems

THERE IS an old saying: "What goes up must come down."

Originally, I suppose, this was applied to anything thrown into the air. But here we want to focus attention on the fact that for any biological system any increase in activity cannot go on for ever: in time the activity level must come down.

This idea provides a starting point for our examination of the reason why, in Hypnotherapy, if we want to *decrease* the activity of a system, we may often succeed by first *increasing* it.

Here are some examples of the use of such a principle. It is not uncommon for someone to say, "I cannot relax. The more I try, the worse I become." The problem here is that the muscles are designed actively to contract when they receive a nervous impulse: ↑{nervous input} → ↑{muscle activity}. But there is no way in which a direct nervous stimulus can reduce activity. Those people who can relax have learned the knack of stopping sending any messages *to* the muscles (via the efferent nerves), often by concentrating instead on messages coming *from* the body (via the afferent nerves).

People who are *trying* to relax, but can't, are acting as if the way to relax is to find the right way of *ordering* the muscles to relax. But this does not work. With such people it is particularly useful to get them to start by *tensing* all the large body muscles as much as possible. We might suggest raising the legs, holding the arms forward with tensed fists, tensing the abdomen, etc. They are then instructed to hold this for as long as possible. This greatly enhanced activity of the muscles soon uses up most of the available energy in the bloodstream which, combined with a build-up of lactic acid in the muscles, soon produces the familiar tiredness and ache.

When this tension is relaxed the muscles are then naturally in no condition to be activated by any nervous impulses, and so relax into a state of very low activity.

In shorthand we have:

$$↑\{muscles\} → ↑\{sense\ of\ fatigue\} → ↓\{muscles\}$$

I have known men who have got into a terrible state because they have been told by someone that they ought to relax more: they have then reduced the amount of sport they have been playing in an attempt to do so. This has only led to hours of increasing tension. When they are instead instructed to play sport again they find the natural consequence: they relax after the game completely and naturally.

We see in these examples the principle that in dealing with some organic systems the best approach to making a change in one direction is to *start a change in the opposite direction*.

As another example of this principle, there is a case of Erickson's in which he dealt with a grossly overweight woman by first *forcing her to put on more weight* (Rossi (1980) vol. IV, pp 182-185). The practical effect of this was that she subsequently lost weight quickly and easily.

A possible mechanism for this can be analysed as follows. There is some system in the body which is responsible for storing fat: let us call this {storing}. There is another system which deals with removing stored fat (remember the general principle that we expect two different systems which operate in opposite directions): let us call this {removing}. In line with our general principles of diagnosis we would like to know what leads to an activation of {storing}.

If we place the mechanism in the environment in which it evolved, which was one in which there were very few means of storing food safely for long periods, and one in which there might be years of plenty and then years of famine, the following dynamics would seem natural. Any sense of there being a shortage of food would activate {storage} in the same way that today any news that there might be a shortage of sugar on the supermarket shelves leads to housewives descending like locusts and packing their larders with it. In the case of a sensed impending famine the early woman would simply find herself eating every scrap available and turning it into fat.

We therefore have the simple process:

$$\uparrow\{\text{sense of shortage}\} \rightarrow \uparrow\{\text{storing}\}.$$

Note that although this is a plausible formula I am by no means saying that it MUST hold for everyone. If there is one certain thing that can be said about people it is that they work in different ways. What I DO say is that the question of whether or not the formula holds *for a particular person* is one which can be determined empirically. If an artificial sense of famine such as is produced by a strict diet leads to an activation of a pattern of compulsive eating and then rapid weight gain we have a strong reason to suppose that the initially plausible result above holds.

With this idea in mind we may see Erickson's strategy as being one of inactivating completely this particular coupling by presenting the woman's body with a world in which there is not only a surfeit of food but one in which it is being forced into her. With this {storing} system inactivated it would then be easy to lose weight.

Incidentally the same method of placing this storage mechanism in the environment in which it evolved would suggest that it is rather more likely to happen in women, who have to carry food within their bodies for both themselves and a helpless baby, than for men, who would more helpfully respond to famine by working harder to glean food by hunting or going further afield - activities not generally helped by being heavier.

Here is another thought on the same lines. What made a woman look attractive a few million years ago? I suggest that it was being well-fed and plump: this would indicate health and being able to mother healthy children. (This remains true, I believe, in parts of the world where food is at a premium.) Therefore if a woman felt *unattractive* then we might well suppose that the primitive mechanism of attempting to pad herself out would be activated:

$\uparrow$\{sense of unattractiveness\} $\rightarrow$ $\uparrow$\{weight\}

A modern woman who has inherited this mechanism is therefore in a terrible position because, thanks to modern ideas, she thinks that weight is unattractive. We therefore have:

$\uparrow$\{weight\} $\rightarrow$ $\uparrow$\{sense of unattractiveness\},

which, coupled with the above primitive mechanism makes, of course, an increasing positive feedback loop for weight and unattractiveness - a loop which is a familiar one to millions of women.

If such a woman attempts to lose weight by dieting, but has also inherited the old storage pattern, then she only succeeds in activating a very strong instinctive desire to binge and grow fat. This is a serious feedback loop:

$\uparrow$\{weight\} $\rightarrow$ $\uparrow$\{diet\} $\rightarrow$ $\uparrow$\{sense of famine\} $\rightarrow$ $\uparrow$\{storage\} $\rightarrow$ $\uparrow$\{weight\},

which underlies the principle, "Dieting makes you Fat" (Carnon & Einzig (1983)). Since an increase in weight will sooner or later trigger another attempt at dieting, there is an increasing positive feedback loop.

For such people Hypnotherapy has to act to eliminate the increasing loops by deftly altering key factors. For example, a strong emphasis on enhancing the feeling of attractiveness will tend to weaken or incapacitate the loop involving it and weight.

Erickson's over-eating strategy would work for many women, but it takes a lot of effort to get most women to accept this approach! But at the least we may note that it is an important part of any healthy eating pattern that there should not be any prolonged sense of being deprived of food.

This book does not provide a detailed account of dealing with such problems. In general there is no one way for every woman. As in the general principles of Hypnotherapy outlined in Part B, the best results are obtained by a careful analysis of how things work in each individual; the systems, internal and external, that are involved; and finally a proper handling of the various possible strategies for change and their outcome.

After the above examples and discussions, which give insight into how *when we are dealing with dynamic systems* the "obvious" change can be in exactly the wrong direction, we can come to a more general perspective on the strategy of creating change by pushing in the *opposite* direction.

We start with the general principle that, in order to maintain homeostasis, organic systems evolve *pairs* of subsystems which operate in contrary directions. (In many cases there are several systems which operate in each direction, but for simplicity we will consider two.) Let us just call a particular pair of systems which regulate some factor X, {up} and {down}. They might be systems for increasing and decreasing salt in the bloodstream, for raising and lowering an arm, for increasing or decreasing weight, for increasing or decreasing adrenaline production, etc. Remember that the systems {up} and {down} will generally have evolved millions if not billions of years ago in quite a different environment and in beings with little conscious control.

We then have the basic formulae:

$$\uparrow X \rightarrow \uparrow \{down\} \text{ and } \downarrow X \rightarrow \uparrow \{up\}.$$

The third factor that we are going to take into account is the attempt consciously to control the system regulated by these twin mechanisms.

Now suppose that consciousness is always striving to alter X in one direction. Without loss of generality we may suppose that it is trying to move it down:

$$\uparrow \{consciousness\} \rightarrow \downarrow X.$$

Inevitably this will bring it into conflict with {up}, which exists to safeguard the organism against values of X which are too low, and this in turn acts to increase X:

$$\downarrow X \rightarrow \uparrow \{up\} \rightarrow \uparrow X.$$

But this increase, of course, completes an increasing loop for X. The increase will be consciously noticed and the process repeated again, and again:

$$\uparrow X \rightarrow \uparrow \{consciousness\} \rightarrow \downarrow X \rightarrow \uparrow \{up\} \rightarrow \uparrow X.$$

Since it is a general principle of organic systems that the more often they are activated the stronger they become - think of muscles or of immunity to disease - the main effect of the above loop over a number of cycles is that {up} becomes *stronger*.

Meanwhile {down} can take it easy. *It* is never needed: {consciousness} has taken over its role. It is inactive. It may even start to atrophy.

One great virtue of getting the conscious mind to act in the *opposite* direction, and to force the value of X *up* for a while, is that it will then activate the lazy {down} system! Erickson's eating strategy did just this.

One of the big problems with people who suffer from panic attacks is that although there are natural systems which will prevent the associated symptoms from getting out of hand, they are often used so infrequently - the sufferer naturally tries to avoid panics at all costs - that they become weakened and less effective than they should be. A strategy of getting a Client to go out and "collect" mini-panics would be an example of a way of increasing the strength of the "down" system.

In our initial example on relaxation we activated a natural system which switches *down* muscular activity by first forcing *up* the activity until the {down} system - the system designed to protect against overwork - was activated.

Many problems which are brought to the Hypnotherapist are a result of one-sided efforts at control. And time and time again they have been helped by an approach which encourages the Client to spend some time activating the opposite mechanisms.

There are millions who have tried very, very hard to sleep, but have never tried to stay awake. Forcing oneself to stay awake and active is a good way of activating the natural mechanisms which reduce arousal and bring on sleep. There are men who have trouble urinating in public. They have pushed and pushed to no avail in an attempt to *start* but they have never practised *stopping*. When they *do* practise they are acting *against* the release system, which therefore gets a chance to grow stronger. There are those who are very embarrassed by blushing. They try very hard to reduce it, but it only makes things worse. By actively trying to *increase* it, they tend to activate more often the systems which tend naturally to limit it: systems which can then operate more often and more easily.

Of course in all real cases the situation is quite complex and the suggestion to reverse the direction of conscious control has other definite useful effects in breaking psychological vicious circles as well.

However there remains an important principle of organic systems, which is that putting pressure on them will, if they do not collapse completely, make them stronger.

We have eliminated smallpox from the world. But most other infectious organisms are getting more and more immune to our best antibiotics: because medicine is always acting to reduce their activity, the long-term effect is to make them stronger.

In society it is so very often the case that attempts to oppress or suppress some section of society leads only to that section becoming stronger in the long run. There are exceptions, as with the diseases, but so many people fail to understand that directly attacking an organic system (without killing it) is most likely to make it stronger in the long run.

Anything that does not kill you outright makes you a little stronger.

- Piet Hein

The introduction of myxomatosis was very successful in reducing rabbit populations when first introduced. But now rabbits have become more immune and have developed different instincts so that they no longer return to the warren to die, which used to increase the chance of the other rabbits becoming infected. This disease is therefore no longer effective in controlling rabbits, and the populations are expanding again.

We may note in this context that one potential problem with many medical interventions is that they are always acting in a one-sided way. They act as adjuncts to the conscious mind's control. The effect will be to weaken whatever system there is in the body to produce the same effect as the drug. Injections of insulin, for example, will tend to decrease the body's own production of insulin. Consequently there must develop a greater and greater degree of dependence on the drug. This is not to say that in many cases the medical intervention is not the best thing to do - particularly in the short term. But it is to say that some practitioners should become more aware of the dynamic nature of the systems they are working with. If, for example, a tranquilliser of any kind is used artificially to reduce anxiety - and this can include nicotine - then inevitably it reduces the demands on the body's own systems which operate to reduce anxiety. These tend therefore to become less active and weaker. Consequently if the artificial tranquilliser is removed there is very little to stop the symptoms rising to high levels. The effect is generally to make the sufferer return again to the artificial help.

As a population, our muscles are much weaker than those of our grandfathers, because we use artificial legs so much: cars. Our natural legs have so much less exercise that they have naturally become weaker.

In general we see that if the function of a system is "assisted" by some other mechanism then there is a definite possibility that that system will weaken. Equally paradoxically, organic systems are often made stronger by being resisted, not assisted. Pruning may strengthen a rose.

The whole principle of vaccination rests on this basis. The vaccination does not directly help to kill off an infection. What it does is to activate and therefore strengthen the body's own immune system by "fighting" it. The vaccination is a mild attack on the body's health. The immune system reacts by growing more effective, and then remains so, often for life.

Notice that in this way it is the complete opposite to drug therapy. Vaccination, by attacking, strengthens a natural system. Drug therapy, by assisting, will tend to weaken a natural system.

But of course there are times, such as when a system has been naturally weakened, and needs a chance to recover, when temporary assistance is the correct treatment.

How do we decide which approach is the better? It is to be hoped that a careful systematic analysis combined with a sympathetic understanding of the Client will enable the right decision to be made. But the mere fact that the two possibilities are in mind should make us aware of the options, so that if the one approach is not going according to plan, then we are well advised to examine the alternative.

It is to be hoped that the need systematically to analyse the dynamics of a situation, as has been done in Part B, will also lead to an automatic awareness of opposing pairs of systems which exist. Recall that we start by asking $\uparrow S \rightarrow ?$, which should reveal among any systems that are activated by an increase in S any which act to limit it. These will be {down} systems. But we also ask the question $\downarrow S \rightarrow ?$, which is to say that we ask what will be the consequence of a reduction in the symptom that is seen as a problem. This should reveal to us any {up} system that becomes active to prevent it changing downwards.

What this chapter adds is the habit of *automatically* looking for paired systems, which act in opposite directions to maintain the homeostasis which is so essential for the survival of an organism.

It also adds the simple but important idea that a change can as often be achieved by starting a change in *the opposite direction to the long-term goal*, with the object in view of activating or strengthening an opposing system which in time will be able to act in the intended direction.

Those readers who are familiar with Ericksonian terminology will find in the above an explanation of why the strategy of "paradoxical intervention" - telling the person to do the opposite of what he or she has been doing to try to get rid of the problem - can often be used to great effect.

A direct attempt to control the habit of thumb-sucking in one of Erickson's cases led only to the girl doing it more and more. Erickson merely *imposed* a certain amount of concentrated thumb-sucking on her, to the point at which she started to feel a strong sense of resistance to the imposed chore (Haley (1973)). The activation of this inner sense was then enough to stop her.

A direct attempt by a parent to control the amount of sweets consumed by a child all too often leads only to a stronger desire for sweets and the habit of obtaining and eating them in secret. All the parent succeeds in activating is a stronger desire for sweets. If, on the other hand, the parent were to impose the consumption of *large* amounts of sweets as a *penalty* for not doing homework or something else, then there would soon be activated a very strong aversion to sweets.

So far we have seen a model of how control of a system may be increased by ensuring that both its {up} and {down} regulatory systems are regularly activated to strengthen them. This explains in a clear way why the strategy of paradoxical intervention works, and why *increasing* the activity that one wants *reduced* can be effective.

But there is another reason why paradoxical intervention may function, which is rather more dramatic, but less common.

We will present this first by means of a picture (which is not unlike what seems to have happened to certain early tribes of people). Suppose that some people move into virgin country, which is wooded. They find that they can cut and burn the trees and reveal fertile ground which can be cultivated. This provides enough food for the population to increase. The increased population can spread out and cut more trees, to provide more ground for cultivation. And this increasing positive feedback loop will continue until they run out of new land. What happens next? It is not simply that the population *growth* will stop, and the population level off: the population is almost bound to *crash*. The reason for this is that there is little warning of the impending danger: as long as there is land still available, the men will go right on exploiting it with increased vigour. If you accelerate towards a stone wall a crash is inevitable.

Businessmen may be aware of similar phenomena in more modern times. The Wall Street crash is an example of a system in which there was an increasing positive feedback loop in a system which was too young to have evolved any negative feedback loops to regulate its growth. When it reached a point where there were no new funds available to fuel the increase, the whole system crashed.

Let us look at this principle and see how it might, in theory, be used to control a predator population. The normal procedure is to work very hard to kill off the predators. But beyond a certain point this becomes very difficult. Not only do you reach a point of diminishing returns in that the smaller the number of predators, the more time and effort it takes to kill another, but also the predator tends to evolve more and more effective ways of surviving your attacks.

The opposite strategy, suggested by the above general characteristic of biological systems, is to *feed the predators*. Let them be able to raise large litters. Help them all to survive the winter. Let their population *grow* exponentially until it is twenty or more times the number that the land can naturally support. Let them grow soft on good living, and lose some of their wariness.

THEN suddenly cut off the supplies at a time when natural food supplies are near a minimum. The large numbers of active predators will very quickly mop up these supplies and then be faced with starvation. There is a very good chance that the entire population will in this way be wiped out: and if you wanted to accelerate this, then there would be a very good chance of killing the last few due to their soft and weakened state.

In these examples, we see a pattern of a positive feedback loop creating exponential growth of a system. But in each case the systems came up against the fact that a resource can drop to zero, and *that can happen with very little warning*.

This, incidentally, is one reason why it can be of great importance to distinguish positive feedback loops which are *increasing* with respect to all their component systems, and positive feedback loops which are *decreasing* with respect to one or more of their systems. In all positive feedback loops we can expect a perturbation to change exponentially, but in the decreasing kind one of the systems can hit zero activity suddenly, and this creates a drastic change in what is happening, as we have seen.

From an ecological perspective, a stable ecosystem is one in which any species which could hit zero activity (extinction) has done so. The remaining species co-exist in patterns of negative feedback loops which ensure that in none does the activity reach zero: as any one approaches zero there must be something in its interactions with the remainder of the ecosystem which ensures that its activity rebounds upwards.

If some change is made to the ecosystem, whether at the environmental or biological level, there is no longer any guarantee that existing negative feedback loops will prevent a species hitting the irreversible zero. Extinctions become possible, or even highly probable.

How do these thoughts have any bearing on Hypnotherapy? Well, we change the ecosystem of someone's mind when we introduce new thoughts. If, in particular, we establish a positive feedback loop to make the problem system increase its activity at a fast rate, then we may find that rather than running up against a natural regulatory system of the kind we considered above, which has evolved to maintain homeostasis, we may have systems running in a totally new mental environment in which there are no such limits. In this case we may anticipate that the exponential growth will at some point cause *some* process in the chain or chains suddenly to hit zero activity due to depletion. This in turn will trigger off sudden shocks in the behaviour of others, and we have achieved a sudden change all around, not unlike the change in an economy when a business which has been growing fast and large suddenly collapses, creating shock waves all around.

This style of "therapy" reminds us of Mesmer's patients who were wound up into higher and higher states of excitement until there was a dramatic "crisis" involving convulsions and a great display of emotion. Such phenomena were once associated with religious conversion, or we may think of initiation ceremonies, or of brainwashing.

I am not happy with such techniques in general because, although they can deliver change, I would have little confidence that it would necessarily be for the better. However this is not to say that they might not be used in a limited way to extinguish a limited and small system.

Some readers may have noticed the value of this aspect of the theory, however, in modelling a nervous breakdown. Typically in such cases there are one or more positive feedback loops which are running ever more strongly under difficult circumstances until one of the systems involved runs up against the brick wall of no further resources. Perhaps the body can give no more physical strength, perhaps the limits of production of certain neurotransmitters have been reached, perhaps the immune system can no longer function on the limited resources it has available to it. Whatever the reason, the sudden stop of any one system in a loop will create sudden changes in all related systems, and the whole complex pattern is likely for a while to stop dead, with all the accompanying symptoms of being totally unable to cope with demands, whether on physical strength, on decision making, or on the emotions.

Of course in time there will be a re-growth which, if well managed, can be much stronger and better than the growth that went before. The American Stock Exchange did not die out after the Great Crash, though it was in the doldrums for some time. It is now far stronger and far better regulated than it was then. An ecosystem which has crashed can also re-grow strongly and often with renewed vigour because a lot of dead wood can get cleared in a crash. In the long term a crash *can* be beneficial, but I would still rather not take the responsibility of initiating a massive crash, because of the enormously difficult task of predicting exactly what will grow again after it. It is true that you cannot make an omelette without breaking eggs, but then it is so very much easier to break eggs and NOT end up with an omelette.

SUMMARY

Organic systems tend to maintain homeostasis: a reasonable equilibrium in the face of changing conditions. To this end negative feedback loops evolve so that any departure of some key parameter from its typical value will be corrected by a pair (at least) of systems, one of which will act to increase it if it drops and the other to decrease it if it rises.

We therefore have a real possibility of reducing some symptom by acting in a way which initially seems to *increase* it, *provided that* this acts to activate the opposing system which will in time reduce it naturally. This is the principle used in vaccination.

We have seen also that repeated efforts directly to reduce a problem may well simply strengthen the system that is producing it, and weaken a system which would naturally reduce it. This will generally aggravate the problem over time. This is the danger inherent in prolonged drug therapy or of any artificial aids.

We have further indicated that under more extreme conditions the activity of a system may be eliminated by forcing it so strongly in the opposite direction that we over-expand it until the system "crashes". This is not recommended, except on a small scale, because of the unpredictability of the consequences. This pattern also provides a model for the process of a "nervous breakdown".

CHAPTER 17

Complex Dissociated Systems

IN PART A we discussed subsystems of the human being which can be identified by means of the associated structures, such as the auditory system, visual system, etc. However these are not the only systems that are involved in Hypnotherapy. There can also be complex systems which are not neatly identifiable in terms of one specific structure. We have already mentioned some of these without explicit comment, but will now pay more attention to them. A useful introduction to such systems is provided by the phenomenon which is known as dissociation.

We may take an example of this from Hilgard's work (Hilgard & Hilgard (1975)). Hilgard is the primary proponent of the modern neo-dissociation theory of Hypnosis, which states that dissociation is the fundamental characteristic of all Hypnotic phenomena.

This example took place in a classroom environment in which the instructor was demonstrating a variety of Hypnotic phenomena, including deafness. One of the students who were participating in this demonstration was also blind, so that the phenomenon of induced deafness would be particularly dramatic for him, as it would leave him awareness of the world through his sense of touch only. He had been hypnotised previously. A standard induction was used, followed by the suggestion that after the instructor counted from one to three the student would become deaf and unable to hear any sound. It was additionally suggested that this would be reversed when the instructor placed his hand on the student's right shoulder. It is possible that had it not been for this reassurance that the effect was to be temporary, the suggestion would not have taken effect, because of the anxiety that might be induced in a person so dependent on sound.

The efficacy of the suggestion was tested by banging together some large wooden blocks: there was no response at all. In fact, at an earlier demonstration the even more dramatic test of firing a starting-pistol near the Subject had been used, also with no effect. Naturally there was no response either to any questions asked of him.

The particular significance of the experiment that day was that another student was motivated to wonder if, despite the lack of overt response, there might be "some part" of the Subject which continued to be aware of what was being said. The reasoning was that since there was no malfunction of the ears themselves, the words might be getting some distance into the brain. The instructor agreed to test this hypothesis and did so in the following way.

He spoke quietly to the Subject, who had proved unresponsive to the loudest noises. He began with the general observation that there are many internal systems of which there is no conscious awareness, such as those that control circulation and digestion. He then added that there might be mental processes of which there may also be no awareness. Next he suggested that there might be a part of the Subject that was able to listen to his voice and process information. Finally he asked for the ideo-motor response of the lifting of an index finger if this last suggestion was in fact the case.

Apparently both the instructor and his class were surprised when the finger rose. So was the Subject, who immediately spoke to remark on the fact that he had felt his finger move for no reason and wanted to know what had happened.

The instructor therefore restored the Subjects's normal sense of hearing by touching him on the shoulder. The Subject's account of events was that he recalled the initial instructions about going deaf at the count of three, and being able to hear again on being touched. There was then only a silence, which was rather boring, and so he had occupied his time with a mathematical problem. While thus employed he had felt his finger lift, and so asked about it.

The Subject was then told what had happened and then the initial suggestions were reversed so that he was able to hear again without a hand on his shoulder.

The next step taken was to use an analogue of the phenomenon of "automatic writing". This is a phenomenon which has been reported at various times in the history of Hypnosis, and had been used by this instructor. It involves the recovery of material not accessible to consciousness by means of one hand being placed "out of awareness" by Hypnotic techniques, and then being allowed to write in response to questions. (This is discussed further in Chapter 18.)

The instructor again went through his Hypnotic induction and talked explicitly of there being two parts of the Subject, and that a certain touch on the arm would put the instructor in touch with that part which had known what was going on when he was hypnotically deaf. He further suggested that *that* part would be able to answer questions, while the other part - presumably the conscious mind - would be unaware even of the fact of talking until "out of hypnosis" again. At that stage he was to be consciously aware of everything.

The instructor then touched the Subject in the specified way and asked questions. The results were very much those which would have been expected if automatic writing had been used instead. The Subject spoke freely of the experiences which had occurred when he had been "deaf", such as the conversations between the instructor and the other students, and the banging of the blocks. But when the touch was removed the Subject reported no conscious awareness of what he had just said.

Finally when all the suggestions were reversed the Subject was able, as suggested, to remember everything that had happened.

The conclusion drawn from this little experiment was that it is possible for one part of the brain to register incoming information even if there is no conscious awareness of it. Furthermore it may be possible to recover such information.

For convenience Hilgard came to talk of this information as being available to a "hidden observer".

Perhaps it should be noted that if this account was our *only* basis for this conclusion then it would be logically quite inadequate. A sceptic can point to the fact that information about what had happened had been given to the Subject after the first episode, and he could easily have re-presented these facts when the supposed "hidden observer" was being questioned. However there is ample other evidence, such as that obtained from automatic writing, to validate the general conclusions, so this account can be taken as a usefully vivid way of introducing the subject of dissociation.

Perhaps the only surprising thing about this account is that the instructor and class were surprised at the finger movement, since they had already seen automatic writing and were therefore aware of the possibility of information not being accessible to consciousness but available by other means.

The "hidden observer" in this example may be regarded as a functional subsystem of the person which is essentially distinct from the system which is active in normal consciousness. The disadvantage of the phrase is that like "the subconscious" it suggests that there exists only one such system. In principle there can be many.

In terms of complex systems the existence of functionally distinct subsystems is no surprise. If we consider that system which is a country, for example, then to an outside observer the outward signs of the activity of that country are those things contained in the media - TV, radio and papers. However, many things happen in a country which are not revealed in the media. And it would be quite possible for an outside observer to pay attention to some different aspect of life - discussions in pubs, for example - which might reveal a totally different picture.

In certain societies there is very little contact indeed between various sections of society. There can be many autonomous sub-societies, which may be deliberately secret like the Masons once were, or simply detached for most purposes like pigeon-fanciers. There is nothing strange about some such subsystem of society responding to and being very agitated about something that the rest of society knows nothing about.

If, by analogy with Hilgard's little experiment, it is arranged that the sub-society has access to the media, then it will tell its story, and then for a while the greater part of society will be in contact with and aware of that sub-society and its preoccupations.

In general terms we may say that ANY complex system will contain subsystems. These are more or less integrated with each other. In this chapter the cases of interest are those systems in which two subsystems are essentially disjoint; they do not communicate; they are dissociated. If they are labelled A and B, then **total dissociation** arises when neither system affects the other:

$$\updownarrow A \rightarrow \bigcirc B \text{ and } \updownarrow B \rightarrow \bigcirc A.$$

We may also define **unilateral dissociation**, in which one system can affect the other but not vice versa. Thus we may say that "B is unilaterally dissociated from A" if changes in A have no direct effect on B, while changes in B *do* have an effect on A:

$$\updownarrow A \rightarrow \bigcirc B, \text{ while } \updownarrow B \rightarrow \updownarrow A.$$

Of course these definitions are idealisations. In practice we may have degrees of dissociation, but this does not diminish the usefulness of the concept.

If we have a strike in a business, then during a period where there is no negotiation we have a situation approximating to a total dissociation between the workers and the management. In a totally autocratic organisation in which the managers order but do not respond to the workforce, we have a unilateral dissociation of the managers from the workforce. If, on the other hand, we have a workforce which does not respond to management, but does affect it a lot, then the workforce may be said to be unilaterally dissociated from the management.

Another approximation to dissociation is provided by a two-party system of government. There seems nothing strange to us in the fact that every so often there can be a complete and sudden change of the principles on which a country is run. Yet, from the point of view of another country, it cannot be so different from dealing with a total character shift in a person. One day foreign policy may be open and friendly, the next it can be protectionist or hostile.

A sensible foreign country will therefore have lines of communication (which are NOT the official channels) to the party which is out of power so that it is not taken by surprise by the change.

The Hilgard experiment can be seen as paralleling just such a communication with a system which was not the one which was primarily in control.

Let us next look at some familiar examples of forms of dissociation in the context of human psychology and psychotherapy.

At one extreme we have cases of split or multiple personality. In such people there seem to be distinct and non-co-operating personalities which can take it in turn to be 'in control'. In extreme cases each personality has its own memories which are quite distinct from those of the other or others. In other cases there can be a one-way flow (unilateral dissociation): one personality has access to the memories of another but not vice versa. Such extreme cases of multiple personality make good reading or films, but seem to be very rare in real life (Ellenberger (1970)).

A second familiar form of dissociation, which is commonly discussed in books on psychotherapy, is one in which a memory of a traumatic event is *repressed*, which is to say, *made* inaccessible to consciousness. Nevertheless the memory can have distinct and often troublesome effects on behaviour and feeling in the present. Here the dynamical pattern is that the two systems - traumatic memory and consciousness - are typically totally dissociated, each having no direct action on the other; but each is competing for control of some third system such as the muscles or the "flight or fight" system activated by perception of a threat.

Let us suppose that a child has been sexually assaulted at the age of four in a garage, and that the memory of this painful experience has been repressed. A typical consequence is that, even when the child has become an adult, it is impossible to enter a garage without experiencing a panic. At such times it is as if the adult personality is replaced by that of a terror-stricken four-year-old again. There is only the most limited communication between the two personalities, since the adult does not have access to the childhood memories which have been repressed, and has little or no control over the child personality. The child, likewise, has very little ability to alter the adult.

A great deal of psychotherapeutic work and Hypnotherapeutic work is concerned with healing such divides. The classic way, going back at least as far as Freud, is of the therapeutic *abreaction*, in which the repressed memories are released - brought to consciousness - together with the associated emotions. This will then often lead to the resolution of the problem. But notice that though it will *often* happen that such a process will work, it is not *necessarily* the case that it will always work. The reason for this, put in a simple way, is the following. Certainly if an adult does *not* know why a child is very upset, then he or she will often not be able to help. But the mere fact that an adult *does* know what is upsetting a child does not guarantee that this is the end of the problem: the adult may still treat the child in the wrong way and make things worse. What is true of the dynamics of a real adult and a real child is likewise true for the dynamics of an adult personality and the "child within".

If we have the pattern that:

$$\uparrow\{\text{Expressed distress; child}\} \rightarrow \uparrow\{\text{Repression; adult}\} \rightarrow$$
$$\downarrow\{\text{Expressed distress; child}\},$$

then it does not matter whether the "adult" system is external or internal: the "child" system will generally be unable to escape the power of this negative feedback loop which acts to prevent any expression of distress. Very often sufferers have, combined with the internal system that reacts to difficulties like an abused child, *also* an adult internal system which acts as if it is wrong ever to complain; so that any complaints from the "child" are responded to by injunctions to the self to "stop being silly," "pull yourself together," etc., which may be effective in the short term but never lead to a resolution of the central problem. The "adult" is forever trying to control the "child", but never quite managing to do it in the long term.

The words, "I do not feel in control," arise in fact very often in the therapeutic context and are a good indicator of some degree of dissociation. The Client may not be in control of their feelings in a certain context, or of their actions in another context, or of their thoughts in yet other contexts. In terms of our present systematic approach we may say that there is a degree of dissociation between that system which is the personality which the Client presents to the therapist and some other subsystem of the body or mind which is seen as a "problem". Some of these cases can come very close to being split personalities, as in the case of severe alcoholics in which the sober and drunk personalities can have little in common, including memories. In others the quasi-autonomous subsystem which is not under control can be comparatively small, as can arise in such problems as incontinence or nail-biting.

One familiar school of analysis of psychodynamics which takes up the above theme and features in an essential way an analysis of a person into large or high-order subsystems is Transactional Analysis (TA), with its division into Child, Parent and Adult (Berne (1964), Harris (1970)). Here the picture is that a particular individual may, in some relationships, continue to behave in many ways like the child he or she once was, while at other times the behaviour can be that of a parent in a relationship. This parental role is commonly based on the role of one of the actual parents. Both parental and childlike roles tend to be rather highly charged emotionally and stereotyped. Finally Transactional Analysis places great weight on a third, or adult, personality which tends to be less emotional and more flexible and helps to resolve conflicts of various kinds in a constructive way.

Although TA deals in this way with subsystems of a person, the primary system of interest is typically a twosome: two individuals who are activating particular personalities in the presence of the other. A typical problem which TA will seek to help is the following. Let C_1 be the childlike persona of the first person and P_2 be the parental persona of the second person. Then problems can arise in cases where an increasing positive feedback loop exists in which the childlike behaviour of 1 prompts or activates complementary parental behaviour in 2, but this in turn activates further childlike behaviour in 1:

$$\uparrow C_1 \rightarrow \uparrow P_2 \rightarrow \uparrow C_1.$$

In the abstract we have no way of telling whether such a loop is beneficial or otherwise - it depends entirely on whether the consequent behaviour is harmful or not. If it is harmful then this positive loop will be seen as a problem and a way needs to be found to eliminate it by changing the pattern of interaction of the systems involved.

A characteristic strategy in the context of TA is to activate an adult personality or system in one or both of the people, which will alter or remove the harmful loop.

Another large-scale analysis of a psychoanalytic nature is of course the Freudian analysis into Id, Ego and Super-ego. These again function like quasi-autonomous subsystems of a person which are often in conflict with each other and may be effectively dissociated.

But we do not need to go into such areas to be aware of the extent to which an individual may have many different personae, each of which may act like a quasi-autonomous system. Many a woman has complained that she is at various times a daughter, a mother, a wife, a mistress, a secretary, a cook, a housekeeper, a taxi-driver, an employee, a nurse, a confidante, a friend, and so on. In most people these different personae are connected reasonably closely, but the divisions between some of them can at times become so strong that it is possible to call them dissociated. Many a professional man, for example, effectively has two personalities - his working one and his domestic one - and there is little contact between them.

As a general point, it seems that some individuals find it relatively easy to compartmentalise their lives. Others find it very difficult. It is possible that some of the facility with which some of the classical Hypnotic phenomena can be produced in an individual are related to such a basic characteristic as this. **In particular note that the fact that Hilgard found such a clear-cut example of dissociation in the particular student does not guarantee that such a phenomenon can be found in everyone.** The fact that Hypnotic processes can at times uncover a dissociated system in certain individuals, or even create one in other people, does not allow us to over-generalise and to deduce that this is the basis of ALL Hypnotic phenomena.

Let us illustrate this principle with our business analogy: many organisations of sufficient complexity naturally subdivide themselves into quasi-autonomous divisions which act independently for nearly all purposes. But this does not allow us to deduce that such departmentalisation can easily or wisely be produced in another company which has always been tightly integrated, with close two-way communication between all sections! Neither should we assume that the whole of business consultancy work is the matter of creating distinct departments.

(As an outsider to the world of management theory it seems to me that the "Management Gurus" (Kennedy (1991)) typically fail to appreciate that different companies not only have different "personalities", but that it is in general better for the general economy if there ARE such different personalities. The Business Gurus, like many a psychological guru, seem all too prone to want every company to adopt the personality which has *their* stamp of approval.)

Finally we have the simplistic analysis into Conscious and Subconscious which is often come across in books on Hypnosis. We meet statements such as, "I will be communicating with your subconscious mind," "Your subconscious knows things that your conscious mind does not and it can signal what it knows by moving a finger," and so on.

This brings us round close to the neo-dissociation theory of Hilgard again, with its two-system analysis. The main point to be made here is that the Conscious/Subconscious terminology creates the limiting idea of there being only *two* large subsystems in the mind. This book should be making it clear that it is far closer to the truth to regard the mind as consisting of an enormous number of subsystems, from the low-level neurological ones up to high-order personae, all of which are interlocked to some extent, and can be dissociated to some extent. If some of these are not accessible to the currently conscious system, then they may be said to be relatively unconscious - an adjective. But to use the words "unconscious" or "subconscious" as nouns gives them a solidity and reality that they do not possess, which is the reason the terms have been avoided as far as possible in this book: though provided that the above point is recognised, they can be used as a shorthand for the large collection of interacting systems involved.

Now that we have taken a wide but brief tour of examples of dissociation, it is time to make an important distinction between two forms of dissociation. These will be termed **weak** and **strong**. Weak dissociation arises if there is simply no reason for association. Strong dissociation arises if there is a natural association, but there is an active principle at work which prevents it.

There are usually certain systems within government which are strongly dissociated from society because of secrecy laws (e.g. the Official Secrets Act in the UK). There are groups of criminals who are actively dissociated from society because there is a death sentence waiting for any individual who lets outsiders know what is going on. We have seen that traumatic memories are often strongly dissociated from conscious awareness, and a man may actively dissociate all thoughts of his mistress at times when he is with his wife. At some times and places it has been the norm that races or classes have been actively or strongly dissociated by strong social forces preventing their sexual or social mixing.

By contrast there is a weak dissociation between the mental systems which deal with inter-departmental memos and with playing ball with a child: there is simply no natural connection, so that neither thought nor activity will ever emerge in the context of the other. Similarly the system of nursery schools and the system of casinos in society have no natural associations: you may change the level of activity of one without affecting the other in the slightest. They are dissociated in the weak sense: no force is needed to ensure that they remain separated.

One way of expressing the nature of a strong dissociation symbolically is as follows. Suppose A and B are two systems where A is naturally associated with B: $\updownarrow A \to \updownarrow B \to \updownarrow A$. But suppose also that there is a third, regulatory, system R which will be activated by any such action of A on B, and will act to eliminate the association. In shorthand this is:

$$\uparrow\{\updownarrow A \to \updownarrow B\} \to \uparrow R \to \downarrow\{\updownarrow A \to \updownarrow B\}, \text{ and/or}$$
$$\uparrow\{\updownarrow B \to \updownarrow A\} \to \uparrow R \to \downarrow\{\updownarrow B \to \updownarrow A\}.$$

We may see this as a negative feedback loop which acts to eliminate any process whereby a change in A can affect B (and/or B affect A). The net effect of this may be reduced to the simplest description of dissociation - $\updownarrow A \to \bigcirc B$ and/or $\updownarrow B \to \bigcirc A$ (total/partial cases) - for some purposes. However, it is important to be clear about when this represents a strong dissociation, involving a third regulatory system, and when it is merely a weak dissociation in which no other system is involved.

In practice the sort of analysis that we have seen in earlier chapters will generally show up such a difference very easily.

There is generally no problem in associating weakly dissociated systems, though it may take continuing effort to keep them together, as there is generally little affinity. On the other hand an attempt to associate strongly dissociated systems is likely to evoke a strong reaction, and will generally be very difficult.

The type of dissociation involved in repression is generally of the strong type, and the literature from Freud onwards contains many references to the ways in which a regulatory system R can act in order to prevent the repressed system from coming into contact with consciousness. If I ask you to associate the idea of a baby with the idea of a lamb there will normally be little problem. If I ask you to retain the association in the context of that lamb being chopped up by the butcher, there is likely to be a strong resistance, because the normal adult has a natural instinctive process which reacts strongly to any suggestion of violence being directed at a baby. An automatic and strong dissociation will therefore arise.

In the context of Hypnosis weak dissociation may well arise spontaneously and with little effort. If the Hypnotist works to establish in the Subject a very unusual pattern of thoughts, feelings and behaviours - even being totally relaxed in a strange room listening without interruption to a stranger's voice is very unusual, after all - then things which are said will have no natural connection or association with other more normal patterns. So that just as thoughts of office memos have no association with playing with a child and so never arise in that context, so the thoughts which arise in response to the Hypnotist's voice need have no association with the rest of life (what the Hypnotist has said is unlikely to be remembered): unless of course a deliberate association has been made.

The creation of a deliberate association is the principle of the post-hypnotic suggestion. As an example suppose that the Hypnotist associates in the mind of the Subject the sound of a piece of music and the idea of marching. This may be done quite strongly if, in accordance with a principle described in earlier chapters, the activity of all other systems is reduced to a minimum. Then the experience of the associating may well be (weakly) dissociated from normal conscious patterns of thought, while the association between the music and the marching remains strong. Then, at any subsequent time, we may find the Subject, even if seemingly normally conscious, reacting to the sound of the piece of music with the suggested marching behaviour, while at the same time the behaviour may not be associated with what happened with the Hypnotist.

There is nothing very strange about this. A similar phenomenon, in systems terms, is as follows. Suppose that in a business some managers are sent on a course to be taught some new technique by training consultants. The rest of the company have no idea what happens on the course. When the managers come back everything may proceed as normal at first, until a particular circumstance comes up which triggers off the newly trained behaviour: the managers then behave in a totally new way, as they have been trained to do.

In a similar way the Hypnotist may tend to isolate one small system or small group of systems and get them to function in a new way in response to imagined circumstances. Later the Subject will behave in a totally normal way until those circumstances arise and then the newly learned behaviour will be evoked in a way which might seem surprising.

In the above examples of weak dissociation the Hypnotist has not established any system designed to keep information about what has happened out of consciousness. It is possible, however, for the Hypnotist deliberately to institute such a system. At its simplest this amounts to introducing the thought, "You will not be able to remember ..." Thus it may be possible to get a Subject to be unable to recall the number "6", so that the exercise of counting the fingers proceeds: "1, 2, 3, 4, 5, .., 7, 8, 9". (There may well be some tell-tale hesitation between 5 and 7 as the regulating system suppresses the knowledge of the missing digit.) With a few Subjects it can be as easy as that. With others the Hypnotist will have to build on some small example of forgetfulness by means of a positive feedback loop, as we have seen in the previous chapter, until the expectation of not being able to remember things suggested by the Hypnotist is confirmed enough by experience to be firmly entrenched.

The dynamics of such a process is not so very different from the way in which many of us make our memories worse by repeating to ourselves, "I have a memory like a sieve!" I have read, but I cannot remember where☺, that to repeat these words is equivalent to punching another hole in the sieve.

Although the dynamics of inducing amnesia in this way shows it to be an example of a strong dissociation, the power of the regulating system is unlikely to be anything like the power of some of the regulators that exist naturally and are involved with repression. These can evoke very strong emotions of terror at the very approach of an association, which effectively prevents any further closeness.

The example from Hilgard quoted at the start of this chapter is of strong dissociation. The auditory system responded to sounds. But the normal pattern whereby the activation of the auditory system activates higher systems was deliberately inhibited by means of the instructor's suggestion. We cannot say exactly where the inhibition took place, but it was at a fairly high level of information processing.

The concepts involved in dissociation throw a very interesting light on a certain basic contrast between Hypnosis as used on the stage and in many simple experimental demonstrations of Hypnotic phenomena on the one hand, and Hypnotherapy on the other.

This contrast may be over-simplified for emphasis by saying that the Hypnotist is generally attempting to dissociate material from consciousness. The Hypnotherapist is generally attempting to **eliminate** such a dissociation.

Let us look at this in a little more detail. Consider what is happening to the Subject on stage. He or she is typically unable to access knowledge that is normally accessible. It may be that the number "6" has disappeared. It may be that a normal ability to control behaviour is gone. Thus if there is a post-hypnotic suggestion to rush about crying "Fire!" whenever a certain piece of music is played, and no recall of the origin of this response in the Hypnotist's words, there is some dissociation. If Hypnotic techniques are used to induce a finger levitation, then the Subject can sense that the movement has nothing to do with the normal voluntary mechanisms for lifting a finger, and there seems no conscious control of the systems which *are* involved in the movement. This again indicates a dissociation, albeit a mild one.

By contrast, the Hypnotherapist is typically faced with a problem in which a Client or Patient is saying, "I have no control over ... ". And this, as has been noted, is very commonly because of a dissociation which has arisen between two (or more) subsystems. The Hypnotherapist (or Psychotherapist) will then typically be acting to *reduce* the dissociation, as we have seen. Efforts will be made to allow repressed material into consciousness; or to allow the conscious mind again to control some function that has become dissociated.

In terms of one of our analogies, the Stage Hypnotist can be seen as showing what fun it can be to replace the personnel of some department of a large firm with stooges who deliberately act in a weird way, and no longer do what is expected of them. (The department becomes unilaterally dissociated.) It would be fun if professional television engineers were replaced by men who had been told to exchange all footage showing the Prime Minister with clips of donkeys, for example.

The Hypnotherapist, by contrast, is dealing with a firm in which some department has become dissociated (perhaps they are disaffected for some reason) and generally works to re-establish good communication and co-operation between that department and others: i.e. the dissociation is reduced.

We have seen then that Hypnotists tend to create dissociations and Hypnotherapists tend to eliminate them. But this distinction is not absolute and there *are* some cases in which Hypnotherapy involves procedures more like those of simple Hypnosis, and may create a system dissociated from consciousness. But such a procedure should be performed with great discretion, because it is analogous to introducing a new species into an ecosystem: if there is a long-term effect it can so easily be worse rather than better.

For example, suppose the problem is caused by a dissociated system which is activating some habit or symptom such as smoking, a nervous stomach, anxiety attacks, etc. Now a simplistic Hypnotic treatment is to "suggest" that these things go away when the Subject's receptivity to new ideas has first been enhanced by standard techniques mentioned in earlier chapters. This amounts to creating a new subsystem in the mind which is partially or completely dissociated and which is designed to act on the symptomatic system in order to remove the symptom. For a while this may work. But since nothing has been done about the original dissociated system, we now have *two* such subliminal systems, both acting on the symptomatic system. The outcome is unpredictable at best. At worst it may create quite undue internal tension and stress.

I once had as a Client a professional woman who wanted help with her blushing. She refused to allow any deeper analysis of *why* she was blushing, and I made the mistake of agreeing to act directly on the symptom. All went well at first; I set up internal systems of thought to suppress the blushing and it stopped for a week or so. Then it came back with a vengeance: worse than before. This may be seen as an example in which the new system seemed effective at first but was then completely overwhelmed by the old.

This is not untypical of what can easily happen if you attempt to suppress the activity of any biological system by force. An initial success is very often followed by a strong rebound, as many a father of a teenage son has found to his cost. Some further thoughts on this principle are in the previous chapter.

Many people, after having watched a presentation of entertainment Hypnosis, come for Hypnotherapy with the idea that it will be very easy to make the requisite changes, but they have often failed to grasp the essential difference between creating a new subsystem where there was none before, and creating one in opposition to one that is already active and entrenched. Any businessman will tell you that there is a big difference between expanding into a town where there is no competition and one where there has been a similar business running for years. In the latter case there may be no problem *at first*, but rivalries will soon start to take their toll, and the entrenched business has many advantages on its side: it knows the customers so much better.

A competent Hypnotherapist will be attempting to make a permanent change, which means that any new subsystem of thought or behaviour must harmonise with existing ones well enough to integrate properly and stay permanently. We have already seen in earlier chapters how a thorough analysis of the dynamics of the situation helps enormously with this task. These show how far from the truth it can be to assume that problems can be solved simply by creating a (possibly dissociated) subsystem directly to control the symptom.

Another analogy for certain Hypnotic procedures which can throw light on the above distinction is that of a skin or organ transplant. If a surgeon replaces a patient's heart, he is replacing a particular system of the body. There was a time when this was thought to be a success if the new heart continued to beat and the patient survived the operation. The fact that death followed within weeks or months was under-emphasised.

Of course it later became apparent that a major cause of such deaths was the rejection of the new organ by the body's defence or immune system.

The procedures of Hypnosis are nothing like as drastic in their consequences, but there are certain similarities. A Hypnotist who establishes a new mental system in a person's mind is doing something analogous to transplanting an organ. For a while it may well continue to function efficiently. But it is generally the case that we have mental processes which act like the immune system in that they reject alien material: material which we do not recognise as "self". If these are working efficiently there will come a time when the new way of acting or thinking will seem alien or uncomfortable, and a little later the alien systems will probably be simply eliminated. We may see such a process happening rather naturally during the teenage years when habits of thought and behaviour which have been passed on to the child by the parents are rejected by the strengthening personality of the adolescent.

Just as there are people whose immune system is weak, so there are people whose ability to reject alien ideas is weak.

I once had a Client, a young woman, who had been to another Hypnotherapist who had, among other things, given her suggestions for "confidence". She had internalised these suggestions, but in rather a strange way. It made her feel as if she were wearing a man's coat - in fact the Hypnotherapist's coat! - which was heavy, large and uncomfortable. In short all the signs were that the subsystem he had created in her was alien to her. (A middle-aged man's sense of confidence will generally be based on quite different things from that of a shy woman in her early twenties.) She had not had the strength when I saw her to cast off that suggestion by herself, but clearly that was what was needed.

Now surgeons have learnt two ways of increasing the success rate of organ transplant. One is to use an organ which is not recognised by the immune system as alien - in the simpler case of blood transfusion this means getting the blood group right - and the other is artificially to reduce the activity of the immune system while the organ is being accepted.

Those concerned, as we are, with transplanting subsystems of mental activity, likewise find that we are most successful if the subsystems harmonise with the existing very large network of systems, and if we reduce, to begin with, the mind's normal and healthy tendency to reject alien material. This latter process is what we have discussed in an earlier chapter under the name of increasing rapport.

The other objective - of attempting to harmonise the suggestions with the personality of the Subject - is not one which can easily be taught. It is NOT easy for us to understand the very different way others' minds work. The average person gives advice on the basis of what they would do in the same situation. A husband who is a golf fanatic will suggest to his wife, suffering from post-natal depression, that what she needs to shake herself out of it is a good game of golf. The woman whose marriage is on the rocks will readily advise her best friend to leave *her* husband. In Gerald Durrell's book *My Family and Other Animals* each of the children gave their mother birthday presents which were things that *they* liked, but were of no use to her.

It takes a lot of listening to other people, and a lot of trying to understand *how* they think, before one becomes good at this side of the job. I *think* I have done well at various times in establishing an understanding of how a modern Druid, and a modern Buddhist and Hindu and Moslem think, so that I can help them to make the changes that they wish to make, but it is probable that, other things being equal, the job could have been done better by someone who shared their world-views.

One moral the prospective Client may draw from this is that in the sphere of Hypnotherapy you should be particularly careful to establish that the therapist listens, and shows strong signs of knowing as a result how *you* think and feel. Otherwise there is a very strong chance that any transplanted ideas will be alien to you. If this happens you will either reject them in a short time, making the whole exercise a waste, or you may end up with a dissociated system that you may well need further help in getting rid of, like the woman with the overcoat!

We may well ask the question, "Why should it *ever* be necessary for a Hypnotherapist to *create* a subsystem which is dissociated from consciousness?" Or to put it another way, "Why should it ever be better for a Client to be unable to remember what it is that the Hypnotherapist has suggested?" or, again, "Why should it ever be necessary for a Managing Director to be strongly excluded from knowing how some of his staff are being retrained?"

If it *is* thought to be necessary, then we may generally presume that the Client would not consciously choose to accept the idea. But this provides *prima facie* evidence that there is a bad mismatch between the new idea and the existing personality, which must make us suspect that it has been badly chosen.

The argument *in favour* of creating subsystems dissociated from consciousness is that IF we know for a fact that the whole being will be the better for the introduction of a new pattern of behaviour, feeling or thought, BUT that this new pattern will, as in the case of an organ transplant, need protecting for a while against a natural rejection, THEN it is worth giving it that immunity by the artificial protection that dissociation gives it while it becomes established.

My personal feeling is that there are very few therapists who are wise enough to be able to be certain of the long-term consequences of a change of this nature and so the procedure of introducing a dissociated system should be used rarely and with great discretion.

Finally notice that the process of creating a subsystem dissociated from consciousness is not the same as creating distinct subsystems. It may well be that in a given small business both correspondence and accounts are handled by the same people in the same department. As the business grows it may well be advantageous to separate the two functions into two different departments. In this way distinct subsystems have been created. If there is no communication between the departments then they will *also* be (weakly) dissociated from each other. But more normally they will continue to interact in appropriate ways, and so they will be distinct but not dissociated from each other. But in either case it is essential that they should not be dissociated from higher managerial levels.

In the same way it can be useful or necessary with certain Clients to enable them to *separate* certain mental functions. For example some phobic reactions arise because a certain situation is *associated* with a certain frightening event in the past. If, for example, a person has had a car crash which involved a lorry, then subsequently all lorries can arouse a strong feeling of fear. Clearly we need to work towards dissociating the fear from a recognition of lorries. In a compact form, we have:

$\uparrow\{\text{perception of a lorry}\} \rightarrow \uparrow\{\text{fear}\}$

and we will need to work towards:

$\uparrow\{\text{perception of a lorry}\} \rightarrow \bigcirc\{\text{fear}\}$

But there is no reason why this change should be achieved in a way which suppresses conscious awareness of the process.

The Hypnotist, again by contrast, is often *creating* strange associations, such as one between a piece of music and an unusual behaviour.

It may help to summarise these ideas by saying that on the whole the Hypnotherapist is more likely to encourage *vertical* association, though he or she may encourage *lateral* dissociations, while the Hypnotist is more likely to be doing the reverse.

SUMMARY

In this chapter we have been considering various aspects of the notion of dissociated systems.

It is clear that **any** complex organic system will have subsystems, and the question then arises naturally within our framework of whether any two are dynamically connected or not. In earlier chapters the emphasis has been on the cases in which two systems are connected. In this chapter the interest has been focused on when two are NOT. In such a case we are dealing with *dissociated* systems.

We have seen that dissociation may be complete or unilateral, and weak or strong. The latter distinction, in particular, is dynamically very important. In the weak case the systems do not associate because there is no reason for it. In the latter they are actively prevented from associating.

A particularly useful distinction between Hypnosis and Hypnotherapy arises out of these ideas. This is that Hypnotists tend to aim to create dissociation between a new system and existing conscious systems. Hypnotherapists tend to work in a precisely opposite direction and to eliminate such dissociations.

This has led to an analogy between the introduction of a new mental subsystem into a Client and an organ transplant. The key consideration is then whether it will be accepted or rejected.

CHAPTER 18

Indirect Questions

A THEME WHICH has run through this book is the asking of appropriate questions. In Part B there were many examples given of the types of questions that might be asked of a Client during the process of diagnosis. We have seen the repeated use of the questions, "And what is the resultant of *that*?" and, "And what is the cause of *that*?" We have seen the problem of determining the best form of intervention reduced to the repeated asking of four questions.

It will be apparent by now that accurate Hypnotherapy depends on obtaining the answers to many questions, at many different levels.

The questions are there to help us to think clearly. At times the answers are obtained by directly asking the Client. But we have already seen that a slightly indirect approach is more useful. In this chapter we are going to dwell on this matter of indirect answers, and in particular on obtaining answers which *cannot* be obtained by asking the Client directly, *because the answers are not consciously known*. In terms of the language of the previous chapter, we may say that the information is dissociated from conscious mental processes.

Let us begin with an example which might arise if we were exploring resultants of a change. Suppose we want to know how it would make a person *feel*. Now there are people who can come out with a quick response if asked, but for many others there is no direct answer. So how can we proceed?

Our approach to Hypnotherapy can help us to analyse the situation in the following way. The primary systems of interest are the verbal (V) and the emotional (E). If we were getting an accurate answer to our question then the following processes would be strong:

$$\uparrow V \rightarrow \uparrow E,$$

so that the verbally suggested thought of the change would lead at once to an arousal of the consequent feelings, and:

$$\uparrow E \rightarrow \uparrow V,$$

so that these feelings would then be able to create a recognition of themselves in the verbal mind, so that they could be reported.

If verbal answers are not being obtained, then there is a failure of one or both of these processes. (In terms of the definitions in the chapter on Dissociation, there is a unilateral or total dissociation between the two systems.)

Now we have seen in the chapter on "inductions" that a Hypnotherapist has quite clear ways of establishing whether or not the above processes can be expected to proceed easily or with difficulty.

Two different pictures may therefore emerge. It may be that the above chains are normally weak, or it may be that they are normally strong, but for some reason are weak in the particular case being considered. (Usually this distinction is the distinction between weak and strong dissociation.) The difference is often of vital importance, for in the latter case the reason can throw a lot of light on the matter in hand.

Let us be more concrete and consider a specific instance of finding the answer to a question that cannot be answered in response to a direct question. We will suppose that a woman in her thirties is unhappy because she has never been able to find a satisfactory husband for some reason. In exploring this problem we will naturally be asking ourselves, in line with the analysis of Chapter 12, "What would the consequence of marriage be?" In a case like this the emotional response is by far the most important. And we will suppose that the woman finds it rather difficult to answer the question in that she reports that she seems to want to get married, but in practice whenever things seem to be moving in that direction, something always seems to go wrong.

A characteristic approach of Hypnotherapy to this situation is the following. It is recognised that the internal visual system is usually more directly connected to the emotional system than is consciousness and so steps will be taken to activate it. These steps are those which are common to a lot of Hypnotic procedures: a systematic reduction in activity of other functions, so that the Client is sitting or lying, comfortable and relaxed, with closed eyes and no distractions and with mind focused with no strain on the visual imagination. We might then, slowly and gently, get the Client to start to unfold, in her imagination, pictures relating to being married, in response to gentle guidance by the Hypnotherapist.

There is no way of knowing in advance what these pictures will be, of course, and it is very unlikely that any two cases will be the same. If we had no evidence to guide us we might conjecture that there might be some hidden fear of sex, or of having children or some generalised inadequacy - the possibilities are endless. And any of these *might* arise in a particular case. **It is the absence of any such specific theories of the origin of problems that is one of the hallmarks of scientific Hypnotherapy. We don't conjecture: we find out.** But to give an idea of how things might proceed I will summarise one case of mine.

This woman soon started to report pictures of a happy house, with plenty of evidence of young children around. There was a very lived-in kitchen and a garden full of swings and toys. The atmosphere was relaxed and domestic. In fact everything went well until we reached the master bedroom, and there the problem turned out to be NOT what you might be anticipating. The problem was that the wardrobe was filled with a man's formal suits! She reported a very strong aversion to these.

So there, in a nutshell, we may see her dilemma. She was drawn to a certain kind of relaxed wife-style. But this coexisted with a preconception that a husband had to be suited and formal, which she did not like at all.

At that stage a Hypnotherapist may instantly move on to the next stage in therapy, which is to change things. In this case the problem system is the limiting belief about husbands, and a suitable change can be promoted by inviting the Client to do something about those clothes in the wardrobe if she chooses. In this particular case it took her very little time indeed to throw out all those horrible stiff suits, and to replace them with jeans, jumpers and so on. She was able to report that this gave her great satisfaction. It was even more satisfactory when she was reporting within months that she had found a wonderful man, and later that they were to get married, and later that the house they were living in was filled with the same feeling and light that she had imagined in her vision, and later that she was pregnant, and later a mother. Her husband does not wear suits!

In this example, then, we have seen one of the major techniques whereby the Hypnotherapist will find answers to questions that cannot be answered directly by the verbal mind. The pattern is simply that if:

$$\uparrow E \rightarrow \bigcirc V,$$

i.e. we cannot get information about a feeling directly to the verbal mind, then we can often proceed indirectly via the imagination:

$$\uparrow E \rightarrow \uparrow I \rightarrow \uparrow V.$$

The idea of obtaining information about feelings via the visual imagination goes back at least as far as Freud, and his interpretation of dreams. But the more modern practice is not to wait in a hit or miss way for a dream to reveal something, but instead gently to guide the imagination towards the required area.

This is far more informative than dream analysis, partly because it allows far more questions to be asked regarding the matters of interest, so that it becomes possible to sift out the important from the irrelevant; but there is also so much more time. A recalled dream may have taken up only a few minutes, while a guided daydream can easily run for ten times that.

In the above case we have an example also of the reverse process:

$$\uparrow V \rightarrow \uparrow I \rightarrow \uparrow E,$$

i.e. instead of the Hypnotherapist attempting to activate feelings in the Client by means of simple words, he is instead talking only about the images, and allowing them to evoke the corresponding feelings.

Such an approach is of course by no means unique to Hypnotherapists. Film-makers and advertising executives pour billions of pounds down the same channel. They provide images whose success is primarily measured by the extent to which they evoke feelings.

But at this stage we are considering primarily the reverse process: not of changing the Client's deeper thoughts or feelings, but of finding out about them. The case quoted above, however, shows that a very precise idea of what the problem is, presented as an image, allows an intervention to be equally precise, elegant and ecologically sound.

Here is another example of the gently guided daydream to illustrate the principle. This time it is of a young man who was, for some reason, not finding a girlfriend. When images started to come to his mind they were of walking down a rather arid valley. Every so often he would meet an older man who would advise him of the dangers of leaving the valley. But he found nothing of interest in it.

This image gives an insight into the probable cause of his predicament, which is that he has been discouraged by his father or other older men from involvement with girls.

The same image was then used to improve matters by suggesting that it might be worth seeing for himself what dangers lay outside the valley. He climbed the hill out of it; walked for some time through a very lifeless region, and then came to fertile farmland on which he found a farm where - surprise! - there was a very attractive daughter with whom he was soon on very good terms.

His discovery of this for himself was possibly one of the more effective ways of creating a change in his attitude to his situation.

In all such explorations notice that the tone of the Hypnotherapist is totally non-forcing and typically of the form, "I wonder if you would like to ... ?" or "I wonder what would happen if ... ?" That is, questions are being asked, but of a very indirect and open kind. It is important that he or she should not interfere too strongly, or the thing which is looked for will be destroyed or missed. This aspect of our work is as unlike the strong, commanding, authoritative Svengali image as possible. We tread as softly as a butterfly on the flowers of which dreams are made.

The above method is the richest and probably the most powerful strategy which is used in Hypnotherapy to obtain answers which are not readily available by direct questioning. The second most common method involves the activation not of the visual system (V) but of the muscular system (M). So if S is some system for which it is impossible to establish the process:

$$\uparrow S \rightarrow \uparrow V,$$

then instead we establish:

$$\uparrow S \rightarrow \uparrow M.$$

The most common response chosen is probably a finger movement, identical to the small movements that arise at the beginning of a hand levitation process. It might be established, for example, that if the answer to a question is "Yes", then a finger on the right hand will move, while if it is "No", then a finger of the left will move. This is sometimes called Ideo-Motor Signalling (IMS).

The problem with such a method is that it is comparatively uninformative, especially if we do not hit on the right question. It is also very slow. A single Ideo-Motor response may easily take more than a minute.

There is one instance in which this particular method can be more informative and faster, which is if it becomes possible to allow S to activate the system of handwriting. This phenomenon goes by the name of Automatic Writing. In some individuals it is possible for the hand to be writing something (often out of view of the Subject) which is making sense, but of which the Subject seems to have no conscious awareness. This is most likely to be possible if there is some high-order subsystem of the mind which has become disconnected from the normal system of consciousness - a phenomenon which is dealt with in more detail in the chapter on Dissociation.

Mechanisms which could facilitate the above methods are the Ouija board, which is like automatic writing in that it can, in time, produce sentences, or a divining rod or a pendulum which, like finger levitation, can produce "Yes" or "No" answers. A divining rod is designed so that a small muscular movement is amplified, and a pendulum uses a dynamic form of the same principle: it takes imperceptible movements of the hand to change a side-to-side movement ("No") to a to-and-fro movement ("Yes"). These do not seem to be in common use in modern Hypnotherapy, probably because those who use IMS find that the amplification of the response which Hypnotic techniques provide makes such artificial amplification unnecessary.

If we are interested in knowing more about the emotional system, however, it makes much more sense to activate NOT a muscular response, but a response which is naturally associated with emotional arousal. Even without making any effort in this direction it is often easy for the therapist to notice rapid breathing, a slight smile or tears as easy pointers to the current emotions. In most cases, of course, the Subject is aware of these and they are interpreted correctly. If, on the other hand, the Subject gives a verbal statement about his or her feelings which is NOT what the signs indicate, then there is a strong presumption that the emotions and the verbal mind are disconnected to a significant extent: a situation which is usually of great significance in therapy.

We may extend this principle by using Hypnotic techniques - suggestion may be enough - to amplify such signs still further. For example we might say, "As you think about what I will be saying, your body will respond quite freely. You need not feel any distress but if your body wants to cry, it will cry freely. You need not feel any anger, but your face or body may show it." Strangely, although Ideo-*Motor* signalling is a phrase often encountered in the literature on Hypnotherapy, I do not recall meeting the phrase Ideo-*Emotive* or Ideo-*Affective* signalling. Consequently I presume that the use of the above device is rare, despite the fact that it can be very useful. I suspect that the reason for the rarity is the absence of a sufficient clarity of thought on what are our goals and our means: a clarity which I believe that a systems approach enhances.

The value of noting emotional reactions is vouched for by those practitioners who make use of an electronic amplifier of emotion. It is a fact that emotional arousal tends to produce a small increase in the production of the sweat glands. If the arousal is intense then the sweat may actually be seen, but for more moderate arousals it is only enough slightly to moisten the skin with salty water. Since this conducts electricity quite well its presence can be detected by measuring how easily a small current of electricity can flow between two points on the skin. A machine which does this is called an Electric Skin Resistance meter. Such machines are often used in the context of biofeedback. Another name for them is Lie Detectors, where it is supposed that they will detect a lie because the liar will be slightly more stressed and aroused when speaking the lie than when telling the truth.

The weakness of the machines is that they cannot distinguish clearly between different *forms* of emotion, but they can nevertheless be useful in practice as a means of detecting emotional activity which is not great enough to affect the verbal mind.

In this context we should note that one of the more useful detectors and amplifiers of feelings is the human being! There are some people who seem to be extraordinarily sensitive to the moods of others. I presume that they are able to pick up small cues from movements, tone of voice, expression and possibly even smell (as animals do) and integrate them into an accurate representation of the other person's emotion at that moment. The representation will often take the form of feeling the same emotion as the other person.

As an example of this, in a small way, I can cite something from my own experience which also leads to a general principle.

Early on in practice I noticed that with some Clients, and for no obvious reason, I was feeling nervous: with me this was signalled primarily by a shakiness in the voice. This could have grown into a considerable problem for me had I not considered the possibility that I was simply feeling the other person's emotion. I tested this by asking, "How are you feeling at present?" On each occasion the answer was, "Very nervous." As I then calmed the Client down, the feeling in me went also.

The general principle is that, for many Clients, there may often be times in which they think that *they* are nervous, when in fact it is the people around them who are nervous, and they are simply picking up the mood.

I have a daydream that in an ideal world there would be a class of therapists who would be termed Empathists. They would have learned to develop an innate skill in assessing the feelings of others in the above ways into a consistent and accurate faculty. Working alone, such an individual is in danger of being swamped by the emotions which are being detected, which can reduce the ability to help. The Empathist would therefore act as a part of a team in which her (or his) role is purely passive - reporting on the feelings of the Client or patient - while others, less able to empathise themselves, would take the lead in directing change while all the time being advised by the team Empathist of how things were going.

Returning now to the general theme of obtaining answers to questions which are hidden from consciousness, we will turn to the phenomenon quoted at the start of the last chapter in which a blind student demonstrated a total dissociation between two parts of himself, each of which was independent of the other, but each of which could take turns in activating the vocal system without any evidence of one going via a different channel, such as the visual. IF we can arrange this, then it is probably the most informative way of getting out hidden information. I have not put it at the top of the list because it does not seem to be an option which is readily available in most people. I seldom find it in my own practice and neither do I read many cases in which it arises. But it needs to be mentioned for completeness.

Before ending this chapter there are some warnings that need to be made.

If you question a nice child, it will tend to give the answer that it thinks is expected. And afterwards it will often believe the answer it has given. Furthermore it is a characteristic of many Clients that the common process of developing rapport will lead to a reactivation of this childlike behaviour pattern. Consequently in the conditions under which the techniques of this chapter are used it becomes very easy indeed in some individuals for the responses to be VERY STRONGLY INFLUENCED by what the therapist wants or expects. Such expectations can easily be expressed by tone of voice or subtle use of words.

In the example of the husband's wardrobe, if I say, "Are the suits nice?" in a tone of slight incredulity, it will suggest the answer "No". If the tone is warm it will suggest the answer "Yes". The professional Hypnotherapist should, as a result of his or her training, be acutely aware of these possibilities, and **guard against them by maintaining a totally open and non-judgmental attitude to all that is said in such conditions, as far as possible.**

How does one know if the Subject is easily influenced in this way? It is usually quite easy. One may test in small innocuous ways. I may say, "This garden that you are in seems a nice place; it needs only a bird-bath to complete it." If the Subject then notices the bird-bath, then I note a strong response to suggestion. If there is no bird-bath, then there is a presumption that there is a weak response, though in either case further examples should be used before jumping to a conclusion.

It is this possibility of a strong response to the suggestion of the therapist which, to my mind, throws doubt on the reported results of many people who seem to obtain amazing results of the type in which they specialise and which they **expect**. There are men who specialise in recovering lost memories of abduction by aliens from Unidentified Flying Objects. There are men who specialise in recovering lost memories of early sexual abuse. There are men who specialise in finding Oedipal complexes. There are men who specialise in finding universal archetypes. There are men who specialise in finding memories of "past lives". There are men who specialise in finding spirit possession. There are men who specialise in finding memories of a birth trauma.

I am not making any statement about whether or not any one of these phenomena is true *in a particular case*. What I am saying is that I believe that the *amazing number of cases* each finds confirming his own ideas is a result of the power of suggestion in at least a preponderance of such cases. When one has worked as a Hypnotherapist one should know how easy it can be with some people to reactivate the open-mindedness of a child to all manner of things. It is usually impossible to persuade the men referred to above that there is any error in their technique, and they are often honest and sincere men. But they seem uniformly unaware of the extent to which ideas and expectations may be communicated by quite subtle cues and be uncritically accepted when the normal mental processes of analysis and resistance are eliminated: a fact which should be obvious to all practising Hypnotists and Hypnotherapists.

There was a time when police forces placed a lot of confidence in the power of Hypnosis to "bring back" forgotten memories which might help them in a case. But the suggestiveness that we are discussing here produced too many "false memories" as a result of the subtle pressure to remember, and so Hypnosis is now used far less in a forensic way.

It is rare to find people reporting sightings of fairies these days. But because I know the extent to which certain people can readily be induced truly to believe that they are seeing things that are not there - any competent Stage Hypnotist will demonstrate this regularly - I know that many people could easily be induced to see fairies again. Or demons. Or to "remember" being abused. Or to experience pains corresponding to an illness they have read about, but which all the tests prove that they have not got.

All such things I will accept as true statements of the person's beliefs and subjective assessments of his or her experiences. (This is what the philosopher Dennet (1991) terms a heterophenomenological position.) But I do not have to accept them as true statements about the world external to themselves without substantially greater evidence.

SUMMARY

In this chapter we have looked briefly at the fact that it is not always possible to find the answers to our questions about the activity of various systems by directly interrogating the verbal mind. One of the strengths of the discipline of Hypnotherapy is that it is familiar with a number of techniques for bypassing the verbal mind and, by amplifying the action of certain other systems, can find the answers to its questions in other ways.

The most informative alternative system is that of the imagination, though the disadvantage of this is that there still has to be a verbal account of what is being seen. The alternatives are the motor system and aspects of the emotional systems, which can bypass the verbal mind altogether, but at the price of being low in information capacity.

However it is important to realise the extent to which the Subject may produce answers which are in line with those expected by the therapist, and that steps be taken to guard against the distortions which can result.

CHAPTER 19

Experimental Hypnotherapy

IN THIS CHAPTER a brief look will be taken at experimental Hypnotherapy from the perspective of the systems approach of this book.

There is something of a chasm between experimentalists and practitioners in the fields of Hypnosis and Hypnotherapy. This can be seen as being a result of the fact that they tend to be asking different classes of questions. The latter are asking, "How can I create a change in this particular person?" The former are asking, "How can we expect a particular process to affect people in general?"

The experimentalist therefore typically works with a particular "induction procedure" - often tape-recorded - which he or she will apply to a group of people, often those suffering with a particular symptom; note the results; and deduce from them whether or not "Hypnosis has been effective" with a particular problem.

To the Clinical Hypnotist or Hypnotherapist, such a procedure seems of very limited value because his or her clinical judgement would often lead to the conclusion that a particular Hypnotic procedure should NOT have been used for many of the individuals, where it would be anticipated to be of little use, and should instead be replaced by a different one.

Furthermore the therapist would say, in the language of this book, "One of my most valuable tools in Hypnosis is the establishing of positive feedback loops both within the patient and between us in order to intensify the effects I am aiming for. This requires correct timing and tuning to the Subject's personality, so that it can be synchronised with the rate at which things happen in the Subject and can be presented in a language and a way which suits the Subject best. All of this is quite simply ignored by the experimentalist's approach."

The argument on the experimentalist's side is quite simply, "But your subjective assessment of the efficacy of treatment is not a good enough basis for the subject. The history of medicine is full of procedures and potions which were claimed to be effective, but careful examination has found that they give no more than a placebo response. We need to establish a hard, factual and scientific basis for your work if it is to be accepted. We are following the standard procedure in such cases."

If we look at this position from a more general perspective we see the following picture. The experimentalist is working within a very simple cause and effect paradigm. The assumption is that we are testing whether a process P will lead to a reduction in a symptom S, which we may represent as:

$$\uparrow P \rightarrow \downarrow S \ ?$$

This is the model used for testing drugs, where P is the appropriate application of the drug.

Now the problem for medical science is that the human body is a very complex system. The connection between the application of a drug and a change in the symptom is therefore not generally a direct one. The drug P may affect one particular system of the body directly, and then this affects a third, and so on through a chain until we get to the symptom. As a further complication, many of the intermediate systems are regulated by negative feedback loops which ensure that there is little long-term change. On top of all that complexity there is the problem that our internal biochemistry varies from individual to individual.

The great advances in medicine this century can be seen to be a result of very careful analysis of the systems most involved in a specific illness and then of designing a drug which will act *as directly as possible* on the system involved. Antibiotics were a great advance because they acted directly on a wide range of infecting organisms. The manufacture of insulin for diabetics, of Factors VIII or IX for haemophiliacs, of the H_2 blockers (e.g. Zantac) which block the acid-producing effect of histamine on the stomach lining for sufferers from stomach ulcers are further notable examples.

These advances are real. They represent a real increase in knowledge and power. Compared with present-day medicine, medicine of a hundred years ago was severely limited in both its understanding and resources.

Medical knowledge has been built on a painstaking analysis of **component processes**. So, I argue, should Hypnotherapy, *mutatis mutandis*.

From this viewpoint the statement, "He is under Hypnosis" seems about as useful as, "He is under Medication". We would immediately ask: WHAT medication? Aspirin? Warfarin? Zantac? Arsenic? Equally we would like to know what Hypnotic processes are being used and how have they been seen to affect what systems.

Of course experimentalists in the field of medicine DO, when a new treatment has been proposed, test its efficacy by means of asking questions of the form: "Does ↑(Treatment) → ↓(Symptom)? But more and more of the experimental side of medicine is devoted simply to asking the key questions ? → ⬦{System} → ?: what are the causes and resultants of any changes in relevant physiological systems? Relief from Alzheimer's disease, for example, is very unlikely to come from a random testing of all known materials. Instead it will come as a result of finding out first, the nature of the process responsible for the destruction of the nervous tissue in the brain which is associated with the disease (my guess being a misdirection of an immune response) and second, of narrowing the search to the discovery of ways of altering or preventing that process.

The liberating implication of this approach for experimental Hypnotherapists, I suggest, is that instead of being limited by the strait-jacket of the idea that the primary process of change is something ill-defined called "being Hypnotised", the emphasis should be on analysing the efficacy of the *component* processes used within Hypnosis.

For example, it is commonly held by practitioners that visualisation is always a better way of getting through to other subsystems of the mind than is verbal direction. My experience suggests that this is an unwarranted generalisation. Even as I am writing this I have just seen a Client who had one of the poorest abilities to visualise that I have ever come across, and yet has performed enormously well on a wide variety of characteristic Hypnotic responses such as dissociation, a seeming ability to regress to "past lives" and so on. However this is just one counter-example, and it may well be that the proposition is generally true in the population. It would be useful to have some extensive studies to establish whether, or under what conditions, this is so.

Another useful experimental exercise would be to focus specifically on the connection between visualisation and another specific subsystem. We might then ask, "Is it true, as is often assumed, that in a particular individual the action of the imaginative system on the other system is stronger *if all other systems are reduced in activity*?"

This is a plausible assumption, which underlies the practice of relaxation and calming that so often accompanies Hypnotherapy. But it should be confirmed by experiment. Notice that we would be avoiding the tendentious question, "Is the subject Hypnotised?", which is very hard meaningfully to answer, and instead be able to use some more precise definitions of when certain key systems are relatively inactive. There could at least be reference to the extent to which the heart rate dropped and the skin resistance increased, and to the immobility of the limbs, face and so on, to establish some criteria other than the vague, "The Subject was Hypnotised". It would be even better if one of the brain-scanning systems were to be used to establish the level of activity in various areas of the brain which are accompanied by certain Hypnotic processes.

The main thrust of the above is the tried and tested principle that science should **AVOID wherever possible concepts which cannot be backed up by measurement**. The concept of "being hypnotised" is so difficult to define or measure that it provides the poorest possible scientific foundation for further work. The concept of changes in activation of a system is by contrast very clear and crisp. (A later chapter dealing with the concept makes it yet more scientifically precise.)

Further experiments could focus on the feedback loops which have been introduced as being quite central to many Hypnotic phenomena. For example, I have stated as a common experience that finger levitation proceeds rapidly only after some initial levitation has been perceived, because there is a presumed feedback loop whereby an expectation of lifting is greatly reinforced by the feeling of some lifting. The experimentalist who already has some experience of bio-feedback equipment may well find that he or she can make some valuable contributions to validating or invalidating this idea. For example we might proceed as follows.

The Subject could be told that finger levitation is always preceded by a certain involuntary response which he or she will be unable to detect, but which will be picked up by a machine and presented in the form of a whistle or pointer moving. We could then examine whether the levitation is quicker if a totally spurious response by the machine is introduced by the experimenter. I would predict that this *apparent* feedback would enhance the Subject's expectation that levitation would happen and therefore serve to initiate the loop.

As yet another specific inquiry: I have often thought that feedback loops are strongest if emotional arousal is high. If this were true then it would follow that many changes would be easier to make if emotional arousal were high. This certainly seems a principle used in evangelical meetings, and it was used by Mesmer at the height of his fame. But it would be good to have more experimental data on it. Does the *nature* of the emotion have any bearing on it?

Again, if the intention were to be to assess the power of Hypnotic techniques to help with physical illnesses, the experiments of real value would seem to me to be those which throw light on the actual systems involved. It is one thing to say lightly, "Saturate the subconscious with thoughts of returning health and it will happen." It is another to establish that Hypnotic techniques can actually change measurably the level of certain antibodies: as has actually been done (Walker et al. (1993)). Better still would be to establish the pathway between the initial thought and the immune system, and therefore the conditions under which such a response could be produced more reliably, and for a greater proportion of people.

Now I am sure that some of this approach is already implicit in much experimental work. The experiments suggested are close to the questions asked in mainstream experimental psychology. The advantage of using the systems paradigm as a framework for experiments relating to Hypnotic phenomena is that the reasoning and results can be made far more explicit and scientific, with advantages all around.

It is my contention that clear and valuable experiments, like clear thought, can only proceed usefully with the help of a clear language and a clear conceptual structure. This book is an attempt to provide just such a structure.

SUMMARY

If Experimental Hypnotherapy were to be based on the theoretical framework suggested in this book, we would find the following innovations.

1. There would no longer appear in the accounts of experiments, "The Subjects were Hypnotised", but rather statements more on the lines of, "Systems a,b,c... were activated, while systems p,q,r... were inactivated, as assessed by criteria x,y,z... As a result it was found that the response of system X to system Y was changed in the following ways: ..."

2. Far more experiments would be made on specific *component* processes involved in Hypnosis and Hypnotherapy. In this way the subject would become more like modern medical and other sciences in establishing a deep, broad and accurate foundation of detailed understanding of its *components*.

It seems to me that the importance of this point cannot be over-estimated. As I look back at the history of the real increases in understanding of our universe I see, time after time, that they have been a result of a *detailed* examination of the facts.

CHAPTER 20

Family Therapy

IN THIS CHAPTER we will take a little excursion out towards one of the boundaries of our subject, to where it merges with family therapy. There are three main reasons for this.

The first is that during diagnosis we may well find that the family enters as a significant system in the creation or maintenance of the problem.

The second reason is that we have seen that it is very important when establishing a new behaviour in a Client to ensure that it will receive positive feedback from the world outside the consulting-room. The most important part of the world for most people as regards personal relationships is the immediate family. For both these reasons we may become involved in many cases with a certain amount of family dynamics.

A third reason is that we are often dealing, as you will find in the chapter on dissociation, with (perhaps partially) dissociated internal systems which are functionally equivalent to parent and child. In such a case we are dealing with something like a part of an internalised family. More generally we may at times find internal systems interacting in a way which resembles other possible external relationships.

Obviously there will be no attempt to give an exhaustive account of family therapy in the space of this chapter. What we will do is to begin by looking briefly at the particular form of family therapy - known as systemic therapy - to which the present systems-oriented approach to Hypnotherapy is most naturally related. Systemic theory originated half a century ago and its ideas have permeated the field to the extent that:

> "All family therapists now accept the idea that families are systems; not believing in systems theory is a bit like not believing in the flag, apple pie, and motherhood. Schools of family therapy vary, however, in the degree to which they actually incorporate systems thinking in their practice." (Becvar & Becvar (1988))

Then an example will be given of a simple family problem using the notation and language of this book. The purpose will be to demonstrate that the same concepts and approaches can be used in family therapy also. Just as it would be useful not to have to learn a new language as you move from country to country, and it is useful to find the same mathematical language used in all the various sciences, so, it is argued, it is useful to be able to use the same theoretical structure both for internal systems of a person and for his or her external relationships. The integrative value of a common structure is further illustrated by reference to the variety of different schools of family therapy.

Systemic Therapy

The roots of systems theory go back to the 1940s. At that early stage it involved workers from many disciplines. Important among these were Norbert Wiener, a mathematician who contributed the word "cybernetics" (Wiener (1948a), (1948b)), which can still be used as a synonym for systems theory, though more often in Europe than America.

The basic innovation of such approaches was to start to think about *processes* and the abstract patterns into which they are organised, rather than to focus on *static* objects. It is equivalent to placing more emphasis on verbs and less on nouns. There is less emphasis on naming and classifying *things*, and far more on describing *how* they behave. In the context of family therapy the focus moved from the individual members of the family to the dynamic pattern of interactions between them. Clearly this whole approach is very much in harmony with the philosophy of this book. (Though I only learned of systemic therapy after having formulated the notions of this book as a result of attempting to understand Hypnotherapy.)

(We might note parenthetically that this change from an emphasis on *things* to an emphasis on *processes* is one which signals the coming-of-age in many a field of knowledge. Before Darwin, species were simply classified. Subsequently attention has been focused on how they form and change. There was a time when rocks were simply classified, and were regarded as unchanging. Then it became obvious that they did change, and geology and related subjects were transformed as attention turned to the more deeply fascinating questions of how rocks form, and how continents form, and how the face of the earth changes with time.)

Another important contributor from the early days was anthropologist Gregory Bateson. He was influenced by the work and ideas of Milton H. Erickson from as early as 1941. He developed systems ideas in the context of studying schizophrenia (Bateson (1956)) and alcoholism (Bateson (1971)), the former paper introducing the concept of a double bind, which will be very familiar to workers in our field. It was co-authored by Jay Haley, who is well known as a student of Milton H. Erickson and now as a giant of family therapy in his own right.

In practical terms the biggest departure from previous practice that systemic therapy introduced was that therapists stopped seeing patients in isolation in both senses of the word. They not only started to see the whole family together - a heretical idea at one time - but also became acutely aware at all times that a "problem" in an individual would often be a result of family factors.

In the process of analysing such family systems a great deal of emphasis was placed on the study of communication and information processing. The emphasis on communication was given its major impetus by Don Jackson, founder of the Mental Research Institute in California in 1959, who was a communications theorist and published extensively as well as gathering around him many individuals who are now well known, such as Virginia Satir, Jules Riskin, Richard Fisch, Jay Haley, Paul Watzlawick and John Weakland.

Although there have been many developments of this systemic therapy in subsequent years, they have been primarily within this context of family therapy and with a high emphasis on communication: it is *inter*personal rather than *intra*personal.

Specific schools which may be seen to have developed in this way are structural and strategic therapies. Structural therapy focuses on the dynamics of communication: who is speaking to whom, when and in what way. Strategic therapy focuses more on the purpose of communication, including non-verbal communication, of which the presented symptom may be an example, in establishing the balance of power within the family.

At the other extreme from systemic therapy we may perhaps place behavioral therapy, which tends in practice to place the most emphasis on the role of operant conditioning, and to say least about the family as a system. However the basic idea behind operant conditioning - the fact that a behaviour which receives positive reinforcement is repeated and strengthened - is one that we have met before in the analysis of positive feedback loops. Consequently behavioral therapy dovetails with the theoretical framework of this book at that point.

This all too brief outline of family therapy is sufficient for our present purposes.

We may now observe that although the basic concepts of the systems-oriented approach to Hypnosis developed here extend upwards naturally and easily to family therapy, there has been no great movement of systemic therapy down to smaller systems within an individual.

Both theories share a common concern with the analysis of processes. Both use the cybernetic concept of feedback, though the present theory applies it in more detail and, I hope, clarity.

The present theory, because of its generality, does not place the same primary emphasis on communication and information, though these concepts will arise in the appropriate contexts.

Systemic theorists tend to see themselves as holistic, and breaking out of a framework of cause and effect. The present approach is holistic in the sense of paying due regard to the influence of all external and internal systems and their interactions, but it remains unrepentantly determined to analyse these interactions in terms of the actions of one on the other. It should already be clear that an analysis of the reciprocal effects of two systems on each other is a powerful tool for understanding their relationship.

Such systems may be systems of thought, of feelings, of relationships, of nerves, of hormones or of society. They may ALL be relevant to a given situation. It is NOT holistic arbitrarily to say, "We will only consider systems of the following kind...", whether the restriction is to biochemical systems, or to social systems or to spiritual systems. "The highest," as it says in *The Imitation of Christ* (Thomas a Kempis (c. 1441)) , "does not stand without the lowest." We have to consider *all* levels and all kinds of systems, and then think very clearly indeed about the interplay between the things that are happening on the different levels.

Next let us look at a situation which might arise in family therapy. Let us suppose that the result of an emotional upset in person A is anger. Suppose that the reaction of person B to this anger is of coldness and withdrawal. Suppose further that this results in yet more emotional upset in A, who regards the coldness as a withdrawal of love or commitment. We can then write this in shorthand as:

$$\uparrow\{\text{anger};A\} \rightarrow \uparrow\{\text{coldness};B\} \rightarrow \uparrow\{\text{anger};A\},$$

which is of course an increasing positive feedback loop. It more or less guarantees that quarrels will have no resolution and will leave both partners feeling very hard done to. This analysis focuses our minds very clearly on the fact that the problem is a *process*, and furthermore that the nature of the process is an increasing positive feedback loop.

If we want to change this loop we can proceed on the same *principles* that we have used in earlier chapters to tackle similar loops in Hypnotherapy. We need to look at each part of the process in turn and see if it can be changed; we need to consider possible changes; we need to check such changes to see if they will last (NO negative feedback loops); we need to think them through to see that they do not make things worse.

There is no way of telling in the abstract which is the best point to work on. In one case it might be quite easy to get A to moderate the expression of anger - perhaps by insisting that it be on paper or in public; in another it might be possible to get B to become angry instead of cold. It may be possible to get either to see that the other is not so much hostile as upset. The best way may take some ingenuity, but the basic patterns of thought used by the therapist can be seen as the same as he or she uses in eliminating a vicious circle *within* a single person in our approach to Hypnotherapy.

In short, the form of the strategies of diagnosis and planning a change can be identical to those used in this book. What will be different is the class of intervention made, though the patterns - ensuring that negative feedback loops are dealt with, ensuring positive feedback for the change - will be the same if the change is going to be viable and sound.

It is worth noting that if we were temporarily to send A out of the room and have a private talk with B, it is analogous to a Hypnotic procedure in which we have diagnosed two distinct subsystems and proceed to communicate with one and not the other (as we saw Hilgard do at the beginning of the chapter on Dissociation), by effectively achieving a total dissociation between them for a while. If we simply talk to one in the hearing of the other, with the other not allowed to intervene, it is analogous to the Hypnotic procedure of communicating with one subsystem - the "child within" perhaps - while allowing another - the internal "parent" perhaps - to "listen in", but not interfere. This would be an instance of a unilateral dissociation.

In the above example the simple loop was presented (unrealistically) as if it were the only problem involved. Of course in general we would have found other, and more complicated, issues. We should have asked, for example, if there was any reason why the individuals had adopted those particular responses, and that might have taken us rather deep into an analysis of the internal systems of each - a process which could easily take us back into the realm of individual therapy. There can be real complexity lying behind such a seemingly simple loop. And the practitioner should be aware of this fact, and not be misled by the fact that throughout this book we are focusing on rather simple examples, in the way in which introductions to most subjects use simple examples to begin with. Remember that the purpose of the book is to establish *a way of thinking* rather than to give an exhaustive account of everything. However, because of the uniformity of the analysis of processes, we can move effortlessly from a family problem down to a personal problem, which might in turn revolve around some quite limited subsystem of that person, and *at all times we will be working within the same systems paradigm, using the same language and the same shorthand notation.*

The above example was also presented without any reference to the process of diagnosis from which it was derived. This throws light on an important point. **In practice the kind of dynamic patterns which the therapist tends to see and work with will inevitably be influenced by the theoretical stance and therefore the questions asked.**

To put this into perspective let us imagine a quite different school of family therapy, which is an economic one. This might model the system of a family from an economic viewpoint. It will have observed that a lot of family arguments are about money, and extrapolated to suppose that money is therefore the basis of the whole thing. A therapist from such a school will focus entirely on the cash value of each exchange between members. He (it would be unlikely to be a woman) will try to establish how each person values such things as making a meal, or having it made and so on. He would focus on processes of negotiation as the "internal market" tries to get into balance. He would be able to assess the activity of "buyers" and "sellers" in any particular commodity or service, and note that activity in one market has to be related to activity in another. For just as when someone buys shares, the money has to come from somewhere else, such as stocks, so it will be the case that if, for example, someone "buys" housekeeping services, they will have to "pay" in perhaps new clothes or nights out, so that $\uparrow\{\text{domestic work}\} \rightarrow \uparrow\{\text{new clothes}\}$. This economic family therapist would therefore see the whole thing in terms of financial subsystems or markets. If his economic model was based on Marxist-Leninist lines then he would be more likely to analyse the subsystems in terms of social class. But the details are not important: the key idea is that *the dynamics discovered will be limited by the types of subsystems felt to be important.*

In a similar way the different schools of family therapy tend to focus on rather different aspects of family life, and involve rather different analyses into subsystems. Consequently they will ask different questions and get different answers. If questions are asked about the family life of parents when they were children, then the answers will reveal patterns involving three generations: the subsystems of the family will be seen to include the behaviour and personality of the grandparents as they were when their children were young. A psychoanalytical approach might see rather different subsystems of the members of the families involved, perhaps with a strong emphasis on the sexual aspects of relationships, Oedipal responses and so on. If, at another extreme, the questions are kept very much to the here-and-now in terms of what reaction there is to any action, as in a behavioral approach, there is going to be comparatively little attention to any history, or any internal ideas or feelings of the individuals involved, and the systems that will be featured in the analysis will be rather simple reactive ones. A communications-based therapy will similarly involve asking questions about the ways in which the communication of one individual is affected by the communication of another, and will derive systems based on the types of communication which are being studied.

Family therapy is not an exact science. There is no reason to suppose that one form of analysis is always better than another. Looking at the situation from the outside, it would seem most probable that for a particular case of a "problem" in a particular family one form of analysis might be the most appropriate, but that each approach will have value in some cases. In an ideal world the therapist would be familiar with *all* possible forms of analysis into subsystems and, as a result of a diagnostic process, determine which is the most useful in a particular case. Such an approach would be "holistic" in the sense used above: of being able to recognise and take account of any systems, of whatever nature, that are involved.

In practice a similar pattern can be seen within Hypnotherapy, though there has been little attempt to classify the different approaches as methodically as has been done for family or psychotherapy. The rough classification of Chapter 4 will, however, give an idea of the way in which different theorists have focused their attention on different systems as being *the* central one in Hypnosis, which is analogous to the way in which different schools of family therapy focus on a different central feature of family dynamics. Such an approach *differentiates* one approach from another. The whole theme of this book is quite the opposite: it is *integrative* in that it shows up what is common in all approaches. There is something of value to be learned from each approach to Hypnosis, but none is a complete theory of the subject.

One of the greatest advantages that the "hard" sciences have over the "soft" ones is their common language, derived from a particularly fruitful and precise shorthand called mathematics, which integrates them and shows what they have in common. Each speciality is differentiated by its raw material, but united with the others by the common discipline which forces it to write down its findings in the most simple and compact way in the common language.

It is this goal which is the guiding principle of this book. The author would like to be able to read case reports on family therapy in which the systems assumed to be important and the dynamics thereof were made explicit and written down compactly. If several different therapists looked at the same case, the different diagnoses could be written in a similar language and compared and contrasted with comparative ease. At present since each field tends to use its own specialised vocabulary, such comparisons become very hard. It is worse than trying to compare the value of petrol at two pumps at one of which it is priced in £/Litre and at another in $/gallon.

Likewise in Hypnotherapy he would like to see case reports and "induction scripts" accompanied by a clear and distinct statement of the dynamics and systems involved, again written in shorthand for convenience, so that he might understand what the therapist believes to be happening.

SUMMARY

The general acceptance within the field of Family Therapy of a systems framework augurs well for a similar acceptance within the field of Hypnotherapy.

The variety of approaches to Family Therapy within that broad framework is also likely to be a feature of Hypnotherapy when it is developed along systems lines.

We have noted the importance of the fact that each approach to Family Therapy is characterised by the kind of systems that it regards as basic.

The value of being able to use the same theoretical framework for working with social groups or families, or individuals or systems within individuals, or even the interaction of neurons, would seem to facilitate thought immensely.

CHAPTER 21

Psychotherapy

IN THIS CHAPTER we will take a brief look at how Hypnotherapy relates to other schools of Psychotherapy. For the non-specialist the descriptions of other schools will not be so detailed as to be tedious. Specialists will be able to supply the missing details for themselves.

Within the present paradigm we have a clear path towards classifying forms of Psychotherapy, as indeed we have to much larger fields of human endeavour.

We first ask:

What are the systems (S) recognised in the field?

We then ask:

By what processes (P) are these systems altered?

The answers then define the field as $[S_1, S_2, \ldots ; P_1, P_2, \ldots]$

Thus the field of classical particle dynamics would be roughly classified as [moving particles; forces]. The field of dentistry is roughly [teeth; filling, removal, replacement]. The field [marriages; divorce] represents a subfield of the legal profession: the field [marriages; discussion, conciliation] is a subfield of counselling: the field [marriages; blessing] is a subfield of the clerical vocation.

These simple examples illustrate that fields may be distinguished *either* by their systems of interest *or* by their procedures, or both.

It should also be clear that a large field can be split into many subfields. Thus modern medicine covers such a large field - [human physical disorders; medicines, physical operations] - that it is split into many small specialities such as oncology = [tumours; drugs, surgery].

Notice that we generally do not need to elaborate all the systems and all the procedures of a given field. If we want to give more detail, then we simply start to enumerate subfields.

We may apply these principles to Psychotherapy and Hypnotherapy to obtain a first-order classification of the fields.

Broadly speaking, Psychotherapy = [problems of the systems of human thought, feeling or behaviour; personal interaction, communication, direction].

We may contrast Psychiatry, which in the UK at present works far more within the medical paradigm and is effectively [problems of systems of human thought, feeling or behaviour; drugs, electro-convulsive therapy].

We may also contrast Teaching = [systems of human knowledge or thought; personal interaction, communication, direction]. The primary difference from Psychotherapy is in the systems of interest, which tend to be more involved with information and less with feelings. Where teaching *does* deal with feelings, as in some of the arts, it is not concerned with feelings as a distressing "problem" which has to be removed.

Next we will roughly categorise some of the principal schools of Psychotherapy. Any practitioner in a school may well object that the brief description does not do justice to the whole: and of course it does not. Just enough detail is given to distinguish it from other forms. The names in brackets are those of the person most associated with the approach.

Adlerian therapy (Alfred Adler) = [behavioral patterns, social systems; encouragement of social involvement, absence of blame, humour]

Assertiveness training = [social skills; self-monitoring, behaviour rehearsal]

Aversion therapy = [behavioral systems; forging unpleasant associations to a behaviour]

Behaviour therapy = [behaviour patterns; desensitization, conditioning, observational learning]

Bioenergetics (Alexander Lowen) = [repressed emotions, muscle tension; muscular exercises, verbal expression]

Biofeedback = [various internal systems; use of feedback machines to amplify small signs of improved control]

Cognitive therapy (Aaron Beck) = [beliefs, thought systems; reasoning, reconceptualising, "running movies"]

Ericksonian therapy (Milton H. Erickson) = [inner and social systems; *very varied,* hypnotic techniques, use of metaphors, pattern intervention, direction]

Freudian therapy (Sigmund Freud) = [id, ego, super-ego, dreams; revealing unconscious conflicts, free association, transference, cathartic release of repressed material]

Gestalt (Fritz Perls) = [here-and-now systems, defences, dreams; encounter groups, integrating subsystems, inner dialogues]

Hypnotherapy = [many systems; activation and deactivation, use of inner and outer feedback loops to enhance change]

Jungian therapy (Carl Jung) = [ego, personal unconscious, collective unconscious, archetypes, personae; activating imagination, use of mandala, connecting to archetypes]

Primal therapy (Arthur Janov) = [Pain, traumatic experiences, repression; evoking the repressed pain]

Rational-Emotive therapy (Albert Ellis) = [beliefs about self; reasoned change of belief]

Reality Therapy (William Glasser) = [Behaviour patterns, self-responsibility; enhancing ego strength, breaking old patterns]

Reichian Therapy (Wilhelm Reich) = [orgone energy, sexual repression, character armour; massage, release of sexual energy; use of orgone box]

Religious Therapies = [God, souls, love; healing of souls, forgiving of sin, establishing bonds of love]

Rogerian Therapy or Person-centred Therapy (Carl Rogers) = [positive regard, parental influence; emotional support, listening, being non-directive]

Self Actualization (Abraham Maslow) = [normal people, hierarchy of needs; meeting needs, becoming more oneself]

Transactional Analysis (Eric Berne) = [Child, Parent, Adult; game analysis, script analysis, I'm OK - You're OK]

The above list gives a reasonably broad picture of the major subfields of current psychotherapy in the UK today, in alphabetical order. However, this list is more useful for didactic purposes than as a way of classifying individual therapists. It is seldom the case that a therapist will be so exclusively trained in one approach that he or she will be ignorant of, and not use where appropriate, ideas and techniques from the others.

Note that although Religious Therapy is included as one item, it is still the case that world-wide this category far outnumbers, in terms of people involved, all the others put together.

Hypnotherapy appears near the middle of the list in the "Morganic" form suggested in this book. It has often been omitted from short lists of therapies because it was thought of as lacking in depth and being, in effect, the field: [conscious, subconscious; trance, direction]. This makes it seem far more limited in scope than it truly is, as I hope this book has shown. I am afraid that Hypnotherapy has long lacked the respect that is its due because of this faulty perception in the minds of those who are not experienced in it. *One of the aims of this book is to elaborate the sound intellectual and scientific basis for the field to prevent such a dismissive attitude in future.*

Not only is this expression of Hypnotherapy near the middle of the list alphabetically, but it is not extreme in other ways. It does not say, "This way, and no other!" (as many of the founders of other schools have said). We have seen that it can accommodate the framework of systems that each of the other specialised therapies use, where appropriate. It is, in principle, broader because it starts with the question, "What are the most appropriate systems for analysing this situation?" By contrast a Primalist, for example, has already pre-judged this issue and answered, "The Pain of a very early suppressed scream."

But there is no reason why a Hypnotherapist should not decide, after the diagnostic process outlined, to work with the set of systems of *any* of the above approaches, but to bring to them some of the particular strengths of the approach, which include a clear sense of the *dynamics* of organic processes; the value of inactivating irrelevant systems; the importance at many levels of feedback loops of many kinds and the ability to make significant changes to different systems at different levels by handling the dynamics properly.

SUMMARY

Different schools of Psychotherapy tend to focus their attention on different subsystems of the human mind, and apply different techniques to them. Hypnotherapy, in the sense of this book, is broader than most, as it deals with levels of systems from the comparatively simple reflexes of the nervous system up to social systems. It includes a prescriptive diagnostic process, a crisp theoretical framework, a sense of the dynamics of feedback systems and a wide variety of procedures to change them.

In particular we note that Hypnotherapy is not *in opposition* to any of the other schools. If it is judged that the particular systems of a school are important in a given Client, then the systematic approach of Hypnotherapy can be applied to those systems.

CHAPTER 22

Activity

IN THE BULK of this book the word "activity" has been used freely without defining it precisely. This chapter elaborates on the idea a little. The following precise definition will now be proposed.

The **activity** of an organic process is the rate at which it increases the thermodynamic entropy of the universe.

(The definition would also be meaningful for an inorganic process, but we are not primarily interested in those.)

Let us see why this is a useful definition.

The first point is that it is well defined. Although the concept of entropy is perhaps rather difficult to grasp for the man in the street, it IS something that can readily be defined scientifically and mathematically.

The second point is based on a very general principle, a form of the Second Law of Thermodynamics, which is that the entropy of the universe is NEVER decreased by any process. This implies that the activity of any process, as defined above, *can never be negative*. This is very satisfactory, since our intuitive idea of activity is that it should be positive or zero.

Note that it is important to define the activity in terms of the entropy of *the universe*, since it is possible for a process to decrease the entropy of *one part* of the universe, but only at the cost of increasing it at least as much somewhere else.

The third point is that it is *additive*. By this I mean that if an organic system is analysed into distinct subsystems, then the activity of the whole will be the sum of the activity of the parts.

The fourth point is that the concept of entropy can be applied to *information* as well as to thermodynamic processes. There is therefore the possibility of using it as a concept which will span the full range of our subject from the atomic processes involved in the simplest biochemical changes to the complex information processing characterising our higher thought patterns.

I am not aware at present of work which directly connects the thermodynamic entropy change involved in, shall we say, a certain neurological process, to the informational entropy change - which is at a different level. Perhaps it is work which has yet to be done. But at least the possibility is there.

At the thermodynamic level it is possible to define the entropy of a process as being the amount of heat that it delivers to a thermal reservoir held at an absolute temperature of 1°K. The activity of a process is therefore measured in watts/°K. Since most biological processes are at temperatures which vary very little from around 310°K (close to blood temperature) we can compare the activity of different processes simply by comparing their heat output. Thus for practical purposes we may identify the activity of a part of the brain (say) with the rate of heat production by the mental processes therein. The activity of a muscle will similarly be measured by the rate at which it is producing heat. The rate of production of heat is power, measured in watts. A two megawatt power station is twice as active as a one megawatt station; a two kilowatt electric fire will be twice as active as a one kilowatt fire; a person climbing stairs twice as fast as another (with the same weight) will be twice as active; two identical neurons firing will be twice as active as one neuron firing; and the activity of each of these different systems can be compared to a good accuracy by comparing their thermal powers, or more precisely by comparing the entropy changes they are producing. The various brain-scanning techniques give measures of brain activity which correlate well with the above definition.

Another way of conceptualising the third law of thermodynamics is the following. Every naturally occurring process results in making energy *less available* for doing work. Energy, as we know, is conserved. There is the same amount of energy in the world both before and after petrol has been burned. But at the earlier time the energy is concentrated and available to power a car, while afterwards the energy is spread through the atmosphere and is no longer available.

The activity of a process is a measure of the rate at which energy is being made unavailable. In today's ecologically conscious age it will be seen that activity is not therefore an unequivocally good thing. An efficient process is one which achieves a given change with the minimum change of entropy: the minimum loss of available energy.

The dynamics of an ecological system may be charted by measuring the flow of energy through it (e.g. Green et al. (1984)). It should be clear that the precise definition of activity used here could be used in such a context. The activity of the rabbit population, for example, could be measured as the rate at which all the processes in which rabbits are involved are increasing the entropy of the universe; or to a good accuracy as the rate at which they are producing heat. On the whole we might expect an ecosystem to evolve in the direction of maximum efficiency as each species uses the energy available to it with the minimum waste.

In the field of economics we might start by noting that a barrel of oil represents a certain number of kilowatt-hours of available energy (if we again neglect the small variations caused by the temperature dependence of entropy). This provides us with a link between currency and energy, since in principle the cost of anything can be measured in terms of the cost of a barrel of oil.

We can therefore establish the economic equivalent to the activity of burning oil, which will be measured not in watts but in £/hr. If we are heating our houses with a two kilowatt fire we are using energy at twice the rate of a one kilowatt fire, and we are spending money twice as fast. The thermal activity and the financial activity go hand in hand.

It may be possible to extrapolate this to other, more complex economic processes, but this would take me too far outside my expertise. For what it is worth my guess is that the concept of entropy at different levels could be a very important one in economic theory: so much economic activity results in order at one level of society (a local *decrease* of entropy) but at the expense of an inevitable *global increase in entropy* (disorder). Just as an efficient machine is one which achieves its goal with the *minimum* increase of entropy, so an efficient business will be one which achieves its goal of producing a product or service with the minimum waste of money.

These ideas will seem very crude to an economist, no doubt. In this book they are simply presented to stimulate an awareness of the potential value of the precise notion of activity which has been presented here, in order to underline the fact that it is applicable to all manner of organic systems. But above all it is worth noting again the fact that a science which uses, as a basic concept, something that can be precisely defined and measurable is in a very strong position to grow on a firm foundation. In particular, therefore, we have a firm foundation for Hypnotherapy when we base it on the notion of the *level of activity of a system*.

SUMMARY

The central concept of activity may be given a precise definition in terms of the rate at which a system is increasing the entropy of the universe. This leads to it being measurable in units of watts/°K, though for most practical situations it is proportional to the power generated in watts.

It can be extrapolated to analyse energy webs in ecosystems with little problem.

It is possible to use this equivalent to obtain an approximate economic equivalent which would be units of £/sec: the rate at which money is being spent. In this way we can make a start on measuring activity on a socio-economic scale if we wish to do so.

CHAPTER 23

Analogies

THE USE OF ANALOGIES in Hypnotherapy is a very common practice. In this short chapter we will look at this and integrate the theory of the practice into our general systems framework.

A good place to start to consider this theme is with the many examples that have been presented in this book of organic systems. Any of these can be taken as a partial analogy which can provide some understanding of the way in which the mind operates. We have considered, for example, ecosystems, or parts of one; we have considered societies and businesses and families, and orchestras. Any of these can be taken as a partial analogy for the workings of the brain. But what exactly is the relationship of one to another?

Of course, at one level what is happening is that I wish to communicate something rather new. I want to teach a way of looking at Hypnotherapy which has not arisen before in my readers' minds. But you can only build a wall by placing new stones on top of stones already firmly in place: they cannot be placed in mid-air. I have therefore been trying to relate these new ideas to pre-existing ideas with which many of my readers will be a little more familiar. (And the little analogy I have used of wall-building is an example of this very process!) But again, what is the relationship?

The relationship, in the examples I am using, is one of **similar dynamic structure**.

I can, for example, explain what is happening in a relationship as follows: "She is a hedgehog. When she feels threatened she curls up and shows only prickles. He is a rabbit. When he feels threatened he wants to snuggle up close for reassurance." Now anyone who can create from these words a picture of the rabbit being upset by the prickles as he snuggles closer, and the hedgehog getting more threatened and prickly as complaints are made about her behaviour, will gain a good *feel* for the dynamics of the relationship. Each is being true to his or her nature, which would make sense to another with the same responses. But each has a response which activates in the other something uncomfortable. His attempt to get her to uncurl makes her worse. Her attempts to ward him off make him worse. We have a clear vicious circle. Clearly the dynamic structure is identical to that of two humans where she reacts to being crowded by being verbally nasty (the equivalent of the hedgehog spikes) whereas his automatic response (perhaps learned in childhood) is to try to get physically close.

In a more abstract form we have the pattern of two systems A and B in the following increasing positive feedback loop:

$$\uparrow\{A, \text{ threatened}\} \rightarrow \uparrow\{A, \text{ prickly exterior to close approach}\} \rightarrow$$
$$\uparrow\{B, \text{ threatened}\} \rightarrow \uparrow\{B, \text{ closer approach}\} \rightarrow \uparrow\{A, \text{ threatened}\}.$$

The virtue of telling someone the story of the two animals is that it gives a simple picture of what is going on in their relationship. Even better is to continue with the little story in such a way that it becomes clear how the animals might make the best of their relationship. "They went along to wise old Badger with their quarrel, and he said to the hedgehog, 'When he gets too close you must ask him to run all the way down to the shops and get you some of your favourite herbal tea. You will feel better when he comes back.' And to the rabbit he said, 'When she gets too prickly you must run all the way down to the shops and get her some of her favourite herbal tea which will make her right in no time.'"

The dynamics of this answer is parallel to a similar answer in the couple, in which it is arranged that the defensive responses trigger off some new pattern of behaviour which breaks the loop. It might be as simple a matter as getting him to do something for five minutes while she calms down and can be open and friendly again.

Notice that we are not saying that the woman snuffles in hedgerows or likes eating worms. We are not saying that the man has long ears or a bobtail. The analogy is not at the level of identity of *structure*, but of identity of *process*.

The use of little stories as analogies in this way is another of the characteristics that made Milton H Erickson so effective. For a volume which gives many examples of this approach read Rosen (1982).

Earlier in the book I quoted the example of a Public Address System which has started to give that loud scream that happens if the microphone is picking up the sound from the speakers, which I used as an analogy for an internal feedback loop within a person which causes a troubling symptom, perhaps of panic, to be produced from nowhere. This does not mean that there is *literally* a microphone in the head, or some speakers. The *structures* are quite different, but the *process*, of an increasing positive feedback loop involving three systems which are involved with perception, amplification and production of the thing perceived, is identical. The analogy then gives insight into the *dynamics*.

It is important to note that the dynamic pattern is always at a higher order than any of its particular embodiments, i.e. analogies which share the same dynamic pattern. The relationship of the theory to its applications is similar to the relationship of the number 3 to all particular collections of three objects. There is an *analogous* connection between any two collections of three things. But the relationship of each to the abstract number "3" is different. "3" symbolises the property that they all have in common.

In a similar way "$\uparrow A \rightarrow \uparrow B \rightarrow \uparrow A$" symbolises the property shared by all dynamic systems which involve two subsystems each activating the other in an increasing positive feedback loop. Any embodiment of this symbolic expression can then serve as an analogy for any other.

This is analogous to the way in which the abstract formula "$2+3=5$" can be embodied in the adding of two apples and three apples, or of two red bricks and three red bricks, or of two pound coins and three pound coins. Any particular such embodiment is analogous to any other. The abstract numbers, however, are at a different level: they encapsulate a common property of all the examples.

Few can doubt that the abstract concept of number and the development of a symbolic way of writing numbers down have together led to enormous changes in understanding of many other things. Mathematics has given its strength also to all subjects in which it has been possible to extract abstract patterns from a mass of particular examples.

It is hoped that in this book we are finding that this same fundamental step can be taken in the field of Hypnotherapy.

There will be people who, having read this book, will say, "Oh, it simply compares the workings of the brain to a society," or "It simply compares the workings of the brain to the workings of an ecosystem," or "To a business" or "To an orchestra". In fact such a statement would reveal that *the reader had failed to make the intellectual leap to grasp the essential nature of what is being attempted*, which is the creation of an abstract theory of a certain very wide class of systems - organic systems - within which the phenomena of Hypnosis and Hypnotherapy can be readily grasped. The principles involved in this theory can have many different embodiments, each of which is analogous to each other.

Returning now to the day-to-day use of analogies in Hypnotherapy, let us explicitly ask the questions, "Why generate them?" and then "How can we generate them?"

Clearly the answer to the former is that we want to change some system in the Client's mind. We want him or her to think rather differently or feel rather differently as a result. But we must then ask, "What changes are we aiming at?" The answer to this should have come out of the procedures of Part B: we have asked questions about the Client's experience which they have answered in their own words. We have then abstracted from these answers the *abstract pattern of the dynamic processes* of the systems involved. We have then decided on the basis of this pattern what things could best be changed. This leaves the final task of getting these changes into the appropriate parts of the Client's mind.

This has to be done at the appropriate level, in a language that those parts of the mind respond to: it may, for example, be visual or verbal or kinaesthetic. But it must also be an embodiment of the change that we know, from our abstract analysis, to be needed. In order to do this well we really need to be able to understand how the Client sees the world, and then translate the change into that context, i.e. we create an analogy by covering the bones of the dynamic structure with the flesh of the person's own thoughts. (That is itself an analogy which does the same thing in a small way.)

For example, suppose that we find someone who is creating problems for himself or herself by continually worrying about some symptom, but we recognise that the very fact of paying attention to it, to see if it is getting better yet, is making it worse.

The abstract formula is an increasing positive feedback loop:

$$\uparrow\{symptom\} \rightarrow \uparrow\{worry\} \rightarrow \uparrow\{attention\} \rightarrow \uparrow\{symptom\}.$$

We clearly want to break this loop. The exact approach will depend on the person. If we are dealing with a keen gardener we will begin by exploring his mind for an example of some problem which might arise in the garden. We might then discover how he would deal with *that* problem. If we find that his approach in that context is sound, then we can make that a basis for an analogy which will get through to him and change his attitude enough to break the vicious circle that he is in.

It might, in a particular case, go like:

"There was a gardener who started to have doubts about how his leeks were growing. They seemed to be lagging behind. So, fearing root-rot, he gently pulled them up to have a look and then replanted them." (The gardener listening to this will understand that uprooting a plant is a very good way to upset its growth.) "But although he found nothing, he was surprised to find that they did even worse. So a few days later he checked them again. There was no sign of the rot, but if anything they got worse and worse. And despite the fact that he checked them every few days and never found any signs of rot, they were the most disastrous crop he ever grew.

"The next year he prepared the bed well and then had to go away for most of the growing season. To his total surprise they did very well indeed!"

At the abstract level the first part of this analogy embodies the dynamics of his presented problem very well. The second part embodies the solution. The preparatory stages of Hypnosis will generally ensure that with no distraction from other mental systems the connection between the problem and the analogy will be clear and run deep. The lesson from the analogy will then generally be applied to the real problem.

It is very important to note that the effective analogy is one which is meaningful to the Subject, NOT one that is merely meaningful to the Hypnotherapist. This can always be ensured in the consulting-room. The problem facing an author in presenting analogies is that he does NOT know what each reader knows. I have therefore presented many analogies and examples, in the hope that one at least will strike a chord.

As another example of this use of analogy, let us suppose the person trapped in the above loop was a loving mother.

> "And there was this caring mother who was worried because her son seemed a bit off colour. So she insisted that he stayed away from school. She did her best to help him. She made lots of nice food, but he still did not seem to have much of an appetite. She read to him, but somehow he lost interest after a few hours. She insisted that he lie down and rest, but he did not seem to improve from it. She sent him to bed early, but he did not seem to be able to get to sleep. Clearly something was wrong. But nothing that she did seemed to help.
>
> "After many weeks of this, the mother had to go to look after her own mother who was really ill, leaving a friend to keep an eye on her son. This friend was rather lax and the next day the boy went outside and played all day long. He came in ravenous and ransacked the larder for all he could find. Then he went out to play again with his friends after they were back from school. He slept like a log. After a few days of this his friends kidded him so much that he went back to school and was right as rain."

Here again the dynamic pattern is modelled in the first part (excessive attention and worrying making things worse), and solved in the second part by a reduction in attention which allows things to get better.

The reader might care to generate a few more examples with different people in mind: a dog trainer, an executive or a nurse, perhaps.

It seems to me that many of the traditional "fairy stories" serve a similar function. I have lost count of the number of times I have retold the story of the Ugly Duckling, for example. It embodies so well the pattern in which a child grows up in a social environment which tries to make it conform, against its own nature. The child feels guilt, a failure, etc. It is only after leaving home and finding the society of others like himself or herself that the child finds life becomes not only tolerable but happy.

It seems to be a fact of human life that all adults can relate to an appropriate analogy, i.e. one that models the dynamics of what is happening to us in terms of another process that we can grasp more easily. They are therefore of universal applicability.

It is also a fact that *not* everyone can abstract general patterns to the same degree. That is one reason why the majority of people find higher mathematics such tough going. The ability to do so is correlated with intelligence and, in terms of the well known theory of Periods of Cognitive Development developed by Piaget (1963), emerges in the final period: that of Formal Operation at around the age of 12 upwards in the development of the child.

I trust that readers of this book can operate at a mental level on which it is possible to abstract the patterns from the examples I give throughout the book, so that they can grasp them at the appropriate level of Formal Operation. If one of the analogies is, however, one that is very familiar, then that will be a particularly fruitful source of ideas and metaphors when it comes either to understanding or to embodying the principles.

SUMMARY

Analogies are used often in Hypnotherapy, and indeed in all learning. They involve relating the new to something already known, so that the new may be understood by analogy with the known.

We have drawn attention to the fact that in Hypnotherapy, which is concerned with changing *processes*, the nature of the relationship of analogy is that of dynamic parallel. The two things have the same dynamic structure.

We have noted that one of the values of an abstract theory is that it makes it easy not only to understand what these analogies are doing, but also to generate them as necessary: it is only necessary to find a concrete embodiment of the dynamics of the systems involved.

It is emphasised that an analogy is only of much use if the Client can relate to it. The skilled Hypnotherapist will therefore clothe his or her analogies with the ideas or experiences of each individual Client.

Finally it has been noted that analogies have been used in this book to help readers to understand the principles of Hypnotherapy by relating it to other fields of knowledge. This is possible and meaningful because many organic systems have the same abstract forms of dynamic processes.

CHAPTER 24

Consciousness: "How?" and "What?"

IN THE BODY of this book I have used the words "conscious" and "consciousness" without defining them. In part this was to avoid complicating the main theme of the book by getting prematurely involved in controversy in what is a lively area of current debate. Since this area of discussion seems to be open to those from all specialities, be it mathematicians such as Penrose (1989, 1994), philosophers such as Dennett (1991) or evolutionary biologists such as Denton (1993), it is perhaps not banned to someone who deals daily and directly with the subject matter: he is the less likely to be accused of ultracrepidating (a useful word meaning the laying down of the law on matters of which one has little experience).

The following thoughts on the subject, then, may be viewed as a possible *starting point* in considering the matter from a viewpoint consistent with that used in the book for other phenomena. Notice that you may choose to disagree with the contents of this chapter, and it need not affect your acceptance of the remainder of the book. I am writing this chapter for pleasure - it is a development of the thoughts running through the book, but it cannot be presented as being necessary to an understanding of Hypnotherapy.

I have taken it as axiomatic that in dealing with a given organic system we must pay attention to all related systems which include BOTH its subsystems AND its supersystems: systems of which it is a part.

This means that in dealing with any organic system we can neither *understand* nor *predict* the behaviour of such a system without reference BOTH to the systems of which it is composed AND to the systems of which it is a part. This is in addition, of course, to understanding its effect on and response to its immediate environment, both physical and organic.

It is a peculiarity of *inorganic* matter that we can deal with it pretty much in isolation. We need to know only a little about its external environment and its internal structure to deal with it. Organic systems are *far* more complex. They generally have complex internal systems that lead to change even in an unchanging external environment. They have far more complex responses to their external environment, and finally they will in general form part of larger organic systems which often determine a large part of their behaviour. For example, the goals of a bee's behaviour are determined by the entire hive, though it has some freedom on a moment to moment level.

Of great importance to us in the present context is to note the related generalisations that:

a) **Systems can NOT be understood purely by reference to their content.**

b) **The nature of higher-order processes relevant to a given system can never be deduced purely from an analysis of its subsystems and their behaviour, nor from its immediate external environment.**

Let us look at some examples to illustrate these ideas. There is a child crying on the mat. How can we understand why he is unhappy? We can ask what has recently happened. He is crying because his father has come home from work and has been angry. How can we understand any further the cause of this? The child, attempting to understand it in terms that he can grasp, may naturally feel that he has been naughty. It is totally impossible *by reference merely to the child* to deduce that in fact the reason the father is angry is that he has just heard that interest rates are going up and this will make his financial situation precarious. Interest rates are not things that can be deduced from the child's experience at all. Nor can they be deduced from the experience of a collection of children. Interest rates are an example of a phenomenon in a higher-order system (the economy) which, while having a significant effect on the life and behaviour of that system which is a child, can never be deduced from an analysis of the child's behaviour.

Let us take another example. Consider, "The cat sat on the ▦▦▦▦." It seems to us easy to supply the missing word. But there is no way that this can be done purely by reference to the pattern of letters within the sentence. If you doubt it, replace the letters by symbols, thus: "¶☐♣ ♥☺¶ !☺¶ ✿♪ ¶☐♣ ▦▦▦▦" It is only because of patterns which exist at a higher level than the simple ordering of the letters that we can supply the missing ones. In this case the correct completion of the sentence relies on the fact that in our society in the UK the sentence, "The cat sat on the mat" has been copied extensively from brain to brain as a typical exercise to be set children who are learning to read. That process cannot be deduced from the pattern of the first five words, because it is a process in a higher-order system. Within the higher-order system the word "mat" completes the sentence with a very high probability. Within the low-order system of groups of symbols, it has a very low probability: we might perhaps expect a three-letter group because four out of five of the previous groups have three letters, and we might expect the last two symbols to be "☺¶" since this has happened in half the three-letter words. But we would not even know what symbol to use to complete the word. How could you guess that it would be "♪" simply from looking at the earlier symbols?

[Readers aware of some information theory (Jones (1979)) will know that an entropy can be associated with the information carried by the last word, which is calculated in terms of the probability of the correct word relative to all possibilities. (Recall that, in information theory, entropy $= -p\log_2(p)$, where p is the probability.) It should be clear to such readers that the entropy *within the higher system* of all known statements starting "The cat sat on the" is far *lower* than the entropy within the *smaller* system consisting merely of a knowledge of a dictionary, which is in turn smaller than the entropy within the still smaller world in which we know only the letters of the alphabet. This is a specific example of what is a rather general rule that we can often reduce uncertainty (decrease entropy) by moving up to a higher system. Or, to put it in other words,. **we can increase our understanding by moving up into a higher-level system.**]

And even if we *did* somehow manage to predict the next group of symbols in this way - by enlarging our data base to include every sentence that has ever been written and spoken in the English language, so that we might gauge the relative probability of the words "mat", "bed", "car", "rug", "rat", etc. and deduce that in fact "mat" is overwhelmingly more probable - then we would still be nowhere near *understanding* it, for this involves placing it within a still larger system which includes real cats and real mats. It is even more certainly the case then that we are unable to understand the whole of the system of the English language merely by reference to the truncated sentence we started with.

For the next example consider a mathematical theorem of great theoretical interest (Gödel (1931)) which says that in any mathematical structure which is at least as big as the system of whole numbers there are propositions which cannot, *even in principle*, be proved true or false within the system itself (cf. Penrose (1989)). But this is not to say that they cannot be included in a still larger mathematical structure in which they *can* be proved true or false (though of course in this new structure there will be new propositions which can be proved neither true nor false without reference to a still larger one). If we note that the question of being true or false is an important one as far as understanding goes, then again we see the principle that full understanding of a system cannot be obtained purely by reference to its content.

Next suppose that we were analysing a brain in great detail, and discovered, as we tend to do, that *this* neuron activates *that* neuron, or even the pattern of activation of a small group of neurons. This gives no insight nor understanding at all into their purpose. It cannot in principle tell us, without reference to the larger system, whether those particular ones are part of the visual cortex or the motor cortex or what have you.

A key can only be understood in the context of lock-and-key, which itself can only be understood in the context of the process of locking, which can itself only be understood fully in the context where some things of value have to be preserved against theft.

The structure of flowers can only be fully understood in the context of the insects which are necessary in order to fertilise the plants which bear them. The reason for their colours can only be understood in terms of the colours that the insects respond to.

Most species of plants or animals have specific features or systems which only make sense, or have meaning, in the context of a particular environment. The long tongue of the ant-eaters only makes sense in a world of ants and termites which can be extracted from deep in their nests most easily by means of a long sticky tongue.

In human beings the bodily systems which are activated by a sense of danger can be understood if we think of the environment in which they evolved: one of enemies or large predators which might have to be either outfought or outrun.

A particular pattern of movements of my fingers at present can be understood at a low level by reference to the external system of the keys on the keyboard of the word processor, but at a higher level it can only be understood in terms of the current thought which certain sections of this community have about Hypnotherapy and related subjects. It would be almost meaningless in the context of mediaeval European thought, and totally so to the stone-age dwellers who once lived on Ilkley Moor above me.

There are countless further examples of this kind. They all underline the facts that **it is the norm to find that the understanding of a system is incomplete unless it is placed in the context of a larger system, and that the nature of this larger system CANNOT be deduced purely by reference to the smaller.**

And I hope that you are finding that this very book you are reading is an embodiment of this same principle. We want to understand Hypnotherapy. Even in principle this is hard to do if we myopically attempt to do so from *within* the subject. And so it is being explained within the much larger context of organic systems, causal chains and feedback loops. In this larger context it CAN be understood far better.

To put all this in a different perspective I suggest that when, in daily talk, we ask the question, "*How?*" - "*How* does this work or happen?" then we are asking for an analysis in terms of *subsystems*. "How does a car work?" leads to a discussion of internal combustion engines and the like.

On the other hand when we ask the question, "*What is?*" it is normally a shorthand for "*What is the purpose?*" or "*What is the meaning?*" and we are then typically asking for an analysis in terms of *supersystems*. The question, "What is (the purpose of) a hand?" is a meaningful one which has an answer couched in terms of the needs of the higher-order system which is the person whose hand it is. "What is (the purpose of) a clock?" is answered not in terms of its workings, but in terms of a higher system which is that of time-conscious animals. If we ask, "What is the meaning of this paragraph?" we are asking to have its content related to a larger system of knowledge.

By now it should be clear that the contention implicit in the approach of this book is that the functioning of the human mind cannot be understood nor predicted without an understanding *both* of the workings of its subsystems *and* of the workings of its supersystems: the social systems, etc. of which it is part.

In particular the highest-order processes of the mind - which I take to be the conscious ones - seem to me to be inevitably those aspects of the person which will *most* require an understanding of processes outside the individual to be understood. Other, smaller, subsystems of the mind may be understood reasonably well by a partial analysis of their subsystems (which will answer the question "How does it work?"), and a partial understanding of the part they play in the whole body or brain, which are their immediate supersystems (which will answer the question, "What is its purpose?").

But conscious processes, being at the top of the pile as regards a single individual, *must* demand explication not only in terms of its subsystems but also of systems *external* to the individual if we are to answer questions related to "*What* is consciousness?" For this NOT to be true would make conscious processes something amazingly unique among complex systems for which, as we have seen, the "What?" questions require the system to be viewed as part of a larger system.

In an attempt to criticise this position I have repeatedly asked myself, "Can you think of ANY organic system S for which it is possible to answer the question, 'WHAT is S?' without reference to a higher-order system of which it is part?" I have failed, but I hope that anyone else who wishes to criticise the position will attempt the same task.

As particular applications of the above principles I would suggest that:

No matter how much knowledge we have about the neurological pathways of pain it CAN never provide an answer to the question, "*What is* consciousness of pain?"

No matter how much knowledge we have about the neurological processes of reasoning it CAN never provide an answer to the question, "*What is* consciousness of truth?"

No matter how much knowledge we have about the emotional or affective system with all its neurological and hormonal aspects, it CAN never provide an answer to the question, "*What is* consciousness of love?"

My humble suggestion is that such things, where we are asking "What is..?", can *in principle* only be answered in terms of a higher-order system or systems. This is not to say, of course, that we are not doing very well in answering the question, "How?"

All the books I have read on the subject of consciousness seem to miss this central point. They argue as if an increasingly subtle use of "How?" questions will eventually give an answer to "What?" But this is *a priori* totally improbable on the grounds that the latter question inevitably requires reference to larger systems.

Perhaps you know a story on the following lines:

A police car was cruising the streets of a seaside town one night, and stopped near a drunk who was crawling on the ground on his hands and knees.

"And what are you doing, sir?" the policeman asked.

"Looking for my losht cufflink," was the slurred reply.

The policeman took a quick look around, but saw nothing, and so asked, "And where did you lose this cufflink, sir?"

"It fell in the sea."

"Then why on earth are you looking here?"

"Talk shence! I can't shwim!"

The snag is, of course, that with our very limited minds we have a very limited capacity to understand very much larger systems (we can't "swim"). The bee does not have a brain large enough to grasp the purpose of the bee-keeper. I have a mind apt only to understand simple things, which is why I have had to look at hopelessly complex organic processes in terms of the simple notions of systems and the interactions of one on another. I could no more understand very much more complex things than I could, as a child of four, understand in the slightest way anything of this book.

Consequently, although it seems inevitable that the direction to look for an answer to "*What* is consciousness?" is *upwards* to more complex systems, there is a poor chance of any of us being able to see far enough in that direction to see anything like a complete answer. However, this is no excuse for looking in a place that the answer *cannot* be, simply because we are unable to look very far in the place where it *is*.

A different, but related, traditional response of some people to difficult "What?" questions is, in effect, to dismiss them. Where in the above it has been admitted that it is *a priori* unlikely if not impossible for me, from my limited perspective, to grasp a phenomenon from a much higher perspective, they will argue, "I cannot answer them by means of my standard methods for answering 'How?' questions. Therefore they cannot be answered." This answer has the undoubted value of focusing the mind on the simpler "How?" questions which can be pursued with considerable success, as the advances in science over recent centuries attest. The act of saying "There is no sea" may well improve our coverage of the ground, but will never help us to find anything in or about the sea. If the sea *is* there and there *is* something of value in it, then even if we cannot swim we may nevertheless hope to find out *something* by some other means.

I am reminded of Isaac Newton's famous humble words:

> I do not know what I may appear to the world, but to myself I seem to have been only like a boy playing on the sea-shore, and diverting myself in now and then finding a smoother pebble or a prettier shell than ordinary, whilst the great ocean of truth lay all undiscovered before me.
>
> *Brewster (1855)*

It will be recognised of course that all the religions of the world are united in taking a third line. They say that an understanding of such basic aspects of our conscious experience as pain, truth and love can only be obtained in terms of a higher-order system or systems - God or Gods. It is my contention that the *direction* in which they are looking - upwards, to a more complex level - is the right *and only* way to look for a full understanding of the nature of consciousness - the "What?" - while not denying the importance of the (easier) task of asking "How?" in understanding the mechanisms of much that is going on.

As to what answers we may find in that direction: they must be left as outside the scope of this book. I am saying that all the examples cited, which stand for millions more, demonstrate that *as a rule* full understanding of anything - in particular the answers to the "What?" questions - can only be obtained from a viewpoint higher than the thing itself: from a perspective which encompasses higher-order systems. I therefore propose that **the question "What is human consciousness?" can only be fully understood from a perspective much larger than the individual**. But since I have merely a human perspective I do not have that higher perspective and so I can say nothing with personal authority. I think we must conclude, however, that the smallest system within which individual consciousness could be understood is that of the society (past, present, and possibly future also) within which it has developed. But who am I to be able to see things from such an enormous perspective? Who can claim to be able to look down on a person with an intimate understanding of a whole society which exists, of course, over hundreds if not thousands or millions of years? And how can I know if that perspective is high enough? Perhaps it will require a perspective high enough to take in the entire system of life on earth - past and future as well as present? And perhaps even that is not enough?

It may help to put the problem in perspective to consider the following. When the human population of the earth has doubled and then doubled again there will finally be about as many people as there are neurons in a typical brain: some 20 billion (Calvin (1983)). (The brain also contains a much larger number of simpler glial cells whose purpose has yet to be fully elucidated.) By that time the communications between people will also, thanks to phones, the Internet, TV, etc., be getting on for being as complex as those between neurons, many of which can be in direct contact with some 10,000 others. We may well expect to see various groups of people collaborating in certain functions just as brain cells collaborate. In brief I am proposing the suggestion that a population of such a size would have a complexity at least as great as a human brain, and reasonably similar processes of operation.

The question which then arises is, "Would there then be a Global Consciousness?" Anyone who argues that consciousness is an "epiphenomenon" of complexity would, I presume, have to accept that the answer could be "Yes". (There are intelligent people who think that a sufficiently complex *computer* could be conscious, so they would have to accept that a sufficiently complex *society* could be also.) But since the relationship of each of us to that Global Consciousness is that of a cell to the entire brain, it should be clear that we can have very little idea of the nature of that Consciousness, though we would be affected by it just as an individual brain cell is affected by our conscious thoughts. Now of course there is no proof that there will be (and perhaps already is?) such a level of consciousness. I am simply proposing the thought to illustrate one kind of supersystem that can plausibly be proposed as one in which the "What?" of individual consciousness might be answered: though it would leave open the question of the nature of that larger global consciousness.

It is of course a rather humbling thought: that of seeing oneself as such a small part of such a large whole. It is so much more gratifying to see oneself as at the top of a complex system than as at the bottom of one: the Managing Director of a firm rather than a junior clerk. And intellectuals, who can often be led to think well of themselves because they can think in more complex ways than their fellows, do not perhaps take all that well to intellectual humility. A study of thinkers of the past seems to show that in every age they have thought that they knew some 99% of all the important things. And later generations have seen that they were laughably ignorant even in matters they thought themselves wise in. I doubt if this generation is any different. We will all probably seem very ignorant in a mere hundred years let alone a thousand or ten thousand.

I suspect that the ideas which I have suggested above will be resisted, when they are resisted, as much from a reluctance to adopt the humble perspective they imply as from a logical critique of the direction they propose.

I should perhaps add the simple point that saying that the answer lies in a certain direction does NOT mean that simply because a proposed answer lies in that direction it is right! A lot of people seem to fail to grasp this point. They may argue, "Morgan has said that the nature of consciousness can only be understood within a larger context. **MY** theory - that it is determined by the position of the stars / a galactic supercivilisation / life force / etc. - clearly involves a larger context, so it MUST therefore be right!"

But that is like saying, "Gold is found underground. I found this stone underground. It must therefore be gold." Or, "Your cuff-link fell in the sea. I have just found *this* (a pebble) in the sea. It must be your cuff-link."

The history of science - the history of the asking and answering of the "How?" questions - teaches us that we have no natural facility either in asking the right questions or in answering them. The past is littered with the most amazing theories and conjectures on all manner of things, such as the idea that the stars are fixed on a crystal sphere around the earth; the phlogiston theory of combustion; the four humours theory of human health; animal magnetism: each of which may be said to give rather superficial understanding of certain areas, but each of which has been demonstrated to be hopelessly inadequate or wrong. (And those theories are among the more successful ones! History says far less about the less successful ideas.) We have only made progress in answering the "How?" questions by means of very careful and honest experiment.

I have no reason to suppose that the human mind is much better equipped to answer the "What?" questions. The *a priori* assumption is that it is worse equipped. The higher may understand the lower more easily than the lower understand the higher. An adult understands a baby better than a baby understands a parent. With my full consciousness I may understand the workings of a single cell: the reverse can never be true. A biologist may begin to understand the workings of the fruit fly. The reverse will never be true. How then can we be expected to understand clearly something which *ex hypothesi* is much larger and more complex than we are?

There is a possible answer to this objection which can be summarised as follows. "The unaided mind is, of course, unable to answer the 'Why?' questions. But God (the 'higher system' as you put it), who is the source of human consciousness, is naturally able to guide it into the paths of truth, *especially on the important matters to do with the relationship of the lesser consciousnesses of His creation to His higher one.*"

For what my opinion is worth I believe that there is some truth in this, but a truth that, like so many others, can easily be misunderstood and misapplied.

SUMMARY

The important phenomenon of consciousness is considered in the context of asking the two important questions, "How?" and "What?", which can be asked of any organic system. The former question requires answers in terms of the functioning of subsystems. The latter requires answers in terms of the place of the particular system within a larger context of which it is a subsystem. We have learned a lot about the "How?" of the mind as a result of experiment and analysis of its subsystems. But such progress will never, of its nature, begin to answer the "What?" questions.

Although we may conclude that to answer the question "*What* is consciousness?" demands a higher perspective than the single human mind, the limitations of an individual mind can be expected greatly to limit any access to that perspective. It is noted that all the world's religions claim that there is a larger system within which human consciousness has its origin and meaning. The above reasoning leads to the conclusion that they are at least looking in the right direction. On the other hand thinkers who are looking to answer it by means which can at best only lead to an answer to "*How* do conscious processes work?" are fishing for whales in a bucket.

Chapter 25

Mathematics

NO MATHEMATICS has been attempted in this book so far. The formulae which have been presented are no more than a form of shorthand. In this chapter I will simply point out directions in which any development of the analysis might continue.

Central to our analysis of Hypnotic, and indeed organic, processes have been feedback loops. The first mechanism which embodied a negative feedback loop is usually cited to be James Watt's flyball governor (1760), but by today they have proliferated throughout society in all shapes and forms.

The theory of such mechanisms is usually dated from the work of Wiener (1948a) on Cybernetics. An alternative introduction to the subject is given by Ashby (1956). Control systems are normally modelled using **linear integro-differential equations**. For a typical modern text on these lines see Stefani *et al.* (1994). These are readily mastered by anyone who can handle the Laplace transform and complex analysis. These approaches have been used to design control systems for such varied systems as artificial limbs (Rauch (1986)) and control of a flexible aircraft (Martin & Bryson (1980)).

Related, but much more complex, mathematics has been used to model feedback in acoustic systems, which are three-dimensional. A particular example of this, which I have studied in depth (Jones & Morgan (1972, 1973, 1974), Morgan (1974, 1975, 1978)) is the generation of noise by jet engines. This involves an increasing positive feedback loop which is associated with the Helmholtz instability of the interface between streams of gases which have different speeds. (Sound generation by the flute is based on the same phenomenon.) Such examples again use a linear model.

However, detailed analysis of biological systems reveals **non-linearity**. The term "non-linear" has a precise meaning to the mathematician, but in practical terms it means "extremely difficult to analyse: can normally only be solved using a computer".

There has been something of an explosion of research into the theoretical studies of such biological systems in recent years. A good compendium with which to start is Murray (1993). Examples of systems which have been treated are population dynamics including predator-prey interactions, nerve propagation, animal coat patterns, morphogenesis and epidemics.

Against the background of all that work, the present book can be seen as simply lifting Hypnotherapy into the twentieth century and making it possible for it to take its place among other sciences which can utilise the power of specific mathematical models. The structure that has been revealed - involving the clear concept of activity as its basic variable - lends itself to measurement. Suitable experimental measurements can clarify the exact form of the interactions between systems. A knowledge of the exact form leads to equations. These equations may be essentially similar to those which have already arisen in control theory or biological systems, in which case we can at once take over the solutions. Alternatively we may find different equations, which will provide the theoreticians with some happy hours of work and many new publications.

It is presumed that the typical reader is NOT versed in mathematical modelling. Nevertheless I will present the simplest possible model of feedback loops in the context of Hypnotherapy to give a flavour of what can happen, and also to illustrate the kind of advantage that comes from a precise analysis. The mathematical formulation chosen is simpler than any of those mentioned above, and should be within the grasp of anyone with a GCSE in mathematics.

Let us consider a common problem which is often brought to the Hypnotherapist for treatment: blushing. The increasing positive feedback loop which drives this problem is typically:

$$\uparrow \{\text{worry about blushing}\} \rightarrow \uparrow \{\text{blushing}\} \rightarrow \uparrow \{\text{worry about blushing}\}.$$

Clearly it takes a little time for the activation of a worry to lead to the activation of the blushing. It takes time, of the order of seconds, for the thought "I am blushing" to activate the change in circulation involved. Equally there is a smaller time taken for the increased blushing, felt as heat, to be perceived by the mind.

If we let the magnitude of the worry at time t be $W(t)$ and the magnitude of the blushing at time t be $B(t)$, then our basic equation deals with *changes* in W and B. This would normally lead us at once to calculus, which deals with the rate of change of quantities like W and B. However not all of my readers are *au fait* with calculus and so I will proceed to discretise: to consider the value of the variables only at a series of discrete times. (This is what is done in any case when difficult problems are solved on a computer.)

This means that we will only consider the values of B and W at a series of times at small intervals apart: in this case we might imagine recording both every tenth or even hundredth of a second.

In this way we would get readings W_0, W_1, W_2, W_3... and B_0, B_1, B_2, B_3.... From these we could calculate the increases in the quantities in each interval as follows:

1) $w_1 = W_1 - W_0$, $w_2 = W_2 - W_1$, etc., and
2) $b_1 = B_1 - B_0$, $b_2 = B_2 - B_1$, etc.

We will next suppose that a change in W will lead to a change in B m time-steps later and a change in B will lead to a change in W n steps later. (Pure mathematicians may be worried that the two time delays could be incommensurate, and could not therefore be discretised in this way, but they can do the continuous calculations with derivatives.)

This will then enable us to propose the very simplest discretisation of our basic relationships between B and W in the following way:

3) $w_i = Jb_{i-m}$ and $b_i = Kw_{i-n}$.

The numbers J and K will be called coupling constants, and are some positive numbers which we might hope to determine by experiment. J is numerically the increase in the activity of the Worry system as a result of a unit increase in the activity of the Blushing system. K is numerically the increase in the activity of the Blushing system caused by a unit increase in the activity of the Worry system.

Notice that in writing these equations we are assuming that b_i and w_i remain positive since our basic relationship $\uparrow W \rightarrow \uparrow B \rightarrow \uparrow W$ only tells us about what happens as a result of increases. At this point we are not examining what happens in a phase in which they are reducing. We have also supposed that there is a direct proportional relationship between the changes in the two variables. In the real world this is unlikely to be more than an approximation, but it is the approximation that applied mathematicians always consider first, in the absence of any better information. This linear approximation, as it is called, is often remarkably good as long as the quantities involved do not become too large. However readers should note that experiment is the only determinant of the exact relationship between the changes in the different systems. They should also note that the equations I have written down are not the ones commonly found in books on cybernetics, in which the equations are typically drawn from an experience of inorganic systems such as electronic circuits, rather than organic systems, as here.

If we put the two equations together we can get:

4) $w_i = Lw_{i-M}$, and $b_i = Lb_{i-M}$,

where $L = JK$, and $M = m+n$.

Now let us consider the situation in which a person is neither blushing nor worrying right up to and including the time $t = 0$, so that $W_i = B_i = 0$ for values of i which are negative or zero. We may then suppose that from that time the worry steadily increases for some reason or other which is not a direct result of being aware of blushing. We can then calculate w_1, which is the increase in the first interval, w_2 which is the increase in the second interval and so on right up to w_M. These may be of any (positive) size until we come to w_{M+1}, at which point we will suppose that increases in W are governed by the feedback loop via equation 4) which says that:

5) $w_{M+1} = Lw_1$.

From then on we will take it that all further values of w_i are determined in the same way. This means that values of w, for $i = M+1$ to $2M$ are simply the values for $i = 1$ to M, but all multiplied by L.

A continuation of the calculation shows that the values for $i = 2M+1$ to $3M$ are those for $i = 1$ to M multiplied by L^2 and so on. In mathematical shorthand we have:

6) $w_{jM+i} = L^j w_i,$

which succinctly expresses the value of w at all future times.

But what we would like to know is not the value of w_i - the increase in the value of W - but rather the value of W itself. We can do this by adding up the individual increases:

7) $W_i = w_1 + w_2 + w_3 + \ldots\ldots + w_i.$

Of particular interest is the value of W_M, which is the value that the worry has risen to at the point where the feedback loop starts to work on the worry to increase it further. We will call this value W. It is not difficult then to see that:

8) $W_{jm} = W + LW + L^2W + L^3W + \ldots.. + L^{j-1}W,$

because after each period of time at which the change has moved around the loop the worry has increased still further by L times the previous increase.

Such a series can be expressed in a different form using a fairly easy result in algebra which, like so much in mathematics, will either be well known to the reader or will have to be taken on trust, as follows:

9) $W_{jm} = W(1-L^j)/(1-L)$

(if L=1 this formula is not well defined, and instead we have $W_{jm} = jW$).

This formula draws attention to the fact that things are very different according to whether L is greater or less than one. If $L < 1$ then the term L^j gets smaller and smaller as time goes by, and the worry only increases up to the limit:

10) $W(t) \rightarrow W/(1-L).$

For example, if $L = 1/2$, then the effect of the positive feedback from the awareness of blushing over time can only increase the initial worry by a factor of two. If the factor $L = 0.9$, then the worry can be increased tenfold by the feedback; if $L = 0.99$ it can be increased a hundredfold and so on.

If, on the other hand, $L > 1$ then the term L^j will go on increasing without limit, and the worry and blushing will in theory go on increasing indefinitely. In the real world this cannot happen of course. As they increase there will come a time when some other factor arises which will prevent further growth, and they will level off at some high value which cannot be predicted without knowing more about the systems than we have built into this simple linear model. This is not dismaying: we knew in setting up this simple model that it was only an approximation. (The exceptional case $L = 1$ also leads to the worry increasing indefinitely, of course.)

The results that we have obtained so far illustrate the virtue of mathematical analysis over simply throwing the equations into a computer and seeing what happens. One might play about with all sorts of values of the parameters J and K and m and n, getting the computer to churn out many different solutions without hitting upon the basic and simple fact that the main features of the solutions are determined by the value of the parameter $L = JK$; nor would it necessarily be easy to determine the way in which the behaviour depends on L.

Some practical conclusions that arise from this simple result are the following. The effectiveness of an increasing feedback loop is determined by the size of the parameters J and K. The job of the Hypnotherapist is therefore to reduce these coupling constants. He or she will therefore be aiming to reduce either the effect of the worry on the blushing, or the effect of the blushing on the worry, or both.

Note that in general the coupling constants between any two systems will be different in different people. If we are using a positive feedback loop in order to produce an Hypnotic effect, then we should not be surprised if it is easier in one person than another because of these differences. The practising Hypnotherapist will have a reasonable qualitative idea in many cases of how large the parameters are. So-called "good" Subjects are often people in which a change in one system produces a large change in another system; a coupling constant is large; the amplification factors tend to be large; positive feedback loops are strong. "Poor" Subjects are those in which it is hard to produce the standard Hypnotic responses: we may characterise them as people in which there is little amplification; coupling constants like J and K are small so that a positive feedback loop has an almost imperceptible effect; the loop is weak; changes in one system have little effect on other systems.

If we need to produce a strong result in a person in which the coupling constants are small, then we are likely to need to put in quite a lot of work to increase the amplification. It is an untested hypothesis of mine that most coupling constants are larger if the person involved is more generally aroused / excited / nervous. Everyday experience certainly suggests that high adrenaline levels produce generally greater responses in most systems. If this is true then there will be times when the current convention in Hypnotherapy of going for deeply calm and relaxed procedures may NOT be the best approach to certain changes, in particular those in which we want to enhance a positive feedback loop.

It is reasonably straightforward to calculate W_i for values of i which are not multiples of M: interested readers should be able to do this themselves. Likewise the values of B are calculable in a similar way. In the example we are dealing with, limiting values of B are K times those of W.

In summary, what we have learned from a close study of this very simple model of a positive feedback loop is the following. It will always tend to amplify a change, but for small values of the coupling constants the amplification will be limited to increasing the change by a factor of $1/(1-L)$. If the coupling constants become large enough for L to be greater than or equal to one, then the amplification can grow indefinitely, until the variables reach values too large for the simple linear model to remain valid. If we had not thought through such a model in detail, then we might have thought that a positive feedback loop would ALWAYS lead to very large values of the activities involved, which turns out not to be true.

So far we have only dealt with the phase of blushing where things are increasing, and have discovered that for $L < 1$ they reach a plateau determined by 10). For $L > 1$ they will go on increasing until some other factor acts to limit an explosive growth: we cannot predict whether this will lead to a steady plateau or a sudden crash.

If we now think of the plateau situation, we will note that there will come a time when the positive feedback loop has been producing very little increase for some time. It is then only a matter of time before some other influence starts to introduce some reduction into the variables. Typically the thought, "At least it is getting no worse!" will act to start to reduce the worry for a few seconds. But this is likely to produce a reduction in the blushing, which will in turn reduce the worry, and so on. In brief we will have a decreasing positive feedback loop: $\downarrow W \rightarrow \downarrow B \rightarrow \downarrow W$. This can again be represented quantitatively as:

11) $w_i = Jb_{i-m}$ and $b_i = Kw_{i-n}$,

but J, K, m and n will now probably have *different values* from those in 3). The important difference between this equation and equation 3) is that the quantities w_i and b_i are now negative, not positive.

We can run through the same mathematics as before and discover that the small reduction induced by the influence of the calming thought will be amplified in the same way as we have seen above. The total possible reduction will, if the new value of L is less than unity, be no more than $W/(1-L)$, where this value of W is a measure of the reduction produced by the calming thought before the decreasing negative feedback loop starts to take over.

There are then a few possibilities. If this reduction is less than the original increase then the resulting level will be somewhere between zero and its maximum value. Some people will report this response: the embarrassment *will* reduce after a while, but can remain at some significant level as long as they remain in the situation. The second possibility is that the expression for the reduction is equal to or greater in magnitude than the original increase. In this case the reduction process will reverse the original increase and bring the variables back down to zero. If the new value of L is greater than unity then the reduction to zero will be simply faster.

When everything is back to zero again we are back where we started. There may or may not be some reason for the increasing process to start up again. An embarrassing remark or a self-conscious thought may do the trick.

As a final comment, we should remember again how very simple the above model is. It can plausibly be supposed in real life that the quantities J and K will depend to some extent on the values W and B. Most organic processes can increase faster at low levels than they do when they are reaching the limits of their resources. Making J and K depend on B and W is not a problem if we are thinking of computerised solution of the equations, but it would take us outside the bounds of what is possible in this book. However, simple though it is, the model has taught us a few simple principles, particularly involving the way the behaviour depends on the size of the coupling constants J and K.

We will next take a look at negative feedback loops in a similar way. The picture now gets more difficult because we have to deal with both increases and decreases.

Let us look at a double-sided negative feedback loop:

12) $\uparrow X \rightarrow \uparrow Y \rightarrow \downarrow X \rightarrow \downarrow Y \rightarrow \uparrow X$.

A similar approach can be used, except that when we come to looking at solutions, we will start not from a solution in which $X(t) = Y(t) = 0$, but from a more general steady state in which $X(t) = X_0$, and $Y(t) = Y_0$ for all t up to and including $t = 0$.

Using similar linear approximations to these relationships, we have the following equations for the increments x_i and y_i:

13) $x_i = -Jy_{i-a}$ (if $y_{i-a} > 0$) $+ Ky_{i-b}$ (if $y_{i-b} < 0$),
14) $y_i = Lx_{i-c}$ (if $x_{i-c} > 0$) $- Mx_{i-d}$ (if $x_{i-d} < 0$),

where J,K,L,M,a,b,c,d are positive parameters.

This is an unusual form of equation in a mathematician's eyes. In the physical sciences it is generally the case that exactly the same form of equation holds for positive and negative values of the variables. Equations like the above are easy to solve on a computer, but the general solution cannot be written down easily.

The solution can be simplified, however, if the delay parameters are the same for increases and decreases, so that $a = b$ and $c = d$. If we then also suppose that $x_i > 0$ for $i = 1$ to $a+c$, then by 14) $y_i > 0$ for $i = c+1$ to $a+2c$, by 13) $x_i < 0$ for $i = a+c+1$ to $2a+2c$, by 14) $y_i < 0$ for $i = a+2c+1$ to $2a+3c$ and then 13) gives $x_i > 0$ in $2a+2c+1$ to $3a+3c$, and the pattern repeats. This can be summarised by saying that there are solutions of 13) and 14) which are periodic and in which x and y will be alternately positive and negative. Furthermore the values of x_i and y_i can be determined in a very similar way to that used for positive feedback loops, which the interested reader may calculate. We can consider only the behaviour of x, since that of y can be determined similarly.

If we let

$$X = x_1 + x_2 + \ldots \qquad + x_{a+c},$$

which is the increase in X(t) over the first positive phase before the feedback loop starts to act on it, then we find that during a negative phase the change in X(t) is -JL times the change in the previous positive phase, which is in turn -KM times the change in the previous negative phase. If we let JLKM=Q, then if Q<1, we find that the departure from equilibrium is followed by a period of oscillation with decreasing magnitude until the values of X and Y reach a new steady state. The limit for X is:

$$X \to X_0 + X(1\text{-}JL)/(1\text{-}Q).$$

If you would like a real situation to think about, then one example is that of the inter-personal distance between two people at a cocktail party. If we let X(t) be a measure of the reserve between the two and Y(t) a measure of the physical distance, then common experience suggests the normal pattern of social interaction is for ↑{Reserve} → ↑{Distance} → ↓{Reserve} → ↓{Distance}. (Note that in this model the important distance is the psychologically perceived distance, as measured by the activity of the appropriate mental system. For simplicity we will suppose that each person estimates it in the same way, and that each has a similar measure of reserve, though there would be an interestingly different, but more complex, analysis if we had two people who judged them differently.) Suppose that the couple are talking happily at some constant level of reserve and distance. Then the above simple mathematics models a situation in which there is some forced change: it may be that for a while a change of topic increases or decreases the reserve or it may be that one is physically pushed nearer or drawn apart by an outside agent. In the solution obtained above, the result is a period of oscillation during which the forced change is overcompensated for, and this overcompensation is again corrected for, until things stabilise at some new distance, which will generally be a different one from the one they started from.

A succession of such episodes may result in the two reaching closer and closer equilibria or more and more distant equilibria.

By contrast, if Q>1 then the situation is unstable, because any small disturbance will quickly build up in an oscillatory fashion. The changes x and y will increase by the factor Q after each oscillation. Of course as this happens we are less able to predict exactly what happens next, as the variables become too large. Thus if the reserve becomes too large or the distance gets too large then the couple will obviously drift apart. On the other hand the mathematics also predicts that after a number of oscillations the distance can become zero: the two will collide. At this point we can no longer rely on our simple linear approximation to predict what will happen. It may be that in some cases the moment will be prolonged to the mutual satisfaction of the two, or it may be that it will lead to an immediate violent emotional and physical distancing.

An important result that emerges from this analysis is the fact that merely because we have established the presence of a negative feedback loop, it does NOT ensure that it will lead to stability. It will certainly act in that way if the coupling constants are not too large. If they are too great then the effect of the loop is to create increasingly large oscillations. We may perhaps call systems which exhibit such behaviour *over-controlled*.

It is typically the case that when a person is highly nervous it can produce behaviour in which there is an over-reaction to all stimuli. Under such circumstances negative feedback loops could easily run into a problem in which the amplification factor Q becomes greater than unity. We might then anticipate such oscillatory phenomena as a shaking hand to become noticeable. The more that the person then tries to control it, the more he or she makes things worse by trying too hard. This phenomenon is quite commonly observed, and may be brought to a Hypnotherapist for treatment. The task is again to reduce the magnitude of the coupling constants J,K,L,M until their product is less than unity, at which point control is efficient again.

It should be remembered however that we have made certain assumptions in deriving the above solution to the negative feedback equations. If, for example, we had not chosen all the x_i to be positive for $i = 1$ to $a+c$, but rather allowed them to vary, with some positive and some negative, then there would be a high degree of cancellation when we came to doing the summation. If the average value of these disturbances were to be zero, then the quantity X would be zero, and the feedback loop would not produce any net change either. The practical implication of this fact is that if the time taken for the loop to operate is significantly longer than the time over which external effects fluctuate, then there is less danger from over-control.

Of more interest is to drop the assumption that $a=b$ and $c=d$. I have been unable to solve the resulting equation exactly, but the effects of the two halves of the loop are no longer in phase, and there is some cancellation, so that although oscillations can still be expected, they do not have the same chance to grow with larger values of the coupling constants. Again there would seem to be the suggestion that over-control is less of a problem if different mechanisms, with different delay times, are used in the different parts of the feedback loop.

I hope that these simple examples will give the non-mathematician at least a flavour of why the exact sciences benefit from their mathematical models. They may not give a full picture and they may not be used to give exact numbers. But they can still give insight, and can predict results which might well not be apparent without the detailed thinking-through that the mathematics forces on us. This leads to a new understanding and promotes new ideas on how to deal with real-life problems.

I know that all of this will seem a million miles away from day-to-day Hypnotherapy for most practitioners. And I am not suggesting that any should need to go into this amount of detail.

We can all drive cars very well without any knowledge of how to tune a suspension system (a primitive cybernetic system). But the engineers who design such systems benefit enormously from knowing the mathematics of such systems. In the same way I trust that if academics and experimenters can give us a more detailed understanding of the way in which the various systems of the mind and body which are involved in Hypnosis and Hypnotherapy interact, then we will all acquire a clearer idea of what Hypnotherapy is about, and also be able to refine and improve our strategies in given cases.

I hope that no one feels that this approach takes all the poetry out of the subject. Think rather that just as the discipline of a strict metre is what has given us the glory of the greatest poetry, just so does the discipline of thinking clearly and accurately about a problem lead to the best therapy.

If the poetry of a body lies in the lines of the flesh, it nevertheless needs the inner strength of the bones to keep those lines firm.

This book on the principles of our subject provides the bones on which its fair form may display its beauty.

SUMMARY

The mathematical modelling of organic systems is a rich and growing field. The principles of this book lead to a description of the methods of Hypnotherapy in terms of the dynamics of organic systems. It is therefore in a far better position than all other theories of Hypnosis or, indeed, of Psychotherapy to take advantage of mathematical modelling to strengthen and illuminate the subject.

In this chapter some simple examples have been presented for the benefit of readers with a little mathematics to illustrate something of what can be achieved by applying mathematical processes to a situation.

Important practical conclusions which have come out of it are the following:

It is NOT the case that the existence of a positive feedback loop inevitably means a massive increase in the activity of the component processes. The increase may be very mild if the coupling constants are small.

It is NOT the case that a negative feedback loop inevitably means a return to the original value of the activities after a disturbance. The new values can generally be different. Furthermore in an *over-controlled* situation, the negative feedback loop may even lead to increasingly LARGE swings in the activity of the variables, and so the situation can be UNSTABLE.

In attempting either to use or to remove either positive or negative feedback loops, the Hypnotherapist will be typically working on the coupling constants between the systems involved.

CONCLUSION

AT THE END of this book I would like to reflect on the fact that a theory is itself an organic phenomenon. The structure underlying it is one or more human minds together with representations of the ideas in books, articles and computer memories. The development of a theory is a *process*. It grows under the influence of a number of feedback loops. While the development has been mainly within my mind I have been conscious of using a variety of mental processes.

The foremost of these is the positive feedback loop:

$$\uparrow \{\text{understanding}\} \rightarrow \uparrow \{\text{satisfaction}\} \rightarrow \uparrow \{\text{further work}\} \rightarrow \uparrow \{\text{understanding}\}.$$

I know that one of my personal characteristics is that the satisfaction I get from understanding something is one of the deepest I know. There is therefore a very strong positive psychological reinforcer in the above increasing positive feedback loop, which has kept it going powerfully over the years since I started Hypnotherapy.

I would say that an enormous part of human achievement is the result of some such loop. If you are a good runner then an increase in speed leads to a satisfaction which leads to more running, which leads to further increase in speed. Part of the art of helping Clients to achieve their goals is to ensure that they close a loop like the above to power the change, as we have seen.

Also central to my way of thinking are two contrary processes (recall the general principle that organic systems tend to arise in opposite pairs). One, which I will call {reject}, acts to reject and criticise an idea. The other, which I will call {accept}, acts to accept and develop a new idea. I regard them as analogous to the systems in the body of which one acts to accept and absorb wholesome food and the other to detect and reject substances that are not food or are poisonous. Each is important. But each can prove fatal without the other. To accept everything is a path to madness. And the other path to madness is to reject everything. To eat everything will soon prove fatal to the body. To eat nothing is equally fatal.

So during the development of the ideas you have been reading there have been countless cycles of thought applied to aspects of the theory, large and small. If we let {idea} be the process of dwelling on an idea, then I have operated at different times *both* $\uparrow \{\text{idea}\} \rightarrow \uparrow \{\text{accept}\}$ *and* $\uparrow \{\text{idea}\} \rightarrow \uparrow \{\text{reject}\}$.

Thus, for example, at one stage I had half the book written, but an exposure to {reject} found it inadequate and I scrapped it all.

Now if the action of {accept} does NOT lead to any increase in understanding, it reduces the satisfaction with the idea, and the idea tends to drop out of mind. On the other hand if the idea resists all attempts to criticise it then I become more satisfied with it and it grows stronger.

We thus have the following possibilities:

$$\uparrow\{\text{idea}\} \rightarrow \uparrow\{\text{accept}\} \rightarrow \uparrow\{\text{satisfaction}\} \rightarrow \uparrow\{\text{idea}\},$$
$$\uparrow\{\text{idea}\} \rightarrow \uparrow\{\text{accept}\} \rightarrow \downarrow\{\text{satisfaction}\} \rightarrow \downarrow\{\text{idea}\},$$
$$\uparrow\{\text{idea}\} \rightarrow \uparrow\{\text{reject}\} \rightarrow \uparrow\{\text{satisfaction}\} \rightarrow \uparrow\{\text{idea}\},$$
$$\uparrow\{\text{idea}\} \rightarrow \uparrow\{\text{reject}\} \rightarrow \downarrow\{\text{satisfaction}\} \rightarrow \downarrow\{\text{idea}\}.$$

Repeated application of these processes tends to continue to alter the ideas in various ways and at various levels. But any that can withstand the alternating mental environments are inevitably more robust. The gardener both fertilises and prunes. The continuing survival of a species involves growth and death. The survival of an idea is no different.

Notice that the sign of an expert in *any* field is the repeated and frequent use of {accept} and {reject}. We may see it in someone who is expert at assessing clothes or wines, or buying and selling cars, or at golf: "Shall I accept that shot as adequate or reject it as not good enough?" It is the continual exercise of both that leads to expertise.

There is another set of mental processes, which I consciously or instinctively use in my thoughts, that parallel the directions suggested by looking at subsystems or supersystems or connected systems of a given system. Of any idea I will tend to ask:

Q1. How does this idea work in a particular example?

Q2. Can I generalise this idea to a broader context?

Q3. Can I find a similar idea: an analogy?

Each of these questions activates a certain kind of process of mental search: {search example}, {search generalisation}, {search analogy}. I will trigger off these processes at random, as a part of the overall process of understanding, and in particular in response to the activation of the feeling of being at a loss as to what to do next.

I think that you should be able to find the influence of this way of thinking throughout the book, as I move between specific examples, analogies and generalisations.

If, for example, I apply the process {search analogy} to the process of asking the above three questions, I can immediately generate the following loose analogies:

a) They might be likened to the three Gunas - Sattva (or Sattwa), Rajas and Tamas - described in the Bhagavad Gita:

"Those who are in Sattva climb the path that leads on high, those who are in Rajas follow the level path, those who are in Tamas sink downwards on the lower path."

b) They might be likened to the three possible spin states of a particle with spin-1 (in quantum theory): the spin takes values that can be labelled $+1$, 0 and -1.

c) They might be likened to the Holy Trinity.

d) Or to the {child}, {parent} and {adult} of Transactional Analysis.

e) Or, relative to a given species, of {predators}, {food} and {competitors for the same food}.

f) Or, in an organisation, to {pass the buck up}, {pass the buck down} and {pass the buck sideways}.

There are many more possibilities, but the above will serve as examples. I would then activate the process {accept} to each of these for a while to see if the analogies help my understanding. Later I would activate the process {reject} to criticise their value as analogies. At the end I might be left with one or two which seemed quite useful.

Another pair of mental processes that I use freely are {search similarities} and {search differences}. For example in dealing with a given Client I will be forever seeking to find similar cases that I have read about or handled, which can be a fruitful source of insight into the present one, but ALSO seeking for the differences between the present one and the others, because these differences may be crucial.

Notice that the first of the two sentences above consisted of a generalisation to which I then applied {search example} in order to obtain the second. If I had activated instead {search analogy} I might come up with the following.

There is a little girl sitting on the floor sorting peas into two piles, big and small. Each time she picks a new one up she compares it with each of the piles she has so far. Some clearly go to one pile or the other. Others have to be compared carefully against the peas in the piles to see how similar or different their size is to those in the other piles. From time to time she may need to re-sort some peas into the opposite pile. But eventually she not only separates the peas but acquires an excellent ability to assess, as a result of these repeated processes, the size of any small object. In the same way, by forever assessing ideas to see if they are similar to or dissimilar to other collections of ideas, one can develop an astute ability to assess a new idea quickly and easily and see where it belongs.

Another principle of thought that I also use is to ask of most things in life, "What process or processes is this a part of?" It is the difference between thinking in terms of still photographs on the one hand and of a video or film on the other. Suppose, for example, that a Client tells me some isolated fact, then the above mental process - {search process} - is activated, and this in turn activates a mental process of creating a (rather abstract) conception of what is likely to have led up to and then followed on from the isolated fact: I am mentally searching for precursors and resultants. I may then activate {test} and ask the Client if I have got the details right and activate {accept} or {reject} on the basis of the answers I get, in order to modify my concept of the processes involved.

Yet another process that I use freely in my thought is, of course, the asking of questions. (The word comes from the same Latin root as does "quest", a search:

it is a process of mental searching.) Furthermore, I do not simply ask questions, but I ask myself, "Is this a useful question to ask?" I use my tools to improve my tools.

I could present this analysis of my thought processes in more detail, but perhaps I have written enough to show that the means I am using to analyse other organic systems are self-referential: they can be applied to the means themselves. They allow us to think about thought, or to think about our thought about thought and so on; at each level rising to a higher level of system. This may remind some readers of Bateson's ideas on Levels of Learning (Bateson (1973)). He is also worth reading for other ideas that parallel some in this book. I presume that other thinkers think about their tools: their thought processes. But with the exception of Bateson and the well-known works on lateral thinking and other mental tools by Edward de Bono, I have come across few references by even the foremost of our thinkers to the way in which they have chosen to think, which is perhaps a little surprising.

You will be able to see that since I regard thoughts as themselves processes, I do not regard them as in any sense fixed or immutable or eternal. Furthermore they, also, depend intimately on the environment in which they exist. And as a part of the process of testing (which contains the subprocesses {accept} and {reject}) it is necessary to involve not only my internal environment but also my external one.

One of the most important aspects of this is in the consulting-room. An idea which does not help me to help people gets a very low satisfaction rating. An idea that *does* help is highly satisfying. (I should add that the pleasure of helping has always been a second strong reinforcer for me.)

The second important external environment is that of the minds of others who work in the field. In order to get feedback from this environment I have presented some of my ideas at the Annual Meeting of the British Society for Experimental and Clinical Hypnosis (1993, to be published); published some of the material in this book as it has been evolving in my mind (Morgan (1993a), (1993b), (1993c), (1994a), (1994b), (1995a), (1995b)); and modified the ideas where appropriate in response to the feedback.

Now, with the publication of this book, the ideas are extending to a larger environment still, to include your mind as well. You will have your own internal systems to deal with new material, and they will almost certainly include {accept} and {reject}, though the criteria they use may well be different from mine. You will understand that I will be most happy if you choose to use *either* or *both* of these systems and then feed back the results to me, for in either case you will be extending my own development of the theory. Then, when new editions come out, they are likely to be changed by this feedback. It is of the nature and glory of life that it changes and grows. A theory which did not partake of these qualities would be a dead theory: dry bones.

I hope that you, the reader, will play some part in actively changing what you have understood: recasting it in your own words, relating it to others, incorporating your own experiences, developing your own life as a result of what you have learned. Only insofar as things like that happen - only insofar as the theory activates thought and action - is it a living, organic thing.

I have enjoyed writing this. It has activated my mind, and helped me to do my job better. I hope that it has activated your mind and that it may contribute in some small way to help your life to improve also.

Finally it might be an idea to think back to what I said in the introduction about the purpose of this book. There you read that this book is NOT intended to present new facts about Hypnotherapy, nor to be a compendium, nor a history, nor a handbook, nor a "Teach Yourself" book, nor the finding of the Elixir of Life. Rather it is intended to present a new view of the subject: a new paradigm which leads to a deeper understanding.

I hope that, through reading as much of the book as you have chosen to do, you have been able to take that new perspective and consequently are able to judge if this intention has been achieved. I hope to have revealed that Hypnotherapy can be treated as highly scientific in the true sense of the word. It has a foundation of clear and measurable concepts and a theoretical framework which underpins its many techniques. It can certainly hold up its head very high among forms of psychotherapy, many of which can get lost in a jungle of ill-defined if evocative terminology and vaguely defined concepts.

It can interface with the theoretical framework of modern medicine in its emphasis on systems in a way that few other forms of psychotherapy or alternative medicine can match.

It includes within itself a diagnostic procedure which is well-defined, specific and free from arbitrary labels and complex patterns of symptoms - "syndromes" - which have no reference to underlying mechanisms or processes.

Of its essence it emphasises the *dynamic* nature of all organic processes, which even medical diagnosis can fail properly to take into account.

It can interface also, thanks to its structure, with theories of society and economics, so that there can be mutual gain from the exchange of models and ideas.

In its emphasis on the importance of the supersystems within which the system of interest is embedded, it is holistic in a meaningful sense of the word, and gives an added dimension to the concept of ecologically sound changes in an ecologically conscious world.

In its emphasis on the importance of feedback loops it is connected to one of the most central features of all the mechanisms of the body and mind, and indeed all organic systems.

It automatically imposes a wholesome mental discipline in the analysis of problems and the generation of solutions, which is again lacking in so many other forms of psychotherapy.

The ways of thinking it embodies are very practical on a day to day level in dealing with Clients. For all its abstract strength it deals with human reality.

It does not demolish existing practices and particular perspectives in Hypnotherapy, but rather strengthens them by uniting them in a common framework.

All those things I claim for the approach, but I do not claim that what is fixed in this book is either complete or without error. There are doubtless mistakes, at many levels, that I have not managed to eradicate. And there is much more development needed not only on the consequences of the approach but also on the approach itself. A crystal may be flawless. A mausoleum may be complete. If the ideas above were complete and without error then they would be beyond change: but to be beyond change is to be beyond life. I would prefer the theory to be organic and to live.

BIBLIOGRAPHY

Ashby, W. Ross (1956). *An Introduction to Cybernetics*. London: Methuen & Hall.

Barber, T.X. & Wilson, S.C. (1978). The Barber Suggestibility Scale and the Creative Imagination Scale: Experimental and Clinical Applications. *American Journal of Clinical Hypnosis*, 21, 84-108.

Bateson, G., Jackson, D.D., Haley, J. & Weakland, J. (1956). Towards a theory of schizophrenia. *Behavioural Science*, *1*, 251-264.

Bateson, G. (1971). The Cybernetics of "Self": a Theory of Alcoholism. *Psychiatry*, *34*, 1-18.

Bateson, Gregory (1973). *Steps to an Ecology of Mind*. London: Paladin.

Becvar, D.S. & Becvar, R.J. (1988). *Family Therapy: a Systemic Integration*. Boston: Allyn & Bacon.

Berne (1964). *Games People Play*. New York: Grove Press.

Bernheim, Hippolyte (1884). *De la suggestion dans l'état hypnotique et dans l'état de veille*. Paris: Octave Doin.

Bowers, K.S. & Meichenbaum, D. (Eds.) (1984). *The Unconscious Reconsidered*. John Wiley.

Braid, James (1853). *Neurypnology or the Rationale of Nervous Sleep considered in Relation with Animal Magnetism*. London: J. Churchill.

Brewster, Sir David (1855). *Memoirs of the Life, Writings and Discoveries of Sir Isaac Newton*. London.

Buranelli, Vincent (1975). *The Wizard from Vienna - Franz Anton Mesmer*. New York: Coward, McCann & Geoghegan.

Calvin, William H. (1983). *The Throwing Madonna: Essays on the Brain*. McGraw-Hill.

Carnon, G. & Einzig, H. (1983). *Dieting Makes You Fat: a Guide to Energy, Fitness and Health*. London: Century Publishing.

Casti, John L. (1989). *Paradigms Lost*. New York: William Morrow and Company.

Crabtree, Adam (1993). *From Mesmer to Freud - Magnetic Sleep and the Roots of Psychological Healing*. Yale U.P.

Dalton, John (1808). *A New System of Chemical Philosophy*.

Dennett, Daniel C. (1991). *Consciousness Explained*. Penguin.

Denton, Derek (1993). *The Pinnacle of Life*. Allen & Unwin.

De Puységur, Le compte M. de C. *Rapport des Cures Operées à Bayonne par le Magnetisme Animal* translated by Tinterow, M.M. (1970). *Foundations of Hypnosis*. Illinois: Charles Thomas.

Egbert, L., Battit, G., Welch, C. & Bartlett, M. (1964). Reduction of postoperative pain by encouragement and instruction of patients. *New England Journal of Medicine, 270,* 825-827.

Ellenberger, H.F. (1970). *The Discovery of the Unconscious*. New York: Basic Books.

Elton, Charles (1927). *Animal Ecology*. London: Sidgwick and Jackson.

Erickson, Milton H., Hershman, Seymour, Secter & Irving, I. (1981). *Practical Applications of Medical and Dental Hypnosis*. Chicago: Seminars on Hypnosis Publishing.

Ferenczi, S. (1916). The role of transference in hypnosis and suggestion. In S. Ferenczi, *Contributions to Psycho-Analysis*. Boston: R.G. Badger.

Gauld, Alan (1992). *A History of Hypnotism*. Cambridge U.P.

Gibson, H.B. & Heap, M. (1991). *Hypnosis in Therapy*. Hove: Lawrence Erlbaum Associates.

Gödel, K. (1931). Über formal unentscheidbare Sätze der Principia Mathematica und verwandter Systeme I. *Monatsshefte für Mathematik und Physik, 38,* 173-98.

Gordon, David & Myers-Anderson, Maribeth (1981). *Phoenix: Therapeutic Patterns of Milton H. Erickson*. California: Meta.

Green, N.P.O., Stout, G.W., Taylor, D.J. & Soper, R. (1984). *Biological Science 1&2*. Cambridge U.P.

Grimes, James Stanley (1839). *Etherology, and the Phreno-Philosophy of Mesmerism and Magic Eloquence: Including a New Philosophy of Sleep and of Consciousness, with a Review of the Pretensions of Phreno-Magnetism, Electro-biology etc.* Boston and Cambridge: James Munro.

Haley, Jay (1973). *Uncommon Therapy: The psychiatric techniques of Milton H. Erickson, M.D.* California: Meta.

Harris, Thomas A. (1970). *The Book of Choice*. Jonathan Cape. Also published as *I'm OK - You're OK*. Pan Books (1973).

Hilgard, Ernest R. & Hilgard, Josephine R. (1975). *Hypnosis in the Relief of Pain*. Los Angeles: William Kaufmann.

Iverson, Jeffrey (1976). *More Lives than One? The Evidence of the Remarkable Bloxham Tapes*. London: Souvenir Press.

James, William (1950). *The Principles of Psychology*, Vol 1. p.8. Dover Publications, reproduction of the 1890 edition: Henry Holt.

Jones, D.S. (1979). *Elementary Information Theory*. Oxford: Clarendon Press.

Jones, D.S. & Morgan, J.D. (1972). The instability of a vortex sheet on a subsonic stream under acoustic radiation. *Proc. Camb. Phil. Soc. 72*, 465-488.

Jones, D.S. & Morgan, J.D. (1973). The instability due to acoustic radiation striking a vortex sheet on a supersonic stream. *Proc. Roy. Soc. Edin. (A), 71*, 121-140.

Jones, D.S. & Morgan, J.D. (1974). A linear model of a finite amplitude Helmholtz instability. *Proc. Roy. Soc. Lond. (A), 388*, 17-41.

Kennedy, Carol (1991). *Guide to the Management Gurus*. London: Random Century.

Krebs, Charles J. (1994). *Ecology. The Experimental Analysis of Distribution and Abundance*, 4th Edition. New York: HarperCollins College Publishers.

Kuhn, T. (1970). *The Structure of Scientific Revolutions*, 2nd Edition. Chicago: University of Chicago Press.

McKenna, Paul (1993). *The Hypnotic World of Paul McKenna*. London: Faber and

Faber.

Martin, G.D. & Bryson, A.E. (1980). Attitude Control of a Flexible Aircraft. *Journal of Guidance and Control (Jan-Feb)*, 37-41.

Mesmer, Anton (1779). *Mémoire sur la découverte du Magnétisme Animal*. Geneva: P.F. Didot le jeune.

Milgram, S. (1974). *Obedience to Authority*. New York: Harper & Row.

Morgan, J.D. (1974). The interaction of sound with a semi-infinite vortex sheet. *Quart. J. of Mechanics and Applied Mathematics 27*, 465-487.

Morgan, J.D. (1975). The interaction of sound with a subsonic cylindrical vortex layer. *Proc. Roy. Soc. Lond. (A), 344*, 341-362.

Morgan, J.D. (1978). *SIAM Journal on Mathematics*, 9, 1172-1178.

Morgan, J.D. (1993a). Time to define a new concept of Hypnosis. *European Journal of Clinical Hypnosis*. October. 26-34.

Morgan, J.D. (1993b). A systems-oriented paradigm for hypnotic phenomena. *Journal of the National Council of Psychotherapists and Hypnotherapy Register*. Autumn. 33-43.

Morgan, J.D. (1993c). Systems Analysis and Diagnosis. *Journal of the National Council of Psychotherapists and Hypnotherapy Register*. Winter. 34-49.

Morgan, J.D. (1994a). Systems-oriented Hypnosis. *European Journal of Clinical Hypnosis*. January. 33-44.

Morgan, J.D. (1994b). Systems-oriented Hypnosis. *Journal of the National Council of Psychotherapists and Hypnotherapy Register*. Winter. 11-26.

Morgan, J.D. (1995a). Positive feedback loops in Hypnosis. *Journal of the National Council of Psychotherapists and Hypnotherapy Register*. Spring. 46-55.

Morgan, J.D. (1995b). Formulating a system to analyse and understand Hypnotherapy. *European Journal of Clinical Hypnosis*. Spring. 44-53.

Murray, James D. (1993). *Mathematical Biology*, 2nd Edition. Springer-Verlag.

O'Hanlon, William H. & Hexum, Angela L. (1990). *An Uncommon Casebook: The*

Complete Clinical Work of Milton H. Erickson, M.D.. New York: W.W. Norton & Co.

Parkinson, C. Northcote (1957). *Parkinson's Law or the Pursuit of Progress.* John Murray, London.

Penrose, R. (1989). *The Emperor's New Mind.* London: Vintage.

Penrose, R. (1994). *Shadows of the Mind: a Search for the Missing Science of Consciousness.* Oxford U.P.

Piaget, J. (1963). *The Origins of Intelligence in Children.* New York: Ballantine.

Popper, Karl (1959). *The Logic of Scientific Discovery.* Hutchinson & Co., London.

Rapport des commissaires chargés par le Roi de l'examen du magnétisme animal (1784). Paris: Imprimerie Royale.

Rathus, Spencer A. (1987). *Psychology*, 3rd Edition. Holt, Rinehart & Winston.

Rosen, Sidney (1980). *My Voice Will Go with You: the Teaching Tales of Milton H. Erickson.* New York: Norton.

Rossi, Ernest L. (1980). *The Collected Papers of Milton Erickson on Hypnosis, Volumes i-iv.* New York: Irvington.

Thomas a Kempis (circa 1441): trans. George F. Maine. *The Imitation of Christ.* London: Collins (1957).